MILLENNIAL AGRICULTURE

The New Eden

A Key to Understanding the Kingdom of God

by

Paul W. Syltie

Triumph Publishing
Box 292
Altadena, Ca. 91001

Paul W. Syltie, Ph.D., North Dakota State University,
Fargo, North Dakota

—in collaboration with—

James E. Wylie, M.S., Moorhead State University,
Moorhead, Minnesota

iii

Dedicated to . . .

Sandy, my loving wife,
and my children Neil, Anne-Lise,
Stephanie, and Jonathan

TABLE OF CONTENTS

Page

LIST OF FIGURES

Acknowledgments

At least ten years of forethought has preceded the writing of this book. For some time both Jim Wylie and I have understood the futile pathway that modern technological agriculture has been taking, its failure to consider first the health of the land and people as part of a basically exploitative economic system. We first met in 1976 at Fargo, North Dakota, where I was a doctoral student in soils at North Dakota State University and Jim was a horticulture instructor at the nearby Detroit Lakes (Minnesota) Vocational-Technical Institute.

As time passed our common interests in God's Word and agriculture began to parallel one another, and the viewpoints expressed in this book began to take shape. It became very clear to us that little has been said about the development of an agricultural system that can continue to exist indefinitely at high levels of productivity, and also is designed with people in mind. Without the inputs of both of us it is doubtful that this writing would ever have been undertaken.

I must compliment Jim Wylie as a highly imaginative and original thinker with a knack of getting to the heart of a matter. Others influential in helping to formulate several ideas expressed here are Zoell Colburn, Dale Schurter, and Allen Stout of Big Sandy, Texas, as well as David Swaim of Crawfordsville, Indiana, all of whom look forward to better days ahead on the land.

In addition, a great deal of thanks is expressed to my father, John Syltie, whose love and respect for the land—and farming as an occupation—have guided me in the search for truth throughout these years. Also, not to be forgotten are Sandy, my wife, the world's greatest typist, organic cook, and source of encouragement, and four young children—Neil, Anne-Lise, Stephanie, and Jonathan—who are growing to love the natural world as much as their dad.

Paul W. Syltie
Fargo, North Dakota
March, 1980

Preface

Something is very wrong with agriculture today. Farmers often sense this error, as do many urban dwellers who understand that all life begins—and ends—with the soil. The feeling is often intuitive and subjective, something beyond the tangible sense of research reports, agri-business advertising, or views of the land itself. Oh, we are assured by professional agriculturalists that all is well, that there is absolutely nothing to become alarmed about . . . that all of this apprehension is raised amidst history's greatest thrust of progress *ever* toward bigger and bigger yields. No matter the fewer and fewer farmers, the endless expanses of modern-day fields, and the hauntingly stark and barren appearance of the countryside, so often bereft of trees, hedges, and wildlife. Don't concern yourself with the probable extinction of the whooping crane or the bald eagle; after all, who is more important, man or beast? What about severe nationwide soil erosion? Aren't our soil resources inexhaustible? And how can 200 bushel per acre corn be bad? Isn't a bushel of corn raised under today's agri-business prescriptions as good as a bushel of corn raised under the "antiquated" techniques of the horse-and-buggy days?

Despite the pleas of the burgeoning agricultural chemical industry and allied Land Grant universities to let all misgivings die in blissful ignorance, a great number of Americans find it impossible to ignore the ugly facts any longer, and have asked questions about the agricultural system we now are immersed in:

Is it good to unsettle the farmlands and crowd these rural immigrants into the hypertensive, sterile, concrete jungle of the city?

Cannot parents have a better opportunity to rear a family close to land and nature on the farm, teaching the work ethic and value of accomplishment to the upcoming generation through a family working together as a team? Was man even *meant* to live in cities?

Do environmental chemicals in our food contribute to the appalling cancer death toll, and the multitudes of ill people, in this country?

Is one bushel of corn the same as another? Do soil treatments cause variations in this quality, and to what degree? What about these modern "green revolution" hybrid crops and quality?

Are crop yield and quality totally compatible towards maximizing the health of consumers?

Has technological, scientific agriculture *really* contributed to the proven establishment of a system of agriculture destined to last thousands of years, leaving the land as fertile and full of vitality as when man first arrived . . . land just waiting to support countless generations of young adults eager to justly care for the preserved wealth inherited from their forefathers?

Are today's agricultural practices and trends leading towards happiness and fulfillment in life for the few still able to pursue farming as a living? What about the millions who will never get the chance?

These are all valid questions one may pose in questioning the practices of modern agriculture; each is awaiting an answer. Indeed, most of them *can* be answered fairly accurately, though the approach one uses in answering is as important as the questions themselves. After all, one is desiring truth, and "there is a way that seems right to man" (Prov. 14:12). On the other hand, "God's word is truth" (John 17:17). What does one choose: the reasonable speculation of man, or the utterly sure revelation of Almighty God as revealed in His Word?

Thus, the first and the final question one should ask, while intent upon answering any of the above questions, is "What does God have to say about agriculture?" This is the big question. Few people have explored it seriously, and seldom with the intent of letting Scripture interpret itself . . . which is the admonition to all legitimate Biblical researchers (Isa. 28:10).

It is the attempt of this work to lucidly outline what the Eternal has to say about agriculture as it ought to be practiced; or, as the title of this book implies, how God intends land to be managed during the millennium, that 1,000-year period during which the laws of nature will be universally followed by all mankind, when virtually all men will be husbanding the land with total respect for natural laws. Those laws, if obeyed, yield untold blessings of field, forest, and flock, but if disobeyed yield dismal, chronic failures in production from the land. Man has chosen the latter course of action, and history's record has borne out the periodic rise and fall of empires, usually closely tied to treatment of the soil and its fertility. From Babylon to Egypt, from Greece to Rome, and from Palestine to China we are met face-to-face with civilizations which prospered, faltered, and finally fell because of disregard for the ultimate source of personal and national strength—the soil.

Are America, Britain, and other Western civilizations also well into the declining phases of civilization due to soil depletion through erosion, crop removal, and chemical practices intent on profit maximization?

Answers to these questions will become more and more clear as the following text is explored. To assist the reader in interpreting the present status and trends of American agriculture, the first chapter describes many such trends. It is not the purpose of this work to elucidate the details of America's current farm dilemma, though an understanding of the unmistakeable negative trends so apparent all through the first chapter should alarm the reader to the seriousness of our plight. American agriculture, like the rest of society, is in trouble . . . deep trouble. The trends illustrated are intended to point out some of these difficulties.

On the brighter side, the text which follows reveals the glorious future which is in store for the entire face of the earth, a world freed forever from the heart-wringing, painful grip of famine, war, and pestilence. It is the message contained in the Bible, directed to all those willing to listen, a message of such incredible hope and tearful joy that all people who have a concern for the future should become familiar with it. It is about a world of luxuriant, green pastures and forests, serene settings of gently-sloping prairies and woods, people fearless of the lion or wolf, basking in a superb, moderate climate within communities of truly liberated individuals free of gossip, drunkenness, and immorality. Banks and their interest charges will be gone. Land will be a permanent inheritance for each family, a homestead ever-present to serve as a focal point for loving families amid a loving society. It is a message of a world where divorce is unknown, where diseases of all sorts have disappeared, and one language and one religion overspread the entire earth . . . world government finally in the hands of God where it belongs, rather than in the hands of wayward, error-prone human despots.

In short, this book is one of great *hope* directed towards all individuals intent upon discovering a ray of light in the darkened world of modern agriculture. Yes, the machinery glitters, the corn fields grow tall, the cattle grow fat, and all may appear well on the surface, BUT . . . it will not continue. It cannot, for the author of its system is opposed to permanence and truth. If two words could be used to describe the present state of affairs in American agriculture they are "deception" and "impermanence." Truth is hidden in the name of money; the ephemeral material goods are worshipped rather than the permanent spiritual entities. A tractor today may look old, dirty, and out of place in a few years; the old "home place" may be sold to a neighboring farmer, the permanent homestead forsaken if the price is right. Corporate advertising of hybrids, pesticides, herbicides, commercial fertilizers, and credit sources promise big returns in high yields but fail to mention the agonizing kickbacks a few years hence. A universal truth is that every cause produces an effect, be it good or bad. Supposed good results (high yields) today are often expounded as truth, but natural laws do not obey man's commands. They remain free and clear of idle declarations of men. As Horace once said,

You may drive out Nature with a pitchfork, but she will ever hurry back, to triumph in stealth over your foolish contempt.

Is American and Western technological, agri-business-oriented agriculture driving out Nature with a pitchfork by its short-sighted, profit-maximizing efforts? May the pages of this text help clarify this and many other questions on the minds of those searching for truth amidst a world of half truths and deception, using as a basis the one and only infallible source—God's Word.

Author's Note on Biblical Translations Used in This Text

Throughout this work a great effort was made to incorporate Biblical references wherever they applied. These references are included directly in the text. Two translations have been used, the particular one used at a specific point in the text being that which seemed to contain the most appropriate wording. In most cases the Moffatt translation[1] was used, this being a modern translation of Old and New Testaments by James Moffatt, a Bible scholar from Oxford, England. The modern English of this recent version helps add great impact to the meanings of statements inspired or directly stated by the Almighty God of the Universe . . . though, as Moffatt stated (p. xiv) in the Introduction to his translation, "I hope there is nothing in the execution, certainly there is nothing in the aim, of the modern translation which would be out of keeping with the tone of these searching words which preface its great predecessor [the 1611 King James version]."

The King James version[2] has also been utilized at times to relate the traditional Scriptural language so familiar to many. It is hoped that the use of these two translations, one in modern English and the other in the English of 1611, will help elucidate the magnificent messages contained within the Word of God which form the foundation of this work—a work in itself of little value if separated from that eternal knowledge and truth revealed by the Creator of land, sea, air, and all they contain.

---

[1]Moffatt, James. 1954. *A New Translation of the Bible Containing the Old and New Testaments.* Harper and Row, Publishers, Inc., New York.
[2]Anonymous. 1971. *The Holy Bible.* Oxford University Press, London.

About the Author

Paul W. Syltie was born near Porter, Minnesota, the son of a crop and dairy farmer within the fertile prairie region of southwestern Minnesota. Throughout his youth he developed a loving kinship with nature upon the rich, rolling farmland and the wooded creek valley just below his parents' farmstead. The violent thunderstorms of summer and blizzards of winter, teeming life of the prairie and woods, and a closely-knit family of Norwegian ancestry combined to enrich the imagination of a youth whose love for the open spaces and rural life has never diminished.

Writing poetry began at an early age but was never engaged in seriously for many years. Mr. Syltie left the local community in 1963 to attend college at South Dakota State University and later the University of Minnesota, receiving a Bachelor of Soil Science degree from Minnesota in 1967. That summer he married his high school sweetheart Sandy. He then began work on a Master's degree at the University of Illinois but was interrupted for two years by military service during the height of the Vietnam War. While in the service he served as a U. S. Army bandsman in Monterey, California, and Bad Kreuznach, Germany, before returning to complete the Master of Soil Fertility degree at Illinois in 1971. He toured much of Europe in 1969, a trip highlighted by a visit with relatives in Norway in the majestic fjord country of western Norway. Those marvelous vistas of sheer rock walls and shimmering blue-green waters were never to be forgotten, and provided continued inspiration as years passed.

An intense love of the land and his home community drove Mr. Syltie back into farming with his father in 1971, a return which was short-lived as the reality of economic pressures bore in. After a year he returned to the educational field, serving with the agriculture faculty at Ambassador College, Big Sandy, Texas. He later managed

xix

a farm in southwestern Wisconsin before attending North Dakota State University where a Ph.D. in Soils, Botany, and Biochemistry was received in 1979. Four lovely children have been added to his family during the past twelve years of married life. Continuing interests include gardening—when the entire family pitches in—and photography, his wife and children often providing the subject matter.

Among his writing accomplishments Mr. Syltie has published not only this book entitled *Millennial Agriculture, The New Eden: a Key to Understanding the Kingdom of God,* which deals with world agriculture as it should, and will, soon be; he has also published several articles in scientific journals beside co-authoring the booklet *World Crisis in Agriculture.* He has completed a detailed history of his family and is presently continuing to write on agricultural subjects and poetry. He is listed in the American Collegiate Poets Anthology, and soon hopes to have published his first major publication in the field of poetry, entitled *Surely Doesn't Nature Itself Teach You?*

Among Mr. Syltie's other hobbies, besides those mentioned, are horseshoe pitching and rock collecting. Academic honors: graduated first in his class of about 250 students at the University of Minnesota College of Agriculture, Forestry, and Home Economics in 1967; completed his Ph.D. program with a 4.0 grade point average. He has two brothers and a sister.

Chapter One

Where Are We Headed?

Why should a discussion of millennial agriculture begin with an examination of present trends within American society? The answer is simple: so that the imminence of the millennium may be appreciated, and the reality of the words to be expressed throughout the text may have an impact on the reader. Never before has man, in all his profoundly destructive military might, been able to speak not just in terms of the possible annihilation of mankind through warfare, but in terms of "overkill." Modern science and technology have hypnotically serenaded men and women to the far corners of the earth into believing that new discoveries in food technology, marital relations, child psychology, nuclear weaponry, transportation, and scores of other areas of endeavor are for our good—our happiness and fulfillment in living.

Chemical, biological, and nuclear weaponry await the day of infamy when roaring, crackling intercontinental missiles lurch from concrete silos and submarines to exterminate cities containing millions of men, women, and children in a matter of minutes, bringing ever-nearer the potential reality of Christ's end-time prophecy, "Had not those days been cut short, not a soul would be saved alive" (Matt. 24:22).

What Modern Prognosticators Say

Today's society, according to the statements of many modern historical figures, is experiencing the throes of death, the first pangs of the breakdown of an unmanageable, ponderous industrial system

1

among Western nations and grossly illiterate, populous, underfed Third World nations. In response to the question, "What's in store for the industrial nations of the West?," Alvin Toffler,* author of *Future Shock*[1] and *The Eco-Spasm Report,*[2] stated:

> That's why I use the term 'eco-spasm' to describe what's happening today. It's not boom or bust, or recession or 'stagflation.' It's an economic shake-up in the midst of an ecological crisis, technological and political upsets, and revolutionary changes in family structure, values, sexual attitudes, military and geopolitical power balances.[3]

According to Robert L. Heilbroner,

> . . . there is an absolute limit to the ability of the earth to support or tolerate the process of industrial activity, and there is reason to believe that we are now moving toward the limit very rapidly.[4]

Dr. Paul Ehrlich, author of *The Population Bomb,*[5] added in a more recent book, *The End of Affluence,*

> . . . the exact timetable of society's decline and the sequence of steps on the down staircase are impossible to predict, *but they are relatively unimportant.* What you need to know is that in ten or fifteen years—twenty or twenty-five at most—you will be living in a world *extremely different* from that of today—one that, if you are unprepared

---

* Toffler stated in *The Eco-Spasm Report* (p. i) an additional very comprehensive and revealing statement:

"What we are seeing today is not simply an economic upheaval, but something far deeper, something that cannot be understood within the framework of conventional economics. This is why increasingly mystified economists complain that 'the old rules don't work any longer.' What we are seeing is the general crisis of industrialism—a crisis that transcends the differences between capitalism and Soviet-style communism, a crisis that is simultaneously tearing up our energy base, our value systems, our sense of space and time, our epistemology as well as our economy. What is happening, no more, no less, is the breakdown of industrial civilization of the planet and the first fragmentary appearance of a wholly new and drastically different social order. . . ."

for it, will prove extraordinarily unpleasant. . . . For the energy mini-crisis [in 1974] illuminated once and for all the hopeless incompetence of our political and business leaders and our institutions when it comes to coping with fundamental changes.[6]

Other voices from the scientific world, such as that of Barry Commoner, add that the poorly understood, tangled knot of problems facing modern America baffles not only citizens, but legislators, administrators, and separate specialists.[7] These problems involve "complex interactions among the three basic systems—the ecosystem, the production system, and the economic system—that, together with the social or political order, govern all human activity."[8] The poet-farmer-philosopher Wendell Berry has voiced the current ecological and societal crisis at the level of the land,[9] while Erik Eckholm in *Losing Ground* predicted that a third of mankind will very soon become mired in hopeless destitution unless there is a major shift in global political priorities, a tragedy with ominous implications for world order.[10] The Club of Rome, in its study, *The Limits of Growth,* concluded

If present growth trends in world population, industrialization, pollution, food production, and resource depletion continue unchanged, the limits of growth in this planet will be reached sometime within the next one hundred years. The most probable result will be a rather sudden and uncontrollable decline in both population and industrial capacity.[11]

The Proof of Where America Is Headed

Statements by prognosticators in themselves may speak truth. Yet, to assure the reader that America, the world's most powerful industrial nation, is indeed sailing upon unfriendly seas, a series of figures is presented based upon official government statistics. These trends are easily viewed by graphical presentations. As shown in Figure 1, a burgeoning urban population at the expense of environmental quality cannot be considered good by any stretch of the imagination. Ralph Waldo Emerson once said, "Cities give not the human senses room enough. We go out daily and nightly to feed our

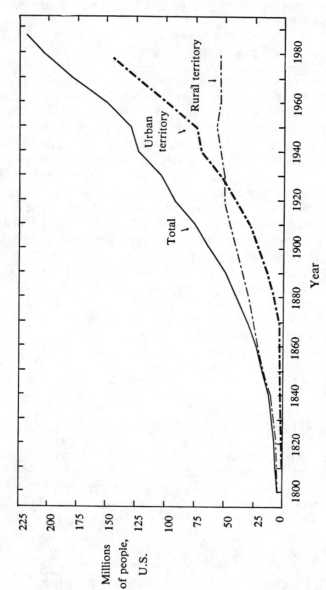

Figure 1. U.S. population: total, in urban territory (areas of 2,500 or more inhabitants incorporated as cities, villages, boroughs, or towns), and in rural territory from 1790 to 1978.[12]

eyes on the horizon, and require so much scope, just as we need water for our bath."[13] The impact of urbanization on individual lives has been immense. Since the Industrial Revolution became the foremost preoccupation of man in the mid-1800s, the eventual urbanization of man became a foregone conclusion: factories needed workers, and low farm-commodity prices forced the respecters of the soil to become overwhelmed by tillers intent upon maximizing profit from the land . . . which they likewise viewed as an exploitation process of an "inexhaustible" resource.

As land additions in the western U.S. increased profoundly until about 1850—then leveled off for the next 100 years (see Figure 2)—population density steadily increased from less than five per square mile (1810) to about 50 per square mile (1950). Despite the addition of Alaska and Hawaii to the total land area in the 1950s, the population density reached 61.2 by 1977, adding sustained pressures on already strained environmental resources: lakes, streams, oceans, land, and air, not to mention human resources and packing of people into cities like so many rats in cages with attendant noise, odor, and visual pollution. The freeway traffic snarls during the weekday rush hours of cities such as Los Angeles were replaced by weekend traffic jams in the national parks within commuting distance—Yosemite, Sequoia, Kings Canyon, and others—as urban refugees fled the hectic pressure cooker atmosphere of the modern smog-ridden metropolis. A recent environmental quality summary confirms the fact that our overall living conditions and resources are indeed steadily waning (see Figure 3).

Motor vehicle numbers and fuel usage increases (Figure 4) hastened the pace of transportation and of life in general, precipitating not only air pollution (and additional disease problems) and thousands of miles of unsightly roadways, but also mental and social problems which accrue to people living beyond their normal pace of living . . . rendering them ever more unable to cope with an accelerating array of problems demanding solutions on all sides. As Toffler has pointed out, "there is widespread agreement, reaching from historians and archaeologists all across the spectrum to scientists, sociologists, economists, and psychologists, that, many social processes are speeding up—strikingly, even spectacularly."[17] In the accelerating scheme of things we have adopted the throw-away milk

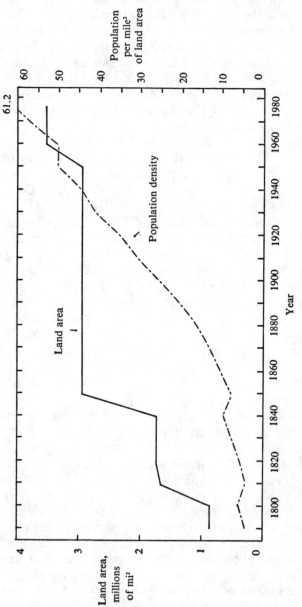

Figure 2. Land area and population density in the U.S. from 1790 to 1977.[14]

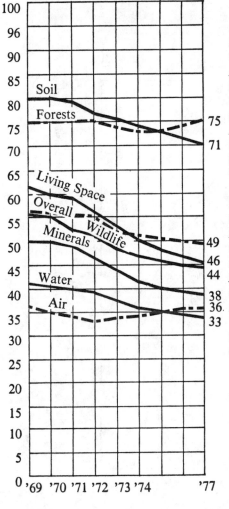

Soil: down, as four billion tons of were lost to erosion in 1977.

Forests: up, as forest lands have improved somewhat, but continued high world demand will add stress to this vital resource.

Living space: down; America is more crowded than ever, and land use planning remains more wish than reality.

Wildlife: down, as bad weather and habitat loss continued to deplete numbers of wild animals.

Minerals: down; mineral depletion continues far ahead of new discoveries.

Air: same; in some ways the original goals of the Clean Air Act seem more elusive than ever.

Water: down; industry is cleaning up its problems but towns and cities are not.

Figure 3. The environmental quality summary for 1969 to 1977 for the U.S. (a subjective analysis of the state of the nation's natural resources).[15]

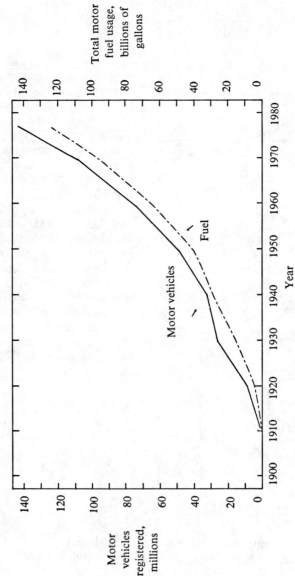

Figure 4. Motor vehicles (automobiles, buses, and trucks) registered and total motor fuel used in the U.S. from 1900 to 1977.[16]

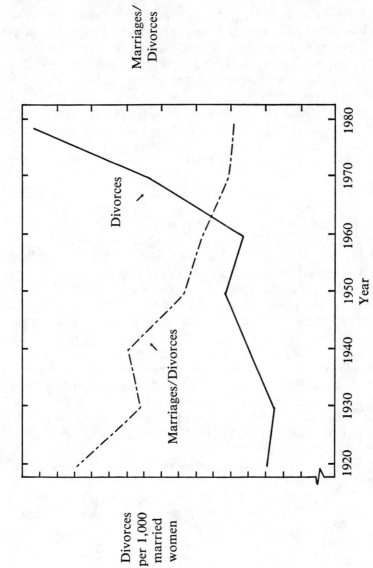

Figure 5. Divorces per 1,000 population and marriages/divorces in the U.S. from 1920 to 1979.[18]

carton, rent-a-secretary, transient and modular friendships, two-week pop best sellers, paper wedding gowns and temporary marriages, communes and homosexual daddies, frustrated and disowned children, pill-popping and drug abuse, and jet-lag syndrome. Figure 5 shows the appalling increase in divorces with about one divorce for every three marriages in 1979. Seemingly coupled to the divorce rate is a paralleled increase in the number of illegitimate births in the country (Figure 6). The crime rate has likewise soared, especially since about 1950, far beyond the rate of population increase. Total offenses have jumped almost exponentially to over 100 million in 1977 (Figure 7).

As lax morality rears its ugly head in the form of broken homes, illegitimate births, venereal disease, crime, delinquency, and pornography, the greed of spending beyond one's means is displayed by burgeoning debt in Figure 8. Private debt reached an incredible 2.5 trillion dollars in 1978, while public debt (debts of local, state, and federal governments) reached 1.006 trillion dollars, leaving a whopping debt of $16,112.13 for every man, woman, and child in the country! Most of this increase has occurred since 1940. The true debt *per taxpayer* in early 1979, however, according to the National Taxpayer's Union, was nearly $113,000 once all annuity programs and commitments were considered.[22] Welfare expenditures (Figure 9) have likewise spiralled since about 1940, the per capita social welfare costs being $701 in 1970, though only 40 years earlier the figure was a mere $33. People in need of legitimate welfare help—widows, the elderly, orphans, and the disabled—have recently been receiving less and less of the total outlays than those able but unwilling to work, or crooks who collect payments illegally.

Annual national health expenditures per capita (Figure 10) increased from a recent low of $22.65 in 1935 to a recent high figure of $646.11, reflecting not only the ravages of inflation and modern innovations in health care, but also the general deterioration of the health status of multiple millions of Americans. The soaring rate of chronic debilitative diseases is under-scored by the fact that one in four Americans is likely to contract some form of cancer during his lifetime, a rate which led to about 3.5 million cancer deaths during the 1970s.[25] At least 20 million Americans suffer from hypoglycemia, and over 300,000 people of all ages die of diabetes

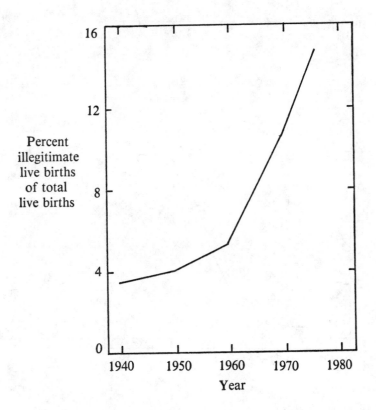

Figure 6. Percent illegitimate live births of total live births in the U.S. from 1940 to 1976.[19]

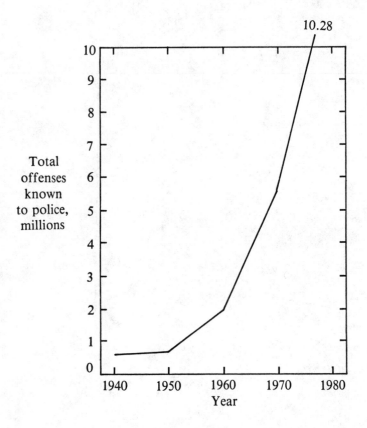

Figure 7. Total criminal offenses known to police in the U.S. from 1940 to 1977.[20]

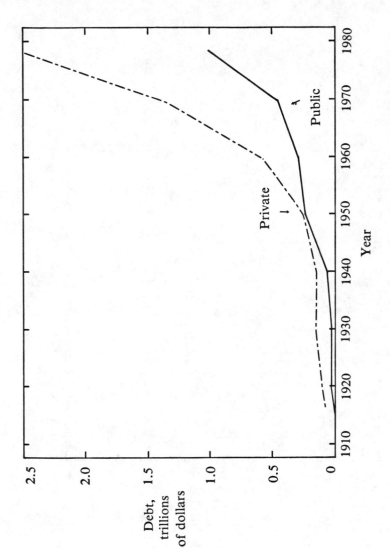

Figure 8. Net public and private debt for the U.S. from 1916 to 1978.[21]

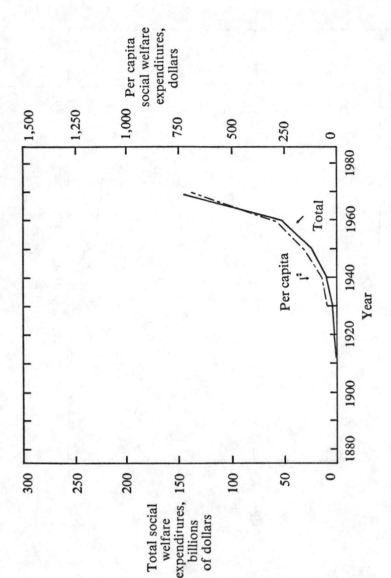

Figure 9. Social welfare expenditures, under public programs, total and per capital, for the U.S. from 1890 to 1970.[23]

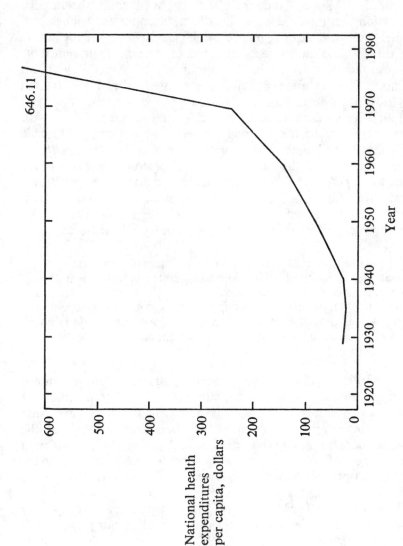

Figure 10. Per capita national health expenditures for the U.S. from 1929 to 1977.[24]

each year.[26] "Minor afflictions" such as head colds, bronchitis, constipation, hemorrhoids, and headaches account for a huge and extremely competitive drug market which claims much of the advertising on TV and radio—aspirin, time capsules, cough remedies, sedatives, and stimulants—for these ailments are endemic within a population feeding upon the highly processed, chemically treated foods of today's food industry. Lack of proper exercise, rest, and fresh air, despondent mental attitudes, and losing contact with nature contribute to the everyday miseries of millions of today's Americans. Rose Hume Hall, in *Food for Nought, the Decline in Nutrition,* speaks of the importance of the perceptive process for human well-being and the fact that it was originally designed for a natural environment, a fact that the food industry and government protective agencies would rather ignore. Regarding the GRAS (generally accepted as safe) list of food additives, Hall states:

> The regulatory agencies strive to present an external aura of rationality, but the process by which the GRAS committee arrives at their decisions is strictly intuitive, although the process is termed scientific judgment. On the other hand, if anyone wishes to dispute the decision to allow a particular chemical to enter the food supply, he is not allowed to use common sense, but must present hard scientific data to prove his case.[27]

Our sedentary, ill-fed, hectic-paced, polluted world is indeed leading us down a dead-end road, with virtually every indicator expressing a degenerative trend. Only a few such trends have been shown in this chapter; many more will be shown throughout the following chapters. Are we entering the end-time period, prophesied by the sages of old, known as "Jacob's trouble," the great cataclysmic upheaval which will envelop the entire earth in such misery and suffering that never again will this tribulation be equalled (Jer. 30:7; Dan. 12: 1; Matt. 24:21)? Trends within the United States indicate we have reached—and passed—the peak of our power, and, true to the guarantee of Leviticus 26:18-19, God is breaking the pride of our power. We have not "hearkened unto God," and are beginning to reap the curses of Leviticus 26:14-39 guaranteed to commandment breakers. We are following in the footsteps of Rome, that city which swelled into an empire, whose "prosperity ripened the principle of decay; . . . as soon as time or accident had removed the artificial supports, the stupendous fabric yielded to the pressure of its own weight."[28]

The Light Beyond the Present-day Clouds

Despite the terrific present and future problems of America and all nations of the earth, problems insoluble in the hands of men, a glorious future awaits those individuals called to inherit the Kingdom once these troubles have passed. It is the purpose of this presentation to shed light upon the nature of that future, to bring hope and vision in the midst of despondency and benightedness so characteristic of the present time. In fact, those truly looking forward to the Kingdom will experience great joy at the appearance of these hideous end-time signs. Isaiah spoke of a day when the Eternal will "lay the earth bare and wild, rendering it shapeless and scattering its inhabitants" (Isaiah 24:1). The earth and sky will droop, wither, and wane, "for earth has been polluted by the dwellers on its face, loose to laws and scorning statutes, breaking the eternal Compact" (Isa. 24:4-5). In verses six to 13 a guilty people in a cursed land is pictured, few in number, dying of famine and disease, finding no joy in life as towns fall to pieces, doors are bolted, and cities are devastated, a backdrop for which Isaiah writes,

> Some at this raise shouts of joy, acclaiming overseas the Eternal's might, bidding the East own the Eternal's might, and western shores acknowledge Israel's God; from earth's far bounds the chorus sounds, 'Now glory dawns for upright men!' (Isa. 24:14-16).

Leaders in politics, science, education, and industry have voiced for decades the necessity of a new world order—a world government—as the only real solution to global problems. Sir Winston Churchill once said,

> The creation of an authoritative all-powerful world order is the ultimate aim toward which we must strive. Unless some effective world super government can be brought quickly into action, the proposals for peace and human progress are dark and doubtful.[29]

U Thant said, in 1969,

> I do not wish to seem overdramatic, but I can only conclude from the information that is available to me as Secretary-General, that the Members of the United Nations have perhaps ten years left in which to subordinate their ancient quarrels and launch a global partnership to curb the arms race, to improve the human environment, to defuse the population explosion, and to supply the required momentum to development efforts. If such a global partnership is not forged within the next decade, then I very much fear that the problems I have mentioned will have reached such staggering proportions that they will be beyond our capacity to control.[30]

The lessons of history have shown, through Babylonian, Medo-Persian, Grecian, and Roman rule, that world government in the hands of man cannot work. Only a force far superior to man—God Almighty—is able to unite all nations into a workable union. Through His supreme laws a Kingdom will soon be established where true peace, harmony, prosperity, and love will reign on the earth. The environment, today sinking into degeneracy, is promised to blossom into its full potential and to be utilized properly and lovingly by men intent upon serving God, not other men.

What will that environment be like? More specifically, what sort of agricultural and agrarian system will spread over the entire earth once the new era begins? It is these basic questions which will be addressed in the following chapters; topics which are as scintillating as they are instructive, the comprehension of which will hopefully lead the reader into a more full and rich understanding of the wonderful, beautiful, productive world on ahead . . . a world designed for you and me, for humble folks that care about other people, the trees, the birds, animals, and fish, and the flowers at their feet.

Cultivators of the earth are the most valuable citizens. They are the most vigorous, the most independent, the most virtuous, and they are tied to their country, and wedded to its liberty and interests by the most lasting bonds.

Thomas Jefferson[1]

Chapter Two

Agriculture—the Foundation of Physical Life Past, Present, and Future

Today in America only 2.4 million farms* feed a total population of 218 million.[2] We are a nation of urban dwellers (see Figure 11), forced from the land by economic and social pressures of greater severity than at any other time in man's history,

---

* According to the 1978 Census of Agriculture's new definition of a farm (places having sales of agricultural products exceeding $1,000), the average U. S. farm is 450 acres with a gross income of about $47,000. These averages, however, have little meaning because of the wide variation in farm size and productivity. There are 55,000 farms with annual product sales of $200,000 or more, only 2.3% of the total farms but accounting for 35.5% of total farm product sales. At the other end of the spectrum, about 1.6 million farms with less than $20,000 in annual sales comprised 65.5% of the total farms but only 10.7% of total product sales. The operators of these smaller farms averaged only $2,300 in net farm income and $13,600 in off-farm income, while the farmers above $20,000 annual income averaged $19,100 in net farm income and $7,100 in off-farm income.[6]

perhaps even exceeding the pressures just prior to the Deluge of Noah's day (Matt. 24: 37-39). Many of us have lost touch with our "mother earth," the soils from which each of us has been fabricated ever since Adam and Eve were fashioned out of red clay and given breath, this despite the fact that George Washington once stated, "Agriculture is the most healthful, most useful and most noble employment of man."[4] Abraham Lincoln echoed his words nearly a century later: "No other human occupation opens so wide a field for the profitable and agreeable combination of labor and cultivated thought as agriculture."[5]

Yet, since that creation day nearly 6,000 years ago one extremely important fact has not changed: "Dust [we] are and [we] return to dust" (Gen. 3:19). Man still must depend on the land, the top few inches of soil covering the continents like a thin film on a globe, for producing food to sustain him physically.

Just as agricultural production now forms the foundational basis of physical wealth upon which all governments stand, so will the increase from the land provide the basis of physical wealth during the soon-coming worldwide millennial reign of Jesus Christ. Although the Kingdom will be ruled by the loving, guiding hand of Jesus Christ and His resurrected spirit brothers (Rom. 8:29; Rev. 5:10), the earth, still being physical, will be governed through the operation of material laws of the universe. The sun will still radiate its life-giving light to nourish and increase the green plants. Plants will require water to grow. Carbon from the air and minerals from the soil will be absorbed and fabricated into the wheat, rice, carrots, potatoes, and livestock which sustain human life.

The major change which will be wrought during this 1,000 year reign of Christ will be that Satan and his negative, degenerative underworld of darkness and subversion of God's perfect, natural, productive, and positive laws of spiritual living will be bound (Rev. 20:2-3). Christ withstood the tempting of Satan in the wilderness, using the power of God's Spirit, and qualified to rule the earth in his place (Matt. 4:1-11; Luke 4:1-13). Christ's rule, however, was not to commence until after 6,000 years of man's misrule on the earth under the sway of Satan's perverted powers. The 7,000 year plan for man, typified by the seven-day week with six days of labor and a seventh day of rest (Ex. 20:8-11)—each day representing 1,000 years (II Peter

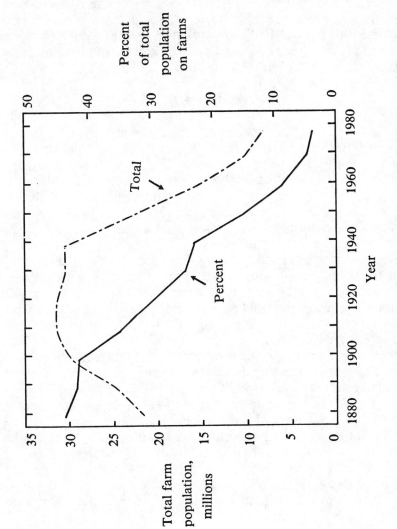

Figure 11. U. S. farm population totals and percent of the total from 1880 to 1978.[3]

3:8)—helps bring mankind an understanding of the true majesty, love, and omnipotence of a God whose ultimate concern with mankind is to extend His Family infinitely beyond the limits of the present "Elohim," or Family of God[7]: the Father, and His Son Jesus Christ.

The Necessity of Vision

With a multitude of signs about us indicating the imminence of Christ's return to utterly do away with Satan's corrupt society, it becomes imperative for God's select firstfruits, the modern-day Church in this spiritual wilderness, to possess a working, growing vision of the stupendous glory and order which will soon become extant on the earth. "Where there is no vision the people perish," remarked a God-inspired Solomon centuries ago (Prov. 29:18). On the converse, it may be said that when God's people possess a vivid, Scripturally grounded image of this Kingdom they will thrive and unite behind this great hope of the "restitution of all things" (Acts 3:21) which greets their enlivened imaginations each new day, which engenders hope and life amid the concrete jungles and unsightly scars of our cities, airports, landfills, and power lines that besmirch the face of our fruitful land.

What is this image of this soon-coming utopian era? What does Scripture reveal concerning its reality to paint us this glorious picture of a land restored to full God-like beauty and productivity? God inspired the words, "what no eye has ever seen, what no ear has ever heard, what never entered the mind of man, God has prepared all that for those who love him. And God has revealed it to us by the Spirit, for the Spirit fathoms everything, even the depths of God" (I Cor. 2:9-10). Here is the guarantee that God's elect in this present age, those chosen by Him to prepare for rulership in the Kingdom, can indeed form a profitable image of that incredibly beautiful, prosperous World Tomorrow.

Keys to Understanding Millennial Life

(1) God's way of love will be expressed in all things. The total emphasis will be on *living,* not on preoccupation with death. Today's

social and economic order express the character of the present God of this world, Satan (II Cor. 4:4; Eph. 2:2), whose way is summed up by GET, compared to God's way of GIVE and SERVICE. Since God created people "good" (Gen. 1:31), it is only through the temptation and deception of Satan—and the weakness of man's judgment when apart from God—that this perfect way of service was forsaken by Adam, Eve, and all of humankind ever since (Gen. 3). Despite near ly 6,000 years of man's Satan-directed rule on the earth the laws governing happiness, fulfillment, and abundant well-being for individuals on earth have not changed. God's laws of nature, such as gravity, if challenged by a skydiver who decides not to release his parachute, bring death. Likewise, laws of human behavior, implanted by the Creator in Adam and within all human beings ever since, exact their toll of spiritual travail if broken. These laws are summarized in the Ten Commandments (Ex. 20; Deut. 5) and have been extended in their spiritual intent by the great Master Teacher, Jesus Christ (Matt. 5: 17-30). They also bring untold peace of mind and abundant living if obeyed (Phil. 4:7; John 10:10).

(2) Man owns nothing in this life. As he was formed out of dust, to dust he must return (Gen. 3:19). He has taken nothing into the world, and he can take nothing material out of it when he dies (I Tim. 6:7). In fact, God's admonition is to seek after the Kingdom and His righteousness in order that all of the material, needful items of life—food, clothing, and the like—will be provided (Matt. 6:33), and then to the degree which He deems necessary (Prov. 30:8). God's ultimate objective is to "put everything under Him," and be "everything to everyone" (I Cor. 15:28), even to the point of wishing that every person having ever lived would not perish but be brought to repentance (II Peter 3:9). All the land belongs to God (Lev. 25:23), the nations being mere "drops in a bucket" (Isa. 40:15), wherein he has established the boundaries for races and nations (Deut. 32:8). All the silver and gold are His (Hag. 2:8). Although all that man possesses is given to him on a temporary basis, his stewardship is to be tempered with care and honesty (Luke 16:1-12).

(3) Nature can teach us God's principles as we observe how the natural environment about us operates. This idea was expressed by Paul in I Cor. 11:14 regarding hair length for men and women: "Surely nature herself teaches you. . . ." One may observe the

vibrant balance among the multitude of life forms in forests or prairies, the protective function of the stronger male gender of most species of animals, and the cycling of plant nutrients in soils from living to dead form, and back to living once again. Science becomes a vital tool for uncovering many truths in this area, although observation by nearly anyone may uncover many basic principles which nature does not easily hide.

Chapter Three

The Millennial Economic System

As soon as one speaks of *agriculture*, or "the science or art of cultivating the soil, producing crops, and raising livestock,"[1] he is thrust into the total lifestyle of man and society; and at the heart of any society lies an economic system. The Bible speaks a great deal about economics. At the present time we see around us a system largely perverted from its pure, God-created form. Yet, God set into action the economic principles by which all men and nations must operate in order that the production, development, and management of material wealth will be expedited to the greatest possible good of all. In fact, the only elements which support our present economic system and prevent its utter collapse are those elements we yet preserve from the Bible.

Profit Maximization vs. Love

At the present time a central theme of economic theory is maximization of profit,[2] essentially through production of the largest quantity of goods or services during the shortest period of time. This tenet is currently practiced in most industries, such as steel and automobile production, railroad and truck transportation, food processing, and even farming. As a recent text in soils has stated, ". . . agriculture has changed from a way of life to a business. . . ."[3] This system leads to dependence of most people on others for their employment and means of subsistence. Employers in turn depend upon the will of those who finance the business through interest-bearing loans. Satan's way is one of bondage, dependence, and quantity production of oftentimes inferior and monotonously uniform products.

God states, in contrast, "my yoke is kindly and my burden light" (Matt. 11:30). His guidelines guarantee independence for individuals and security for all, the production of quality products based on individual expertise, and spiritual principles by which quality and fulfillment are incorporated into the whole of life. These principles, summarized by the concept of "love" (Matt. 22:37-39), are based on the Ten Commandments and are expressed as "joy, peace, good temper, kindliness, generosity, fidelity, gentleness, self-control" (Gal. 5:22). The economic fruits of such a way of life—the very imprint of God's character—are extremely positive; for development of the individual character becomes the primary step toward the establishment of a system that provides the physical goods and services which aid in living life to its fullest. All actions, words, and thoughts become directed towards becoming a Son of God (II Cor. 10:5; II Cor. 6:18), a resurrected spirit being who may assist in lovingly but powerfully ruling as a king and priest during the Kingdom on earth (Rev. 5:10), a brother or sister to Christ (Rom. 8:29). Love of God (Matt. 12:30) and of one's neighbor (Matt. 19:19) replaces the love of money (I Tim. 6:10), for money of itself is cold and lifeless, good to no one, and if sought after before the one true God becomes idolatry (Matt. 4:10). One indeed can serve only one master, either God or money (Matt. 6:24). This present world, under Satan's sway, has chosen the latter master to serve. The difference between today's perverted system and that of the coming Kingdom is basically the difference between a civilization where the profit of living is *cash* and a civilization where the profit of living is *life*. The buying and selling of money has become the major concern of modern business, rather than the buying and selling of useful commodities as would naturally occur in a God-fearing society.

God's Simplistic System

A foremost characteristic of today's world is its hectic nature. We speak of the "rat-race", or the "dog-eat-dog" world where joy in awakening each morning to face the day is oftentimes replaced by the hopeless din of trucks, automobiles, and industrial machinery. Our frantic race to outproduce the unseen, vile monster of last year's profits drives executives to ulcers, hospitals, divorces, and delinquent children, all of which drain true productivity for the individual and for the nation. Mental and physical illnesses increase in proportion to the degree of technical sophistication one's environment places about him . . . to the degree one becomes removed from the ordered, fragrant, wholistic nature of the land around him. Demands of the job become too great, and the repercussions on one's personal life so pervasive after work hours, that oftentimes energies are depleted or misdirected for engaging the Christian's tools: prayer, Bible study, fasting, and meditation (I Thess. 5:17; II Tim. 2:15; I Cor. 7:5; Psa. 1:2). In fact, there appears to be a law of nature that as most of society tends to move further and further away from a pastoral life toward a highly sophisticated machine-oriented, gadget-ridden type of life, the amount of truly free, unencumbered time that individuals possess becomes proportionately reduced. Many rural citizens of less developed countries such as Indonesia[4] and Ecuador[5], while often not prosperous by modern Western standards, yet provide well for their physical sustenance while enjoying ample time for family and community activities. E.F. Schumacher in *Small is Beautiful: Economics As If People Mattered* has reiterated this law of economics:

> The amount of real leisure a society enjoys tends to be in inverse proportion to the amount of labour-saving machinery it employs.[6]

Moving from the industrial strains of Germany and the United States to a country like Burma, very low on the industrial scale, one finds an enormous amount of leisure time that people have to enjoy; the burden of life rests much more lightly on their shoulders than on Western workers' shoulders.[7]

Schumacher sees technology acting as a foreign body, whereas nature knows where and when to stop. Three crises have emerged today: (1) a revolt of human nature against inhuman technological, organizational, and political patterns, their being suffocating and debilitating; (2) the living environment that supports human life aches and groans and gives signs of partial breakdown; and (3) nonrenewable resources face exhaustion.[8] This way of life, based on materialism, cannot last long when permanent, limitless expansion is superimposed on a finite environment. Modern technology has "deprived man of the kind of work he enjoys most, creative, useful work with hands and brains, and given him plenty of work of a fragmented kind, most of which he does not enjoy at all."[9] When work is not enjoyed human energy levels decrease, debilitating the nation in an insidious but very direct way.

In the United States the Amish have largely shunned modern petroleum-based technological developments in their farming operations, preferring a horse and man-powered agriculture. They have reaped, in general, a harvest of strong family ties and marriages, few debts, little crime, and an active, personable community life.[10] Satan's way is one of forcing farmers from the land through economic pressures and the glittering lure of cosmopolitan life, packing them like so many rats into nauseatingly similar housing developments or apartment cubicles. Personal independence is largely replaced by dependence upon utility companies and the food industry to provide the essentials for living.

In contrast, God's way is simple, though one requiring diligent, concerted effort (Eccl. 9:10; Col. 3:23). Paul charged that "If a man will not work, he shall not eat" (II Thess. 3:10), and that a father must provide for his own family (I Tim. 5:8). The principles which govern economics are likewise simple, for they are inborn into the human race and operate because of the very design of man. Rather than following human reason, as did Adam and Eve when they disobeyed the Creator (Gen. 3)—following the desire of the flesh, the desire of the eyes, and the pride of life (I John 2:16)—man will automatically in the Kingdom reap the blessings of following God's ordained precepts governing individual and national economics.

The Principles of Giving and Service

As mentioned earlier the primary motivation of Godly individuals is that of giving—for "it is better to give than to receive" (Acts 20:35)—and service (Gal. 5:13). These ideals will be all-pervasive during the millennial reign of Christ. The model prayer given by Christ in Matt. 6:12 states, "forgive us our debts as we ourselves have forgiven our debtors." *Debt* is translated from the Greek *opheilema*, meaning "what is owing, or indebtedness."[11] A dual meaning is implied by this Scripture, in physical terms meaning the forgiveness of personal debts owed to another party but which for some reason were unable to be repaid, and in spiritual terms meaning a forgiveness of wrongs another person may knowingly or unknowingly have perpetrated against you (Matt. 6:14-15). The forgiveness of sins (debts) is so important in God's creative plan that His Son took the form of fleshly man, in all of its weaknesses, to be sacrificed to pay the price of sin for all of us. The Divine system of economics has this same element of sacrificial love: free sharing with those willing and able to share, and the forgiveness of debts.

God's instructions to Israel, as recorded in Deuteronomy 15, make clear this principle of giving without necessarily expecting anything in return (Luke 6:35). Although ideally there should have been no poor among the Israelites because of God's prosperity showered on them (Deut. 15:4), due to failure to completely follow this divinely-ordered economic system poverty did strike some. In such an eventuality God's directive was as follows:

> If you have a poor man, one of your fellow-countrymen, in any township of the land which the Eternal your God gives you, you must not harden your heart nor shut your hand against your poor brother; you must open your hand to him, lending him enough to meet his needs. Beware of letting the mean thought enter your head, 'But the seventh year, the year of remission is near!' so that you grudge help to your poor brother and give him nothing, till he cries to the Eternal against you, and you incur guilt. You must give to him and give cheerfully, for that will make the Eternal bless you in all your work and in whatever you undertake. Poor folk will never cease to be in the land; hence I command you to open your hand to your fellows, to the destitute and needy in your land (Deut. 15:7-11).

Jesus Christ restated this immensely important principle, giving it added spiritual importance and providing a glimpse at the attitudes which will be commonplace during the Kingdom:

If you only lend to those from whom you hope to get something, what credit is that to you? Even sinful men lend to one another, so as to get a fair return. No you must love your enemies and help them, you must lend to them without expecting any return; then you will have a rich reward, you will be sons of the Most High—for he is kind even to the ungrateful and the evil (Luke 6:34-35).

The Jubilee Year

Rooted at the very base of God's system of economics is a unique program of land ownership. "No land is to be sold in perpetuity, for the land is mine, and you are only guests of mine, passing wayfarers; you must allow land to be bought back anywhere in the country you hold" (Lev. 25:23-24). This system of land ownership which God instituted through Moses in ancient Israel provided the foundation for all economic activity of that "church in the wilderness" (Acts 7:38) amid a world of pagan economic systems. Each family had its own homestead, its own nucleus of property *never* to leave the family. Additional sons at birth received title to their own estate, compared to the present system of inheritance of land by reason of someone's death. A birth certificate was a title deed to an estate. Thus, in Israel children were an addition to the nation's wealth and not a drain upon its strained resources.

According to D. S. Milne, the clans of Scotland followed the patriarchal system of the Old Testament.[12] Every crofter had his own holding. The yeoman of England were also free and independent by virtue of their land, though the industrial revolution and the enclosure of land changed all this, creating a great landless laboring class at the mercy of others for their precarious and ill-paid jobs.[13] Even though working conditions and wages have improved during this past century, money and the machine—the products of modern economics—have become our ruthless masters instead of the beneficent servants they ought to be.

Every 50 years was a jubilee year during which, on the Feast of Trumpets, each man was to return to the homestead he had been given when first entering the land. Any buying or selling of land was done "in view of the number of years and crops till the next year of jubilee; as the years are many, you must increase the price, and as the years are few you must lower the price, for what is sold is the number of the crops" (Lev. 25:14-16). Land was always retained by the original title holder, eliminating land speculation and a fluctuating land market. Because of the payments made by the better managers to the owners of the land who may have fallen into hard times—whose land they rented—the income of families tended to be equalized. There was far less incentive to greedily absorb adjoining tracts of land into a gigantic "labor-efficient" operation when one acknowledged that a neighbor owned the land and would receive it back after several years. The reminder, "You must not defraud one another, but stand in awe of your God" (Lev. 25:17) tended to remind one of his responsibility to his neighbor, to love him as he loves himself (Matt. 19:19), and to "do unto others as he would have others do unto himself" (Matt 7:12).

A major point of present day economic theory which has baffled economists is the "Law of the Cycle."[14] The term "business or economic cycle" is ominous with a suggestion of hard times, such as occurred in the United States during the early 1930s. Economists have studied the problem from many angles and have confidently announced that these cycles should be conquered. They have supposedly designed financial devices, such as the F.D.I.C. (Federal Deposit Insurance Corporation), the F.S.L.I.C. (Federal Savings and Loan Insurance Corporation), and interest rate manipulations of the Federal Reserve System, to smooth out the business curves . . . all to no avail. The cycles continue to appear.

Yet, cycles in business should be no mystery, for cycles are inherent in virtually everything God has created: day and night, where the night repairs the ravages of the day; work and rest, rest restoring to the body the energies to continue productive work; the seven-day week; the seven-year land cycle; nutrient cycling in soils; the hydrologic cycle; life to death, and from death to life; planets cycling around the sun, and stars circuiting the galaxy; electrons encircling the atom's nucleus at nearly the speed of light; the cycling of experiences, and repetitions of history. Alongside the daily, weekly, and seven-year cycles appears the God-ordained 50-year cycle. Instead of being a time of heartache, repossession of land, and gloom this Jubilee year is pictured as a time of joy and restoration of lands! An examination of economic charts for the past 180 years tends to reveal periods of business contraction (recession) approximately each seven years, and deeper dips every 50 years (Figure 12). Instead of debt loads being heaped upon individuals and corporations until paid, God's system calls for a *release* from corporate obligations, and a return of all land to the original owners. This was not a form of Socialism or Communism, but God's justice in setting up the freest and most helpful type of individualism imaginable!

Men have been blinded to the true ways of God that would lead them into the brilliantly uplifting knowledge of economic law (II Cor. 4:4; Rom. 1:20-22). This law of the Jubilee is cast in letters of iron on the Liberty Bell in Philadelphia, Pennsylvania: "Proclaim liberty throughout all the land to all the inhabitants thereof."[19] This proclamation of liberty is meant to imply economic liberty, the economic liberty of the Jubilee year from which this Biblical passage was quoted (Lev. 25:8-13). Our ignorance makes the Jubilee a time of distress and agony.

The Land Sabbath

Every seven years a land sabbath was to be observed, during which time the land rested: it was neither sown to a crop nor were vineyards pruned. Six years were allowed for tilling and sowing fields, pruning vineyards, and gathering the produce from them. The sixth year was to yield a triple blessing of crops which would provide food on into the ninth year; only natural produce of the land could serve as food for the Israelites during the seventh year (Lev. 25:1-7, 18-22). In addition, all loans to fellow Israelites were cancelled after the sixth year. No pressure was to be applied to collect this debt except in the case of collecting from a foreigner, who could be coerced to pay (Deut. 15:1-3). Again, the principle of giving is seen as an integral part of the Divine economic principles instituted from the beginning of man's brief tenure on earth by an all-knowing, all-powerful God.

This land sabbath, while providing numerous physical benefits ("The sabbath was made for man, not man for the sabbath;" Mark 2:27) was above all a matter of faith . . . for the entire nation of Israel was to observe it, meaning utter faith had to be placed in God to provide a triple yield the sixth year *or Israel would cease to be a nation!* Without food, starvation and disease would decimate the

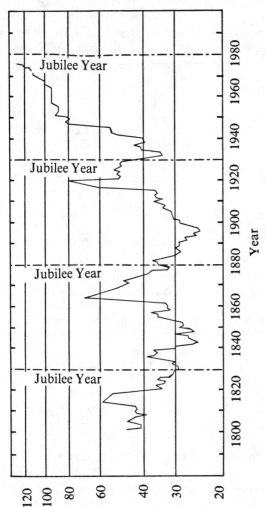

Figure 12. U.S. average wholesale prices and Jubilee Years from 1800 to 1980.[15] Business cycles are characteristic of industrial economies and have been attributed to a number of causes such as individual consumption and saving habits, overinvestment by business in capital goods, psychological factors, the amount of money and credit circulating in the economy, the rate of inventions and innovations, and wars.[16] Financial panics and crisis often precede depressions, occurring during recent U.S. history in 1819, 1837, 1857, 1873, 1893, and 1929.[17] A period of depressed business activity and prices follows these financial crises, as indicated in the above graph. Although wholesale prices do not reflect the total economic atmosphere for a certain time span, they do strongly indicate upswings and downswings of economic activity in highly industrialized capitalistic societies. If the Jubilee Years are indicated correctly on the graph,[18] then in every case that a Jubilee has occurred in the U.S. since 1800 a corresponding period of depression has also occurred, beginning before the Jubilee and bottoming out some years after. What is to occur after 1980?

population, and the inhabitants would be forced to forage for themselves. Total faith in a very real physical sense was needed by ancient Israel to assure physical survival of individuals and that "church in the wilderness," just as faith on a spiritual plane is required to assure spiritual existence and growth among those called out of this society (Hab. 2:4; Rom. 1:17).

Among the physical benefits of the land sabbath are (1) resting and rejuvenation of the soil after six years of treatment by man, (2) rest for the people from their agricultural labors, providing time for planning the next six years of farming and extra study and travel, and (3) the economic benefits of debt release already mentioned. While these and other benefits may accrue to those keeping the land rest, surely faith comprises a major part of God's purpose in having man observe this holy time.

The common thread running throughout God's economic principles is *provision dependent on need*. In the "Sermon on the Mount" Christ clearly pointed out the following:

> Ask and the gift will be yours, seek and you will find, knock and the door will open to you; for everyone who asks receives, the seeker finds, the door is opened to anyone who knocks. Why, which of you, when asked by his son for a loaf, will hand him a stone? Or, if he asks a fish, will you hand him a serpent? Well, if for all your evil you know to give your children what is good, how much more will your Father in heaven give good to those who ask him? (Matt. 7:7-11).

If Christ provides for even the wild birds of the field, and man is worth so much more than they are (Matt. 6:26), then people as well ought to be as Christ (I Peter 2:21) and provide for those in need. His command to His 12 disciples on their being sent to the lost sheep of Israel was to "give without being paid, as you have got without paying" (Matt. 10:8). When the Israelites were about to leave Egypt an instruction from God was "if any household is too small for a lamb, then the man and his next neighbour must take one between them, reckoning the lamb in proportion to what each member of the family can eat" (Ex. 12:4). Less wealthy Israelites were assisted in their need by those able to help. A type of millennial sharing according to need also occurred among the believers in Jerusalem after having received the Holy Spirit: "they shared all they had with one another, they would sell their possessions and goods and distribute the proceeds among all, as any one might *be in need"* (Acts 2:44-45).

A brief comment by Josephus on life during the pre-Deluge world, before Cain's great perversion of Divine precepts, indicates a world closely akin to the ideal of providing according to need:

> He [Cain] also introduced a change in that way of simplicity wherein men lived before, and was the author of measures and weights. And whereas they lived innocently and generously while they knew nothing of such arts, he changed the world into cunning craftiness.[20]

Usury and Taxation

A major flaw of the present world Satanic economic system is the charging of interest (usury) on loans by the banking system, or money for the use of money. Money collected by banks on loans, using deposits of other people's money, is channeled into the coffers of a nonproductive system of stone, pillared edifices. Yet, the taking of interest is condemned throughout the Bible (Psa. 15:5; Lev. 25:36; Prov. 28:8; Ezek. 18:8). In Ezekiel 22:12 the charging of interest for loans is grouped along with extorting one's neighbor, on the heels of lasciviousness, bloodshed, and desecrating the Sabbath in previous verses. God's system requires that credit be given as a help, a lift, and a true favor to the man in need. Contrary to the present banking system which multiplies credit through the multiplication of debt (see Figure 13), God's credit system creates loans *without* the multiplication of debt, a true masterpiece of economic legislation.

This same Divine law that prohibits interest also practices *increase* all of the time. Instead of "dead money" artificially yielding a paltry 3, 4, 5, or 10%, Jesus Christ declared that the interest he pays to men yields in some instances thirtyfold, some sixty, some a hundredfold (Matt. 13:8, 23).

Since man does not own the land, man should not be expected to pay taxes on this foundational source of national wealth. Neither does the land have any assessed valuation. Yet, God demands a "tax," or "tithe," of all the increase from the land (Lev. 27:30-33). How, then, can this tax be paid by the individual? It should come as

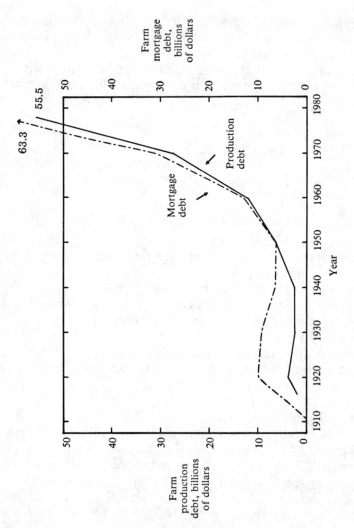

Figure 13. Farm production and mortgage debt in the U.S. from 1916 to 1978.[21]

no shock that *God* is the one who pays this tax, but this tax, in God's system, is not against the value of the land; it is against the annual natural increase of the land! The produce consumed by the family's living is not taxed in the lease, but only the surplus over and above this amount by a mere 10%; this amount rises and falls annually with the abundance of the increase. The property tax is a form of piecemeal confiscation by the government imposing the tax, bringing citizens into greater and greater subservience to a governmental system which Satan heads (Luke 4:6); see the present trends in farm taxation in Figure 14.

Tithes collected were used to support the Levitical priesthood (Num. 18:24) who had no inheritance of land from which to pay tithes (Num. 18:23). Their function was to administrate the religious and governmental affairs of the nation (Num. 1:50-51), for in ancient Israel Church and State were one. The tithe supported all public activities, much more than taxes do: government, religious worship, legal matters, health care, education, and public welfare. Today in the United States taxes consume more than 36 cents of every earned dollar,[23] these local, state, and federal taxes supporting public activities much less effectively and comprehensively than in ancient Israel.

Besides the first tithe a second tithe was saved for attending the various seasonal festivals (Deut. 14:22-26), an "enforced vacation" to enrich the nation spiritually and keep them in mind of God's Master Plan for mankind. Every third year a tithe was deposited in the home and used that year and the following two to support the needs of the Levites, resident aliens, orphans, and widows in each community (Deut. 14:28-29). Never before has a system been devised which so thoroughly complements human needs but maximizes personal incentive and productive work, while encouraging independence in living and assisting the development of strong family ties and community life based upon the laws of love.

With this economic backdrop as a starting point, what then are the brilliantly optimistic realities to look forward to in the Kingdom of God? The answers to this question are quite shocking at times, though always uplifting as the knowledge that the present system with all of its inequities, turmoil, and heartaches will soon be past.

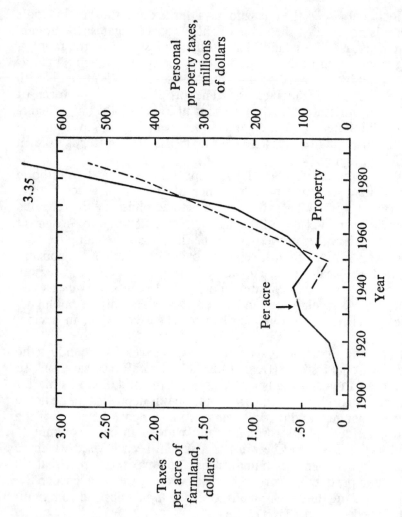

Figure 14. Taxes per acre of farmland and farm personal property taxes from 1890 to 1977 in the U. S.[22]

Chapter Four

Millennial Land Use and Community Setting

T o step back and view the present world's system from
without, as if one is not a direct part of it, is at times difficult
to do but is essential to grasp the vision of the Kingdom.
God's people are indeed ambassadors on Christ's behalf to this
world's nations (II Cor. 5:20). One must be willing to challenge entrenched thoughts to gain insights into the glorious Kingdom soon to
overtake the earth as surely as the sun rises in the east each day.

The principle guiding land use in the Kingdom will be to fit use of
the land into God's natural scheme set into play at the re-creation of
the earth's surface 6,000 years ago. Today man attempts to bend
nature to fit into his own plans, plans largely oriented around the
profit maximization motive of big business; in the Kingdom land will
be allowed to produce only what it is able under a natural system of
land management. Instead of gargantuan four-wheel drive tractors
plying hundred-acre fields, neglecting to care for an eroding hillock
here or a pheasant nest there, every acre of land will be tended as a
valuable resource to be upgraded and preserved for generations to
come. With land remaining in the family perpetually, the joy of
maintaining the productivity and proper use of each land parcel will
continually spur each land tenant (for God owns the land) toward
righteousness in land management.

Sizes of Individual Holdings

A key to understanding proper land use is to visualize how large an average land holding might be. Micah 4:3-4 states, in referring to the Kingdom,

> He [God] will decide disputes of many races, and arbitrate between strong foreign powers, till swords are beaten into plowshares, spears into pruning-hooks; no nation draws the sword against another, no longer shall man learn to fight, but live each underneath his vine and underneath his fig-tree, in terror of no one.

Here *each* man is pictured as possessing land. Indeed, if God's Spirit fills the earth as water fills the oceans (Isa. 11:9) all people will learn to be humble (Greek *praus,* or "meek, easy, mild;" Matt. 5:5) as God stamps His character on all mankind (Isa. 2:3). God's promise is "Blessed are the humble! They will inherit the earth" (Matt. 5:5), a dual prophecy that spiritually applies to God's chosen firstfruits who will be resurrected at the commencement of the millennium (Rev. 20:6) and given rulership over "cities," or regions of the earth (Luke 19:11-24), but which has been applied physically perhaps countless times throughout man's history. Witness the case of Judah's downfall when Nebuchadnezzar, king of Babylon, removed the remnant of those in Jerusalem to captivity in Babylon.

> But Nebuzar-adan the captain of the guard left of the *poor* of the people, which had nothing, in the land of Judah, and gave them vineyards and fields at the same time (Jer. 39:10).

During the "America fever" days,[2] when hordes of Europeans traversed the Atlantic Ocean to settle the newly opened lands under the Homestead Act of 1862, 250 million acres of land were distributed within 40 years. Even the poor, landless immigrants could afford the $1.25 per acre fee to acquire ownership of 160 acres.[3] The inscription attached to the base of the Statue of Liberty typifies the character of these people flocking to settle the fertile, virgin lands of America: "Give me your tired, your poor, your huddled masses yearning to breath free, the wretched refuse of your teeming shore . . . ."[4]

Virtually all families, as in ancient Israel, will be given permanent land holdings to be passed on to sons and daughters forever, as long as the earth exists, which land ownership has already been shown to form the basis for Godly individuality within a nation of future saints, whose express purpose in life is to develop character to become Gods. The size of these holdings will be small enough to (1) support the food, fuel and cultural needs of the family as well as (2) enable the land to be properly cared for in the interest of upgrading and maintaining the soils, grasslands, forests, and living creatures. In 1880 the average U.S. farm size was 134 acres[5] when 4'.8% of the work force was in farming.[6] By 1960 the farm size had jumped to 297 acres on which 8.7% of the population lived and farmed.[7] An average American farm in 1979 averaged 440 acres,[8] and only about 3.5% of the population farmed it[9] (see Figures 11 and 15) using a higher per capita capital investment than for any other industry in the world. For earning a modest $20,000 profit in 1978 a $300,000 or greater investment was needed for an eastern Nebraska corn-swine farmer, or $2,000,000 for a sizeable cow-calf operation in northern Nebraska![11] In order to squeeze out an income once interest and debt payments (most farmers exist year-to-year on borrowed money), income, property, and other taxes, and soaring, inflation-fueled production costs are met, the farmer must foresee widely-fluctuating prices for his produce and confiscation of much of his land by inheritance taxes should he even be able to purchase his land before he dies.

These pressures by government policies that encourage bigness of farms and smallness in farm population[12] will be nonexistent in the Kingdom. As mentioned earlier, land and commodity speculation will be eliminated through permanent, non-transferable land holdings. Taxes will be minimal and proportional to the increase of the land God provides over and above personal family needs. Since God and His perfect laws and personality will be entwined within the very fabric of day-to-day living among individuals farming the land, and within the government of spirit beings lovingly administrating these laws, the fruits of the Spirit will be extant in all things (Eph. 1:18-23). Rather than today's world of ulcer-ridden apprehension about getting the crop planted and harvested with the threat of foul weather, machinery breakdowns, low prices, unavailability of fer-

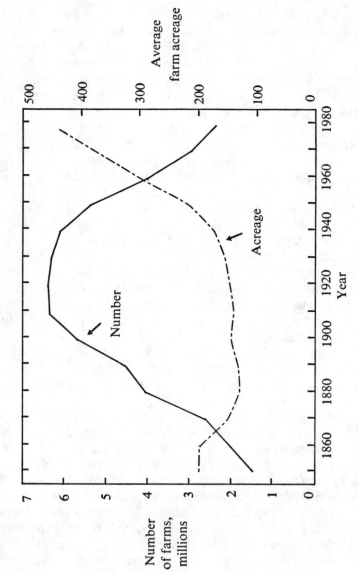

Figure 15. Number and average size of U. S. farms from 1850 to 1979.[10]

tilizers, seeds, fuel, herbicides, and pesticides, and burdensome loan and tax costs, a society filled to the brim with "whatever is true . . . whatever is just, whatever is pure, whatever is attractive, whatever is high-toned, all excellence, all merit" (Phil. 4:8) will greet farmers bent on serving God.

Actual farm size may vary from place to place depending on the regime of the country and natural productivity of the soil. Total land area in the United States in 1970 was about 3.5 billion acres.[13] Total farmland that year was 1.1 billion acres[14] when the population of the country totaled 203 million.[15] Average family size was 3.6 people per family,[16] giving about 56.4 million families. If this farmland was equally divided (for purposes of calculation) among all of these families, then each would possess 19.5 acres, or roughly 20 acres per family. In most areas of the country where rainfall is adequate to grow field crops, 20 acres is ample to raise enough vegetables, fruit trees, livestock, grain crops, pasture, and timber to supply the needs of an industrious, independent family . . . even in the present age! How much more would a family be able to support its livelihood on land even better suited for crop growth through proper land management and livestock raising techniques, as well as vastly improved weather conditions nationwide. Rather than the present energy-wasteful system of producing food on farms and transporting it to wholesale marketers for processing and retail distribution, food will be used where it is produced. Rather than the present attitudes of affluence, waste, and impermanence, sufficiency (Phil. 4:10), permanence (Heb. 13:8), and resource conservation will be the rule.

Cycling Within the Millennial Setting

Millennial land use will be in full harmony with the God-ordained tenets of the natural world, obvious to anyone wishing to notice them. A principle concept of this natural world is *cycling,* the cycling of water, plant nutrients, energy, organic matter, and even beauty that is inherent in every natural environment one may encounter. Figures 16 and 17 illustrate this cycling for two major elements (carbon and nitrogen) and all materials which flow through the ecosystem; these figures, however, oversimplify the vast number of

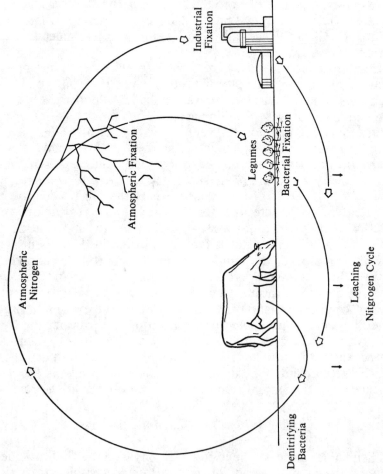

Figure 16. The cycling of nitrogen and carbon within the environment.[17]

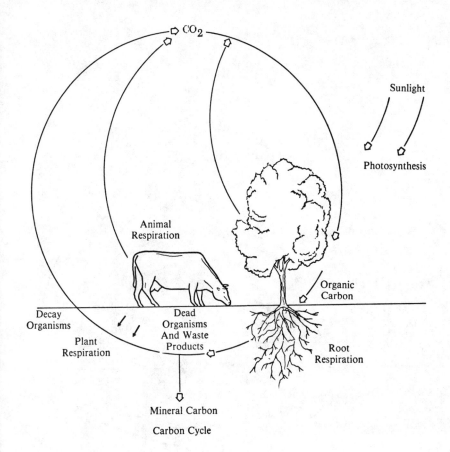

Carbon Cycle

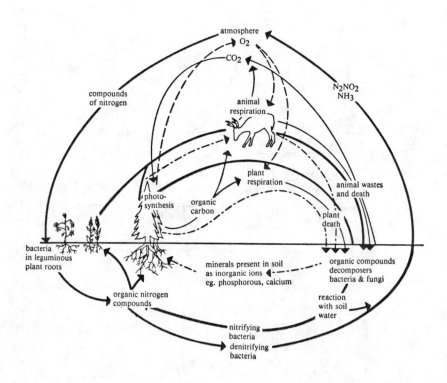

Figure 17. The cycling of materials through the ecosystem.[18]

materials and transformation states which involve subatomic particles, photons and "energy," molecules, bacteria and other microbes, and visible plants and animals in land, sea, and air. In a forest the leaves fall from trees and shrubs, only to be decayed with passing months to yield a rich, humic layer that seals the forest floor from the destructive forces of erosion. Plant nutrients are released by microbiological action from this decaying mat for reuse by the trees as rains continually replenish stores of moisture lost through evaporation and transpiration. Carbon dioxide is "fixed" within the cells of chlorophyll-rich leaves to fabricate the compounds necessary for growth, and life-giving oxygen is released to the air. The carbon dioxide is eventually released from the decaying leaves and organic matter by oxygen-consuming microorganisms, an intricate, dynamic balance being reached within each specific forest environment around the world from tropical jungles to Arctic boreal forests. Earthworms, centipedes, actinomycetes, algae, fungi, bacteria, protozoa, and a host of other live creatures mix and mingle, mostly in the upper few inches of soil and decaying organic remains, synthesizing acidic compounds that aid in the release of mineral elements and sometimes fixing nitrogen from the atmosphere, making it useable to the tree. As leaves flourish, die, and are replaced by additional leaves the entire face of the forest is renewed. Trees and undergrowth die but are soon replaced by other foliage springing from seeds or expanding from nearby growth. Ugly scars of death are quickly healed by the rejuvenating forces of life as beauty itself is cycled from a disfigured scene.

A prairie environment follows the same laws of cycling, but with grasses, a dense mat of roots in the surface foot or so of soil provides added organic enrichment. America's native grasslands have bequeathed to the country the world's richest, most productive soils, the native topsoil organic matter content oftentimes exceeding 10%.[19] The cycles of nutrient elements, organic matter, water, carbon dioxide and oxygen, function as in the forest. The massive carpet of stems and roots is virtually immune to erosion, even under moderate grazing.

In order for man to live in harmony with these natural laws of cycling he must dramatically alter the social, economic, and environmental setting of his communities. Today, food is transported to cities where it is consumed and flushed into sewage systems, and from there to rivers and on into the ocean. The system is "open-ended" according to Barry Commoner, a circle that is not closed aimed at extracting mineral wealth from the soil and funneling it to the oceans with no hope of return.[20] Attempts to recycle sewage from cities back to the land have been met head on by prohibitive transportation costs of the slurry, high costs and other difficulties of application, and heavy metal contamination due to the presence of industrial wastes and modern home chemical agents which find their way into the drain. The rich mineral and organic content of sewage is viewed as a filthy, odorous burden to be quickly gotten rid of rather than used as a potentially valuable fertilizer. Again, economics dictates the cheapest short-term solution to the problem: dumping the sewage into the river, letting it become the problem of every other city along the river's course to yield the modern Mississippi, Rhine, and Thames Rivers, veritable dead bodies of flowing synthetic chemicals and refuse.

The Self-sustaining Community

In contrast to Satan's present system, whereby plant nutrients flow one-way to cities and produce unused, polluting waste products, God's system is simple and energy efficient. With small land holdings upon which people live and work, producing their material and spiritual contributions within an energic, healthful social setting, food sufficient for each family would be produced right on the land. It would also be consumed at or near its point of origin. The waste products, both human or animal, could easily be returned to the land from which it came, completing the cyclic flow of plant nutrients from soil to table to soil again.

This concept of a self-sustaining community would not be limited to food sources. Since neighbors would be relatively near and relationships uniformly loving and congenial, with all citizens of God's nation encouraged to perfect God-given talents (Matt. 25:14-28), there would be no lack of abilities and skills to contribute to a vibrantly fulfilling and abundant family and community social structure. Playmates for growing, untainted children would be across the meadow, or down the pathway a few minutes' walk away. There would be no fear of wild animals, for their very nature will be changed (Isa. 11:6), and dangerous roads with automobile traffic will not exist. God's Spirit rulers will be everywhere, educating people in how to live loving, uplifting, righteous lives . . . to lead each individual towards reliance upon God's ways (Obad. 21: Micah 4:5). Since land holdings would not be large a family could quite easily raise the vegetables, fruits, and livestock necessary for its sustenance in relatively little time each day, the remaining time being devoted to gaining the essentials required for living in a civilized society ("reading, writing, and arithmetic"). Individual abilities will likely expand on an apprentice-type basis, learning skills of those already skilled. Principles of astronomy, physics, chemistry, the biological world (all pointing to God's existence), and especially of God's truth (II Pet. 3:18) will likely be everyday topics of advancing intellects as individuals come to understand that growing is a never-ending, uplifting, God-plane process (Eph. 4:13; I Thess. 5:21). Satan has pictured the learning process as negative and morose in his attempts to conceal his true identity. Thus, he attempts to lead mankind into a knowledge of evil, as he is indeed the "father of lies" (John 8:44) and confronts mankind with an assault of deception, conflict, and perversion through television, radio, printed matter, and evil examples of behavior through other people.

Land Use According To Its Potential

Today's system of land use management casts a dark, strangling net over the freedoms and hopes of people nearly everywhere in the United States. Recent federal legislation permits the establishment of 10 regions across the nations which have been empowered to dictate land use planning. As early as 1934 the U.S. government was calling for federal control of all land, public and private.[21] Assistant Secretary of Agriculture Rexford Tugwell stated,

We have depended too long on the hope that private ownership and control would operate somehow for the benefit of society as a whole.

That hope has not been realized. . . . Private control has failed to use wisely its control of the land. We are preparing a land program not merely for the benefit of those who hold title to it but for the greater welfare of all the citizens of the country.[22]

Tugwell, incidentally, authored the Newstates Constitution, a document designed to replace the present Constitution once the present government has fallen in ruins.[23] His conclusion that private citizens cannot judiciously manage land for the optimum good of the public is, of course, true; however, his rationale that a government in Satan's power can do better is a bit hard to grasp.

In 1968 Robert Weaver, former head of Housing and Urban Development, expressed in testimony before the California state legislature that "Federal regionalism means federal control of all the land wherever it may exist, anywhere in the United States."[24] Under the guise of "environmental concern," farmers, ranchers, and businessmen are being convinced to give control of the land back to the government which first gave control of the land to its citizens.[25]

Farmers could potentially be told what crop to plant in a field, or be refused government subsidies or threatened with fines or imprisonment for not falling into step with federal land use plans. Even with full federal guidelines for land use, planning the countryside would still be oriented around the burgeoning cities—where most people, power, and money reside, and urban understanding of the value of soils and crops is seldom realized. This is Satan's no-win plan, a confused, ill-constructed patchwork of men's laws.

God's plan for land use has already been largely outlined. Each parcel of land with its unique combination of soils will be treated lovingly by permanent owners intent on building the land for future generations. There will be no square mile sections of land with no woods or pasture and little wildlife to break up the landscape:

Woe to men who add house to house,
Who join one field to another,
Till there is room for none but them
In all the land! (Isa. 5:8).

In the same paragraph the Eternal through Isaiah proclaims the fate of people who construct cities and farmlands in this manner:

Many a mansion is to lie forlorn,
Splendid and spacious and—empty!
For ten acres of vineyard shall yield
   but eight gallons,
And the harvest shall only be a tenth
   of what is sown (Isa. 5:9).

The entire setting of this prophecy pictures almost precisely our modern urban and rural society. An atmosphere of "get," or forcing from the land all it is able to give, is the pervading theme, a theme will be dealt with in the following sections.

In the extremely fertile prairie pothole region of the Upper Midwest, sloughs and swales were commonly the heavens of ducks, geese, and multitudes of other waterfowl and game before large-scale drainage, beginning about 1835,[26] largely eliminated their habitats. Tractors with their large machines were difficult to maneuver around the cattail-bordered ponds. An abundance of ducks was delightful but cold cash spoke more loudly, and large-scale drainage commenced. Then floods increased in frequency and severity, for water normally held in sloughs and slowly released to the groundwater now swept quickly through.

Pastures are overgrazed as they have been for centuries, inviting accelerated erosion and the proliferation of undesirable plant species. Forests have often been eliminated from lands best left wooded for the sake of erosion control and most profitable long-term land use. Even today forests are at times clear-cut rather than selectively cut, the former usually being more economically expedient in terms of today's profit-worshipping economic theory, but being death to many slopes which are left bereft of protective cover.

Erosion Eliminated—Organic Matter Retained

Millennial agriculture will also incorporate the principle of zero soil erosion. Like erosion of moral character, family life, music quality, and a host of other facets of modern society, the erosion of the soil insidiously and relentlessly reaps its grim toll. As with unprotected Godly character, an unprotected soil loses the most valuable life-filled fraction first: the organic matter. This organic fraction of the soil may be compared to the spiritual content of a Christian, in a state of continual equilibrium between additions and losses: reduced by excessive tillage but enhanced through judicious husbandry, able to absorb rainfall (spiritual food) liberally when high in organic content (a full spiritual life; Heb. 6:7), but shedding the rainfall to bring destructive, erosive floods when low in organic life and improperly managed (James 3).

Unless this fraction is somehow replaced year-by-year through crop residue additions, the trend of soil life is downhill . . . and with it the soil properties so vital to a highly productive soil environment.* Soil structure or aggregation, perhaps the foremost property of a soil, depends primarily on organic mucilaginous substances and plant roots for its development and strength.[28] Though wetting and drying, freezing and thawing, tillage, and soil cations all play a part in generating and stabilizing soil aggregates,[29] the influence of soil life—decaying organic matter and the slimes from microbes and other forms of life, together with the physical activity of roots and soil animals—is the greatest in promoting soil structure.[30] Intimately related to soil structure are porosity, bulk density, and water permeability and percolation, all of which are in turn related to the

---

* The functions of soil organic matter are as follows: (1) reduces the impact of falling raindrops and permits clear water to seep gently into the soil, reducing runoff and erosion; (2) produces slimes and microbial germs that help form a desireable soil structure; (3) live roots decay and provide channels for luxuriant root growth and water percolation; (4) provides food for earthworms, ants, and rodents; (5) trashy organic remains reduce losses from wind and water erosion; (6) surface mulches lower soil temperatures and keep soils warmer in winter; (7) reduction of evaporation losses by organic mulches; (8) on decomposition, some of all nutrients required for plant growth are provided, as well as many hormones and antibiotics; (9) enhances available water capacity; (10) buffers against rapid chemical changes when lime and fertilizers are added; (11) organic acids released during decomposition help dissolve minerals and make them available to plants; (12) humus provides a storehouse for exchangeable and available cations; (13) fresh organic matter makes soil phosphorus more available; (14) certain plant diseases may be inhibited by adding organic residues.[27]

rate at which water may enter the soil and move through its mass to the subsoil for storage. Less organic matter generally implies less granular soil structure, fewer and smaller pores, a lower bulk density, less absorptive capacity (the organic matter benefits soil water-holding capacity more through favorable effects on structure than through added capacity of the sponge-like humus; the humus has a high wilting coefficient)[31] and lower rates of water movement into and down through the soil. Thus, less organic matter leads to more runoff of precipitation, increased flooding, and soil erosion with its attendant loss of additional organic and mineral matter, muddying of streams, and covering of fertile lowland soils by poorer hillside deposits. The ravages of runoff and erosion tend to be compounded even further by structure-destroying practices such as tillage with heavy farm equipment, high-speed tillage, and tillage under wet conditions, all three practices common in today's pressure-packed "get the corn in before May"[32] syndrome. Perhaps no other single soil component has such a far-reaching influence on total soil properties as does organic matter, necessitating its continued maintenance at near-virgin levels for a nation to achieve the full use of its land resources.

Because of the concentration of organic matter in the surface soil and its low density, organic matter is among the first constituents to be removed through erosion but among the hardest to replace.[34] Nitrogen, a crucial plant nutrient and oftentimes the limiting factor in crop production, parallels organic matter losses, with enrichment ratios* of 3.0 to 5.0 for each being common.[36] Oftentimes more nitrogen, phosphorus, and other elements are lost to erosion and leaching each year than to crops harvested (see Figure 18). For South Dakota soils during 65 years of farming, a very *short* period of time compared to the farming histories of European countries, a full 40% of the original organic matter has been lost (Figure 19). Since about 1950 when this survey was made additional losses have occurred.

---

* Enrichment ratio = $\dfrac{\text{concentration of the element in soil}^{35} - \text{materials in runoff}}{\text{Concentration of the element in soil from which runoff originated}}$.

Different cropping systems produce different rates of organic matter loss as revealed in Figures 20 and 21. In South Dakota (Figure 20) all crops, including a grass harvested for forage, diminished the organic matter level, whereas in Ohio annual gains in soil organic content were registered for grasses and legumes (Figure 21). Total soil losses vary widely, from high values of up to 89 tons per acre in 16% sloping corn fields (Wisconsin) down to 0.002 tons per acre for 10% sloping forested areas (North Carolina).[41] Pimental and his co-workers have estimated that average erosive soil loss in the U.S. on agricultural land is about 12 tons per acre;[42] Brink and others estimate the loss to be from 5.2 to 8.6 tons per acre annually.[43] Since Mc Cracken has estimated that soils form at a rate of only 1.5 tons per acre per year under normal agricultural practices (one inch every 100 years)[44] the growing deficit of soil loss is dramatic indeed!

An estimated one-third or more of the topsoil on U.S. croplands has been lost in 200 years or less of farming, with about 200 million acres ruined or seriously impoverished for crop cultivation by soil erosion before 1940.[44] Besides promoting stream eutrofication by washing soil sediments and associated nutrients (nitrogen, phosphorus, potassium, and others), pesticides, and herbicides into streams, erosion clouds water and reduces light penetration and resultant food production for the aquatic ecosystem.[45] Spawning of fish is sometimes hampered by stream sediments, as is the survival of the eggs. Fish fry are greatly reduced in numbers due to sediments covering hiding places in streambeds.[46]

Barry Commoner sheds some interesting light upon the matter of organic matter's importance. He cites the current circumvention of the traditional scheme of combining animal and plant production on the same farm to cycle organic wastes from animals back to the land. Today this cycle is broken when crops are grown in one place and fed to animals in another; the manure is not returned to the soil from which it came, but accumulates as a waste product.[47] Thus, nutrients cannot re-enter the biological cycle, nor can the organic carbon which provides energy to drive it. Commoner adds,

Organic matter is the fuel that drives the great cycles of the ecosystem which support not only agriculture, but all life. Solar energy, trapped by the living plants, provides that fuel. . . . The basic fact that agriculture is absolutely dependent on the energy contained in photosynthetically produced organic matter . . . has, of course, long been recognized in traditional farming practice.[48]

The current status of American soil exploitation is summed up well by F. I. Scott, editor of *American Laboratory:*

. . . no civilization except for the Chinese has been able to farm in one place for more than 2,000 years without ruining the soil. The record of soil destruction in the United States offers no hope that this nation will rank high in long-lived soil fertility. Despite dedication and hard work on the part of the U.S. Soil Conservation Service, economics pressures tend to increase soil erosion. These pressures include more continuous crop culture, more land in crops, and intensive efforts for all-out agricultural production. If family-owned farms with a greater stake in preserving the fertility of their land cannot resist such pressures, it is difficult to believe that corporately owned farms, whether foreign or domestically controlled, will even try to resist such pressures. Even the well-intentioned land-grant colleges of the U.S. are chartered to further the *exploitation* of the land. Land is considered to be simply a static resource, not the living source of the planet's well-being, requiring replenishment and nourishment.[49]

God's system will be pure and pristine (Rev. 22:1), where water from rivers and lakes everywhere becomes drinkable and refreshing. The tiny amount of erosion that does occur naturally ("geologic erosion") will be easily replaced by natural soil building processes just as today it is being replaced in natural environments. A lucid foretaste of this pristine, fruitful landscape is provided by Colonel William Byrd, a Virginia farmer who in 1728 wrote concerning the Dan River Valley of Virginia:

The soil we passed over this day was very good. Charming valleys bring forth like the land of Egypt. Grass grows as high as a man on horseback and the rivers roll down their waters to the sea as clear as crystal. Happy will be the people destined for so wholesome a situation, where they may live to the fullness of their days with much content and gaiety of heart.[33]

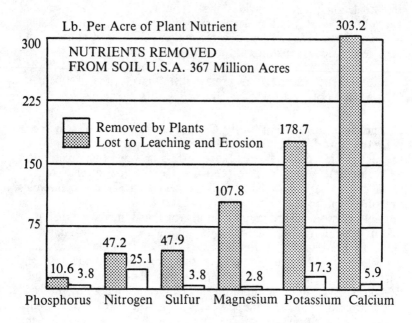

Figure 18. Nutrients removed from soils in the U.S. during a typical year.[37]

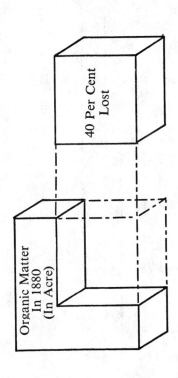

Organic Matter
In 1880
(In Acre)

40 Per Cent
Lost

Figure 19. The loss of total organic matter from South Dakota soils has been heavy during 65 years of farming.[38]

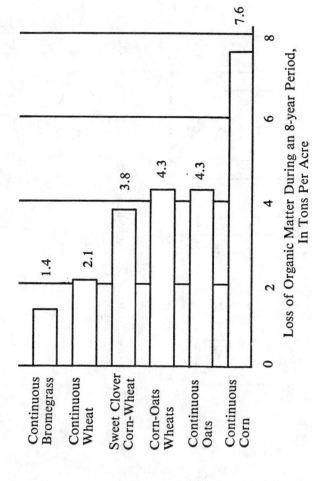

Figure 20. Losses of soil organic matter during an eight year period under different cropping systems in South Dakota (average annual precipitation, 20 inches).[39]

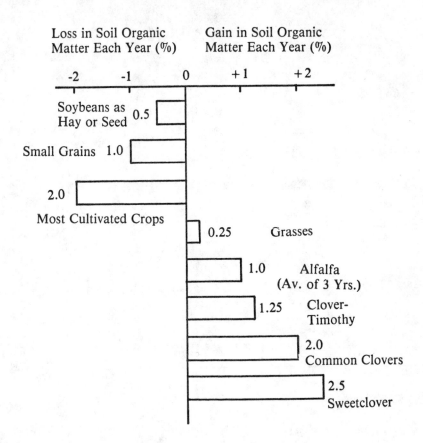

Figure 21. The annual gain or loss in percentage of soil organic matter under different cropping systems in the Corn Belt (average annual precipitation, 30 to 40 inches).[40]

Chapter Five

Energy in Agriculture

O f prime concern for any discussion of agriculture are energy sources. Without energy, life could not exist, nor could it be perpetuated. In fact, along with the discovery by Einstein that $E = mc^2$ (E = energy, m = mass, c = speed of light in a vacuum) came the understanding that all matter, in a sense, is an extremely condensed form of energy.[1] Energy itself may be defined as "the ability to do work" and may exist in various interchangeable forms: radiant, electrical, chemical, mechanical, heat, and atomic.[2]

When considering a permanent agricultural system as envisioned in the Kingdom, several criteria must be met by whichever energy sources are used. These energy sources must be (1) renewable, (2) compatible with the size and type of operation, (3) locally available, (4) non-polluting, and (5) safe to operate. If fields are relatively small (say, 10 acres or less on the average homestead) the feasibility of utilizing today's high-powered gasoline and diesel tractors with their large implements appears out of the question. Even the unlikely probability of 100-acre fields does not require the machines now considered essential for our capital-intensive, labor-efficient, energy-inefficient farming operations.

The Emergence of Oil

Not until after World War I did tractors and trucks really become important on the farm scene, increasing from a mere 1,000 in 1910 to nearly 7.5 million in 1977.[3] Work animals at the same time decreased from a high of 21 million in 1910 to less than 1 million in 1970 (see Figure 22). Figure 23 reveals how several farm machines have increased along with tractor power.

Not only have tractor numbers increased; so has horsepower. Figure 24 indicates that tractor size has steadily risen since at least the early 1960s, accounting for the increasingly common sight of four-wheel drive "behemoths" racing across fields in many parts of the country. This increase in tractor size parallels the reduction in farmers and increases in farm size, though increasing total horsepower on a slightly decreasing total land area can leave only two possible explanations: an excess of power, or soils more difficult to till due to reduced organic matter content and poor soil structure.

For each unit of fossil fuel energy that the American farmer puts into the system, he receives back about 0.2 unit of energy in the form of edible food.[7] In contrast, the Chinese wet rice farmer has been estimated to produce as much as 53.3 British thermal units* (BTUs) of energy for each BTU of human energy he puts in,[8] meaning the American farmer must utilize about 268 times as much energy to produce the same amount of field crop as the Chinese farmer. This is inefficiency of the highest order! The only thing "efficient" about the U.S. farmer is his ability to produce a large amount of food, all at the expense of machines requiring tremendous energy expenditures. Over 150 gallons of gasoline are needed to feed and clothe one person for one year.[9]

Dependence on petroleum products has become nearly total, and so has the reliance upon unstable Arab and South American governments who now supply nearly half of America's oil needs. According to Figure 25 the output of refined petroleum has skyrocketed from virtually zero in 1910 to nearly five billion barrels by 1977! Petroleum is a nonrenewable energy source; none is being formed within the earth's crust today. Despite massive worldwide reserves, supplies are projected, based on present trends, to run out anywhere from 35 to several hundred years from now.[11] Petroleum is seldom

---

* One BTU = the quantity of heat required to heat one pound of water 1° F.

locally produced, usually transported hundreds or thousands of miles to refineries before final distribution to retail stations at rapidly inflating prices. In addition, the emissions of petroleum-powered engines are polluting to the air because of oxides of sulfur, nitrogen, carbon, and other elements found in or added to the refined product. Noise pollution is another common trait of these engines as well as safety problems: a tractor running but without an operator has no sense to stop, claiming many a farmer's life and limb.

If petroleum is not the ultimate answer to farm energy problems then what is? Some have cited nuclear power (fission or fusion) as a possibility. Yet, radiation and disposal problems have raised some as yet insoluble long-term environmental and health questions.[12] Hydrogen gas, produced by electrolysis from farm wind-powered generators, is another possibility,[13] as is fuel alcohol distilled from fermented grains or wastes. These and other possibilities, however, base their fate upon the continued existence of some facsimile of the tractor, truck, and automobile, the very machines which have given rise to many of the current crises facing us today! These crises include huge acreages of land nationwide occupied by roads and urban areas which are unavailable for farming (72 million acres in 1970[14]), the unsightliness of roads, auto junkyards, and barren fields cultivated to suit the needs of huge machinery, discarded human factors, and polluted air and water from millions of belching engines, refineries, and manufacturing plants. Among discarded human factors one finds the separation of a man's home—his very consciousness—from his workplace and his family, made possible by the advent of modern engine-powered vehicles and public highways, and the increased speed of life in general, pressing man's psyche to the limit as he feels rushed, harried, and frustrated in the vain quest for more and more . . . bigger and bigger . . . higher and mightier, the "death of permanence" as Toffler[15] put it, dictated by modern economic theory.

The very existence of the automobile and tractor is up for question. From 1921 to 1970 the miles traveled by automobiles increased from 55 million to 1,120 billion vehicle miles.[16] From 1920 to 1979 divorces per 1000 population increased from 8.0 to 21.6,[17] and between 1940 and 1976 the percent illegitimate births of total births in-

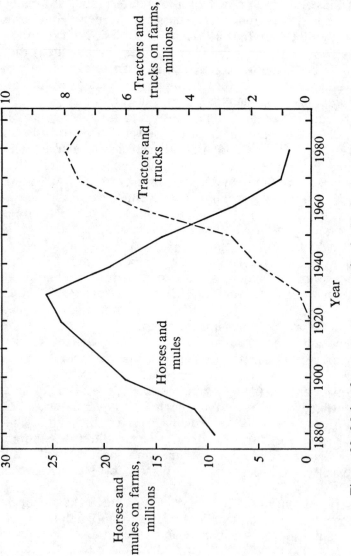

Figure 22. Major farm power sources in the U. S.: horses and mules vs. tractors and trucks from 1870 to 1977.[4]

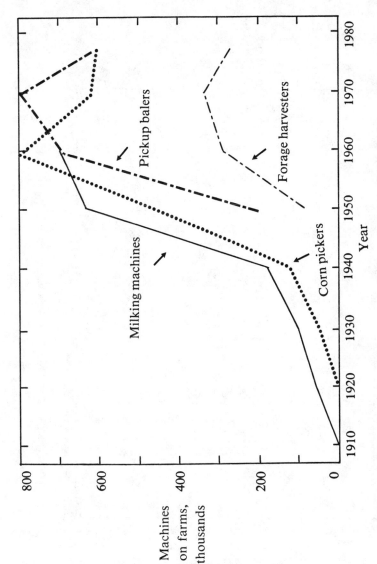

Figure 23. Numbers of corn pickers, milking machines, pickup balers, and forage harvesters on U. S. farms from 1910 to 1977.[5]

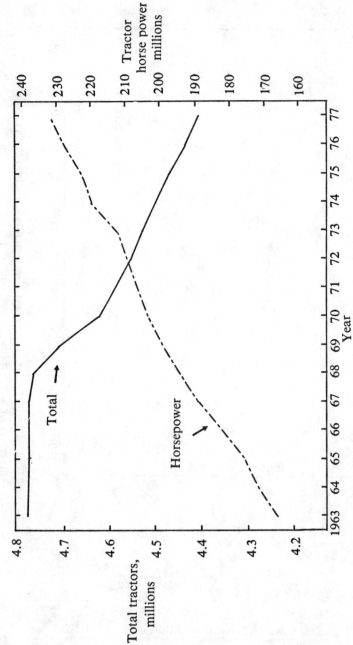

Figure 24. Total tractors and tractor horsepower in the U. S. from 1963 to 1977.[6]

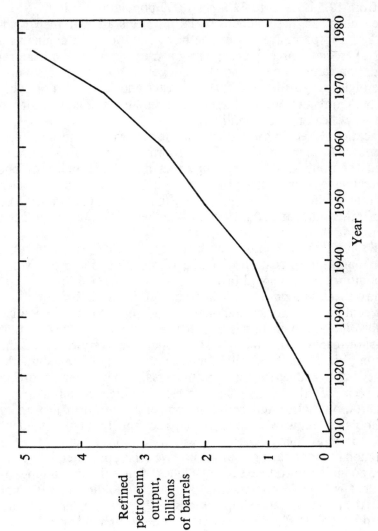

Figure 25. Output of gasoline, kerosene, fuel and lubricating oil in the U. S. from 1910 to 1977.[10]

creased from 3.5 to nearly 15 percent.[18] Juvenile court cases have risen from 10.5 in 1940 to 32.3 per 1,000 population in 1970.[19]

The causes for these hideous social problems are extremely complex. Yet, the pervasiveness of the petroleum-powered engine as a powerful social force causing fragmented families and moral degradation cannot be ignored. We are going, both in the field and on the highway, further and further, faster and faster at a dizzying pace, but enjoying it less and less . . . and in terms of conformity to God's ways heading down and out!

A fact tied closely to the mass production of tractors, automobiles, and modern farm machinery is that corporate factories are necessary. Millions of mine and factory employees must work in conditions degenerative to their health, producing at times diseases such as black lung among coal miners, emphysema, cancer, metal toxicities, and a host of other ailments. Many do not see the light of day or a green plant during their work hours.

Paul stated that "the body is the temple of . . . God" (I Cor. 6:19), a temple that is not to be defiled. While it is possible to improve working conditions in mines and factories for the betterment of workers' health, yet to attain *optimum* health and fulfillment in life for all—a major goal God has for each human being—monotonous, repetitive assembly line employment has no place. Air as pure and fresh as that of a snow-capped mountain will be the rule everywhere in the Kingdom. Water and food will be untainted and wholesome. Superb, vibrant health and energy will be universal. The system involving every step of the economic process—mining, manufacturing, transportation, sales, and consumption—must conform in totality with God's perfect ways of love. Perhaps cottage, family-oriented industries on individual homesteads would be more practical for the production of labor-saving equipment. Even this approach, however, were it possible to produce such machines while still maintaining independent workers scattered over private landholdings, would not remove the innate negative implications inherent within a petroleum-oriented society. Perhaps the words of God through the apostle Paul ought at this point to ring in our ears: "Yet shew I unto you a more excellent way [of love]" (I Cor. 12:31).

Nucleotide Power

People in general know what nuclear power is, but how many have considered "nucleotide power"? This concept is as old as creation itself, and just as powerful as it was then. Nucleotide power is based upon the expenditure of energy stored as high energy phosphate compounds, the principle form of energy utilized in the cells of animals, plants, and man. It is the most efficient means known of converting chemical energy to mechanical energy (useful work) within muscle and other cells. In certain plants, for instance, a 90% efficiency is estimated by Beevers in the conversion of respiratory energy to high energy phosphates.[20] Other workers, however, have shown the true figure may be near 62%;[21] a 75% efficiency may be near the correct value.

In converting the chemical energy of gasoline to the mechanical energy of forward motion, oftentimes only 38% efficiency is obtained; diesel fuel is somewhat more efficient, around 43%.[22]

For century after century nucleotide power has been used successfully in growing crops worldwide, and continues to be used in widespread areas of most continents. Even in America the Old Order Amish employ horses for farm work just as they have since the 17th century.[23] Animal power in America was not phased out until largely after World War I when petroleum became the major fuel source; before that time the entire recorded history of man mentions only the use of men and animals—oxen, horses, mules, etc.—for farming operations.

The Bible makes frequent mention of beasts of burden. David said, "That our oxen may be strong to labour" (Psa. 144:14), and Solomon added, "Where no oxen are, the crib is clean: but much increase is by the strength of the ox" (Prov. 14:4). The statute "You must never muzzle an ox when it is treading out the corn" (Deut. 25:4) directly implies the use of animal power in performing farm work. The patriarchs of old were uniformly wealthy in livestock, using oxen rather than horses for their source of power: "I [Jacob] have oxen, asses, flocks and slaves. . . ." (Gen. 32:5); "He [Job] had fourteen thousand sheep and goats, six thousand camels, a thousand pair of oxen, and a thousand she-asses" (Job 42:12).

No mention is made in Scripture of the use of horses for field or farm work. The horse, rather, was employed primarily in war because of its speed, and then generally among the heathen nations such as Egypt (Ex. 14:9). God's direct order to Israel was "he [the king] must not multiply his war-horses, nor ally the nation again with Egypt, in order to multiply war-horses; for the Eternal has forbidden you ever again to turn in that direction" (Deut. 17:16). When Israel did multiply war horses in the land, God eventually abandoned His people (Isa. 2:6-10); He will likewise abandon His people in the future for their multiplying modern war horses: tanks, battleships, missiles, and aircraft.

The use of horses is not strictly forbidden, for the ass, a close relative of the horse, has already been shown to be a common animal owned by God's people. The implication in Deut. 22:10 is that asses were used for plowing, though never when paired with an ox; the ass was generally used for transportation of people and goods (Num. 22:21; Ex. 23:5; Matt. 21:7).

The superiority of the ox as a more profitable animal than the horse or ass for farm labor is outlined by Clarke in his commentary:

> Except merely for speed, he [the ox] is almost in every respect superior to the horse. 1. He is longer lived. 2. Scarcely liable to any diseases. 3. He is steady, and always pulls fair in his gears. 4. He lives, fattens, and maintains his strength on what a horse will not eat [the ox being a ruminant, will digest cellulose from forages to obtain energy, and synthesize vitamins and other nutrients which a horse cannot do nearly as well], and therefore is supported on one third the cost. 5. His manure is more profitable. And, 6. When he is worn out in his labor his flesh is good for the nourishment of man [Lev. 11:3], his horns of great utility, and his hide almost invaluable. It might be added, he is little or no expense in shoeing, and his gears are much more simple, and much less expensive, than those of the horse. In all large farms oxen are greatly to be preferred to horses. Have but patience with this most patient animal, and you will soon find that there is much increase by the strength and labor of the ox.[24]

From God's viewpoint it appears that the ox, a beef animal bred primarily for strength, endurance, and longevity, is a more honorable animal than a horse and will likely become the major source of power during the millennium.

Additional benefits are derived from a beast of burden when contrasted to a modern farm tractor.

(1) It has a brain which will direct its powers, of itself or on command, to avoid accidents, eliminating most, if not all, of the machine-related injuries and deaths due to modern, "unthinking" tractor-powered machines.

(2) It will not walk in fields too wet to till, providing a self-protective mechanism for eliminating tillage of wet soils, a major soil management problem.

(3) Being an animal, it gets tired and must be rested, providing the farmer as well with a safety valve to avoid overwork, a common problem with hard-pressed modern-day farmers using tractors needing no rest.

(4) One may develop a kinship with a living creature quite unlike that with a cold, steel machine.

(5) The animal is generally quiet in its labors, allowing the songs of birds, the chirping of insects, and joyful chants of the farmer himself to be heard across the fields, whereas today within an insulated tractor cab the farmer is virtually cut off from the multitude of joys associated with communing with the natural world—watching a field mouse scamper away, avoiding a pheasant's nest, or hearing the honk of geese overhead. To say that the man behind the wheel of a tractor will more naturally emulate God's character is a gross misstatement. The development of Godlike character will become the whole business of life during the millennium; just as we tend to become more like the people with whom we associate (Prov. 22:24-25), so we tend to become more like cold, loveless machines through continual close association with them (compare the present machine-oriented "loveless" age with Matt. 24:12).

(6) The animal is better adapted to small-scale operations which will be the rule during the Kingdom.

(7) The farmer will be required to maintain his physical condition (see I Cor 6:19-20). Caring for the animal and guiding it during the field operation requires considerably more exercise than sitting hour after hour on a tractor seat, mesmerized by the din of the engine and the passing sameness of the furrow, one's flesh less than firm and overweight a definite likelihood.

(8) An animal is usually self-healing when injured or diseased, re-

quiring primarily rest for recuperation, whereas a machine must be repaired with parts produced by others, reducing one's independence and financial status as a farm operator.

About the only advantage of tractor power, if it may be called an advantage, is the increased speed with which farm work may be completed. Yet the progression from manpower to ox power, then to horse power, and finally to engine power, is yet another sign of man tied to Satan's wavelength, of doing more and more in less and less time—impatience (Rom. 1:29). God's way is a way of patience, love, and perfect well-doing with an accent on quality in completing a job . . . which takes time. As Thomas Hardy wrote around 1917,

Only a man harrowing clods
   In a slow-silent walk
With an old horse that stumbles and nods
   Half asleep as they stalk.

Only thin smoke without a flame
   From the heaps of couch-grass;
Yet this will go onward the same
   Though Dynasties pass.[25]

An additional observation in favor of the ox as the primary work animal of the Kingdom is its use among the early settlers of America. This newly opened land of Israel with its endless sea of prairie grasses and boundless forests attracted a pioneer people that in the beginning used oxen for power. Witness the early photographs and stories of the great western movement which reveal that oxen were used;[26] work horses came to the fore later, especially during the 19th and early 20th centuries when the Satanic forces gathering to destroy mankind were gaining strength. With man now being led to total reliance on petroleum, Satan is nearing the point he has worked towards for millennia: he can cause a cut-off of fuel sources to rural and urban dwellers and, through the forces of modern oil-based nations, ignite warfare so horrendous that all flesh would be destroyed except for God's timely intervention (Matt. 24:22; see also *Armageddon: Oil and the Middle East Crisis*[27]).

Other Energy Sources

Besides field power sources there will be numerous other sources of energy needed. Should there be a need for significant heat in the Kingdom (see a later section dealing with climate) wood will be a primary source:

> In cutting timber for this purpose a man will fix upon some plane or oak, which God planted and the rain nourished to serve as fuel; men kindle a fire with it to warm themselves, or start a blaze in order to bake bread (Isa. 44:14-15).

Here it is shown that a primary heat source in today's world is wood, a source that will undoubtedly also be used in the Kingdom.

Numerous other renewable sources of energy exist that will very likely be significant sources for the Kingdom. These include direct solar (*indirect* solar energy is that trapped by green plants in the form of food, fiber, structural, or fuel products), indirect solar (plant oils), geothermal (hot water or steam at or near the earth's surface), wind, water, and gravity. Any of these energy sources can be converted to other forms to provide electrical power should this be appropriate on an individual homestead basis.

Wind power has been used for hundreds of years to pump water in the United States, and in more recent years to generate electricity. Water power in streams has been long used as a source of power to drive lumber and flour mills, and during the last century for electricity generation. With no need to control excessive watershed run-off, however, any dams constructed would likely be small, picturesque, and durable to serve the needs of a local community. Geothermal energy potentials may become more widespread after the coming cataclysmic earthquake (Rev. 16:18), when the earth's crust will become markedly altered. Solar energy may more effectively be used for home heating through advanced home designs; modern heat collecting devices are oftentimes expensive and oftentimes require a highly technical, factory-oriented society for their construction. Harnessing of gravitational forces has not as yet been developed, but poses a potentially valuable source of energy for a new world. Other possible sources of energy cannot be ruled out.

Efficiency? For What?

Need a farmer be ashamed if his personal productivity drops so that he produces for the needs of few others besides his own family, his productivity dropping because his production is tied to human and animal power rather than petroleum power? Need he feel ashamed if he, like the Chinese rice farmer, multiplies his collection of the sun's energy nearly 54 times above his own input, through photo synthetic activity in his fields, while a fossil-fueled mechanized approach drains five units of energy from a nonrenewable source for each unit of energy captured from the sun? Does the vanity of "efficiency" through the use of monstrous machines, high-speed field and feedlot operations, hybrids, monoculture, the concentration of livestock in large beef, swine, or dairy operations really yield happiness and fulfillment in life, drawing one closer to his Creator . . . which, after all, ought to be man's quest on this earth? What of the family? Is it being strengthened? Are the children able to gain the God-required loving guidance and discipline from parents willing to give of their valuable time to their most precious resource (Prov. 23:13-14; I Tim. 3:4-5; Dobson, *Dare to Discipline*[28])?

As shown in Figure 26, the average farm worker has increased his productivity 14 times since the early and mid-1800s, from a mere four persons supplied per worker to a whopping 56 persons in 1978.[30] Most of this surge in productivity occurred after World War II when excess industrial war capital was turned to the production of machinery and petroleum products (especially commercial fertilizers). The number of man-hours to produce 100 bushels of corn dropped at the same time as revealed in Figure 27, from 344 in 1800 to a mere 7 in 1970; corn yields during the same period increased 2.9 times[32] due to commercial fertilizers and hybrid seed.

As already indicated, farm productivity increases occurred primarily due to tremendous outlays of petroleum energy. Virtually all categories of agricultural production rely on petrochemicals (see Figure 28): crop drying often uses propane gas; irrigation relies upon electric motors or gasoline or diesel engines; transportation and field machinery require gasoline or diesel fuel; pesticides and herbicides are usually modified oil chemicals; and fertilizers rely heavily on industrial acids and petroleum fuels. The entire food system uses one-sixth of all energy used in the U.S.[34] Of this one-sixth, production energy shown in Figure 28 accounts for only one-fifth of the food system's total energy use; food processing, marketing and distribution, commercial eating establishments, and home food preparation and use account for the rest.[35] Since 1950 fertilizer usage per acre has increased five times while corn yields have only doubled.[36] Clearly the returns per unit of added fertilizer are decreasing, an omen that further yield increases may be achieved only through increasingly heavy fertilizer additions . . . which depend upon increasingly scarce and expensive energy.

Is this energy-intensive but labor-efficient approach to agriculture really the best way to produce our crops and livestock? Is there a better way? Why not eliminate the need for petrochemicals which account for this perverted definition of efficiency, and bring the urbanites unto the land where they could exert their energies alongside nature? After all, not until this century did oil replace human and animal resources in agriculture. For thousands of years crops were dried in the field or corn crib. If food is consumed at or near the place of production the need for tremendous outlays of fuel for transportation is eliminated. Fuel needed to power machinery may be eliminated by animal and human power as most families individually work their homesteads. With individual attention given to the land by farm operators working in harmony with the forces of nature—animal wastes and crop residues recycled back to the land, an abundance of birds and animals to hold insect populations in check, and genetically diverse farmer-selected crop varieties which resist plant disease and maximize nutritional quality and yield—the need for herbicides, pesticides, and commercial fertilizers would be eliminated.

Are such thoughts progressive? Are they rational? Yes, and not only are they progressive and rational but they are workable . . . but under an economic system based upon love and concern for God and people, and within an environment radically altered where species competition, storms, bitter cold and torrid heat and greed find no place.

Some statements by modern-day Isaiahs should help clarify the nonsense behind the all-out drive toward efficiency in production and elimination of small landholders. E. F. Schumacher has stated,

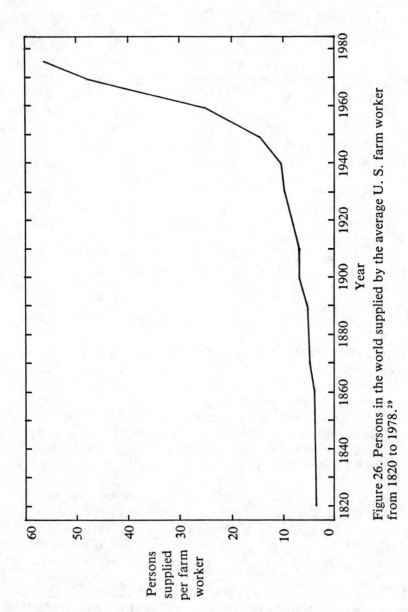

Figure 26. Persons in the world supplied by the average U. S. farm worker from 1820 to 1978.[29]

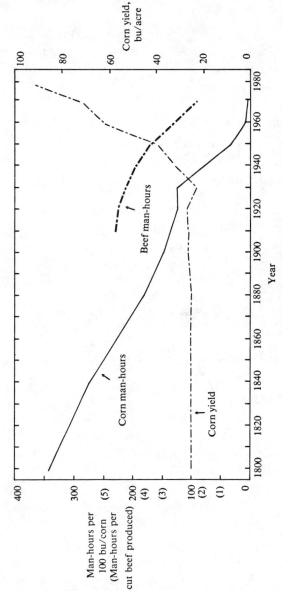

Figure 27. Man-hours per 100 bushels and yield of corn for U. S. farms from 1800 to 1979, and man-hours per hundredweight of beef produced from 1910 to 1977.[31]

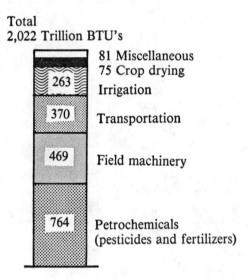

Total
2,022 Trillion BTU's

81 Miscellaneous
75 Crop drying
263 Irrigation
370 Transportation
469 Field machinery
764 Petrochemicals
(pesticides and fertilizers)

Figure 28. Energy use in agricultural production (1976 data).[35]

On a wider view . . . the land is seen as a priceless asset which it is man's task and happiness 'to dress and to keep.' We can say that man's management of the land must be primarily oriented towards three goals—health, beauty, and permanence. The fourth goal—the only one accepted by the experts—productivity, will then be attained almost as a by-product. The crude materialistic view sees agriculture as 'essentially directed towards food-production.' A wider view sees agriculture as having to fulfil at least three tasks:

—to keep man in touch with living nature, or which he is and remains a highly vulnerable part;

—to humanise and ennoble man's wider habitat; and

—to bring forth the foodstuffs and other materials which are needed for a becoming life.

I do not believe that a civilization which recognizes only the third of these tasks, and which pursues it with such ruthlessness and violence that the other two tasks are not merely neglected but systematically counteracted, has any chance of long-term survival.

Today, we take pride in the fact that the proportion of people engaged in agriculture has fallen to very low levels and continues to fall. Great Britain produces some 60% of its food requirements while only 3% of its working population are working on farms. . . . These declines in the proportion of workers engaged in agriculture are generally associated with a massive flight from the land and a burgeoning of cities.[37]

Lewis Herber adds, in regard to city life,

Metropolitan life is breaking down, psychologically, economically, and biologically. Millions of people have acknowledged this breakdown by voting with their feet, they have picked up their belongings and left. If they have not been able to sever their connections with the metropolis, at least they have tried.[38]

Within these modern megalopolises and strip cities the urbanite is more isolated than his ancestors were in the countryside: "The city man in a modern metropolis has reached a degree of anonymity, social atomisation, and spiritual isolation that is virtually unprecedented in human history."[39]

Yet, as Schumacher states, the citizen tries to get into the suburbs and becomes a commuter.[40] Because rural culture has broken down the rural people are fleeing the land, and because metropolitan life is breaking down urban people are fleeing from cities. Since "nobody can afford the luxury of not acting economically,"[41] life everywhere tends to become intolerable except for the very rich.

Wendell Berry, known for his probing views of American agriculture, states:

> To answer the official call for more production . . . farmers are plowing their waterways and permanent pastures; lands that ought to remain in grass are being planted in row crops. Contour plowing, crop rotation, and other conservation measures seem to have gone out of favor or fashion in official circles and are practiced less and less on the farm. This exclusive emphasis on production will accelerate the mechanization and chemicalization of farming, increase the price of land, increase overhead and operating costs, and thereby further diminish the farm population. Thus the tendency . . . is to complete the deliverance of American agriculture into the hands of corporations.
>
> The cost of this corporate totalitarianism in energy, land, and social disruption will be enormous. It will lead to the exhaustion of farmland and farm culture. Hubandry will become an extractive industry; because maintenance will entirely give way to production, the fertility of the soil will become a limited, unrenewable resource like coal or oil.[42]

Berry admits this total demolition "may not happen." Indeed, it cannot! All society would come crashing down alongside the collapse of its most valuable resource—the soil. An abrogation of natural law cannot stand for long: every cause exacts its effect. If man was designed from creation to exist upon the land and live in loving harmony with it, nothing in the world can change this fact, including modern agri-business advertising and practice.

Efficiency? For what? Thomas Jefferson, in a letter to James Madison on October 28, 1785, answered this question simply and well:

> . . . it is not too soon to provide by every possible means that as few as possible shall be without a little portion of land. The small landholders are the most precious part of a state. . . .[41]

Chapter Six

A People-oriented Technology

One of the marvels of today's world is the emergence of a technology that has placed men on the moon, produced television sets for nearly every Western home, and enabled the average American farmer to feed 56 others by 1976.[1] However, at the same time that technology has enabled the farmer to become so labor-efficient—or should we say *forced* him to—he has been backed into a corner so tightly fitting that if he attempts to break out of it he is punished in a number of ways. In the process of becoming labor efficient he has become a slave to his profession in order to prevent bankruptcy. Government farm policies and economic pressures have forced the farmer at times to work longer, more torturing hours than workers in perhaps any other profession, largely because he is able to maintain his incentive through the ideal of relative independence on the land. Yet, in order to maintain his grasp on that relative independence he must increase his acreage, purchase ever-larger machinery to till that acreage, and become nearly totally dependent on herbicides and pesticides for weed and insect control . . . and on the banker for credit to fund his land, machinery, and production expenses. Fear or greed-ridden advertising by chemical and machinery companies and peer pressure from ambitious neighbors—besides the sheer economic squeeze of grain and livestock prices far below parity level—add to the social and economic pressures bearing upon the farmer, forcing him to "toe the line" of modern agricultural methods.

As pointed out in chapter five, the conventional Western farmer has become totally dependent upon oil for his production. The oil industry has sprung up largely since the early 20th century at the same time farm size began to increase and the countryside began to rapidly empty. Not only are tractors fueled and lubricated by oil products, but farm chemicals are largely manufactured through the use of petroleum: anhydrous ammonia is manufactured from natural gas, and most herbicides and pesticides are petroleum-based compounds. Without tractors and oil Western agriculture would immediately grind to a halt. Fields could never be planted, and growing crops could not be cultivated or sprayed, much less harvested. Storage facilities and distribution channels as well depend upon oil and other centrally controlled utilities such as electricity. Credit and interest rates, the financial backing for most agricultural production today, is also centrally controlled. The centralized control of the media and its fear-producing, demoralizing, negative tactics of newscasting and programming, preaching the "gospel" of greater and greater yields through modern agri-chemical advertising, amply illustrate Satan's greedy, lustful, and morose character spread abroad upon the air waves ("prince of the power of the air," Eph. 2:2) and published on the printed page. Satan's system is again revealed to be one of dependence upon one's neighbor. To produce tractors one needs miners, machinists, oil drillers, steel workers, and a host of backup men. The same may be said for the producers of oil products, chemicals, or crop seeds.

In the face of such a highly organized, complex, but *dependent* system of widely separated growers, processors, distributors, and consumers, God's technological system stands in sharp contrast. Millennial technology will be *people* oriented, based upon love, peace, and contentment for all. Within a society of God-dependent but largely man-independent landholders it is difficult to conceive of much more than cottage industries where each individual has developed one or more talents to a very high degree, which can be offered as enrichment to others within the community. Whether the skill is making harnesses, producing cutlery, singing, building carriages, casting metals, or growing walnuts, the technology achieved must be oriented about a society of individuals seeking to build strong bridges to God, while assisting one another when the need arises (Js. 4:7-8; Gal. 6:10). Personal daily living will be bound and intertwined with one's animals and machines to maximize righteousness and Godliness, not profit and materialism as today's society now encourages.

As already shown, the principle field power source in the Kingdom will be animal power and other renewable energy sources in harmony with personal economic independence: wind, solar, gravitational, geothermal, and water. What naturally follows is a technology based on muscle power primarily geared towards providing lasting machines to complement the needs of individuals for the highest quality and safest production of crops and livestock. Implements will need to be perfected that will ease difficult work but encourage optimal physical conditioning for individuals. The incredible physical abuses which the early settlers of America often heaped upon themselves were a result of (1) personal greed in farming an excessive amount of land, and (2) failure to obey all of the laws of health; i.e., proper nutrition, rest, and exercise. At times these settlers overextended themselves to an incredible degree, in battle against the elements, homesickness, and Indians. Ole Rolvaag in *Giants in the Earth* spoke of the great hardships experienced by Norwegian settlers during the great settling of the eastern Dakota Territory:

> Many and incredible are the tales the grandfathers tell from those days when the wilderness was yet untamed, and when they, unwittingly, founded the Kingdom. . . . But more to be dreaded [than the Indians] . . . was the strange spell of sadness which the unbroken solitude cast upon the minds of some. Many took their own lives; asylum after asylum was filled with disordered beings who had once been human. It is hard for the eye to wander from sky line to sky line, year in and year out, without finding a resting place! . . .
>
> Then too, there were the years of pestilence—toil and travail, famine, and disease. God knows how human beings could endure it all. And many did not—they lay down and died. . . . The poor could find much wherewith to console themselves. And whiskey was cheap in those days, and easy to get. . . . And on the hot summer days terrible storms might come. In the twinkling of an eye they would smash to splinters the habitation which man had built for himself. . . . Some feared most the prairie fire.

And it was as if nothing affected people in those days. They threw themselves blindly into the Impossible, and accomplished the Unbelievable. If anyone succumbed in the struggle—and that happened often—another would come and take his place. Youth was in the race; the unknown, the untried, the unheard-of, was in the air; people caught it, were intoxicated by it, threw themselves away, and laughed at the cost.[2]

Examples are numerous, however, of hearty sodbusters who thrived in the vast prairies or virgin forests, living moderately and patiently to a ripe old age.

Man in Control of Machines

Machines can be built, using today's technological advances, to assist man in perfecting the fruits of his hands. Metals of all sorts of strengths and durabilities are now available, though usually producible only by the means of modern industrial ingenuity. It is conceivable that the tools of man's future world could be readily constructed on a cottage industry basis using the basic metals—iron, copper, manganese, zinc, aluminium, tin, and others—to produce exquisitely-engineered tools and implements for farmers, potters, carpenters, musicians, coppersmiths, and others. In a society where all men will be building items with the ideal of perfection ever in mind (Matt. 5:48), and of service to his family and fellow citizens, quality products of unheard-of durability and utility can be envisioned. Some have also envisioned that use and decay of metals and wood may be reduced or eliminated.[3] With the drastic climatic changes which are sure to occur, this is a distinct possibility, alluded to in Rom. 8:21: " . . . the hope being that creation as well as man would one day be freed from its thraldom to decay and gain the glorious freedom of God's children." Man's ingenuity to produce physical goods in today's Satanic system is phenomenal; when this ingenuity is redirected along spirit-serving lines one can only faintly grasp the wonderful world awaiting those who will live in that Kingdom:

What no eye has ever seen, what no ear has ever heard, what never entered the mind of man, God has prepared all that for those who love him (I Cor. 2:9).

Today man has graduated to cars, tractors, trucks, computers, power tools, and electric typewriters. He feels he could not exist without them, and indeed he could not within the present social and economic system. In the name of relief from heavy or tedious labor, machines have now driven man from the pedestal of commander to the humble status of slave. By increasing his productivity through machines he has become entwined inextricably into a system which demands more and more of his total life commitment, reducing the amount of real leisure time he commands[4] and often causing him to enjoy both work and leisure time even less.

An interesting observation by E. F. Schumacher is as follows:

> The question of what technology actually does for us is therefore worthy of investigation. It obviously greatly reduces some kinds of work while it increases other kinds. The type of work which modern technology is most successful in reducing or even eliminating is skillfull, productive work of human hands, in touch with real materials of one kind or another. In an advanced industrial society, such work has become virtually impossible. A great part of the modern neurosis may be due to this very fact; for the human being . . . enjoys nothing more than to be creatively, usefully, productively engaged with both his hands and his brains. Today a person has to be wealthy to be able to enjoy this simple thing, this very great luxury: he has to be able to afford space and good tools; he has to be lucky enough to find a good teacher and plenty of free time to learn and practice. He really has to be rich enough to not need a job; for the number of jobs that would be satisfactory in these respects is very small indeed.[5]

How perfectly this modern repressed desire—fostered by today's machine-oriented industrial society—pictures what man is to pursue during the Kingdom . . . when man will have time to explore and perfect his talents, when he will not be enslaved by governments and corporations in order to provide food, clothing, and shelter for his family and still pay taxes. As an independent land holder he will be responsible directly to God's free government, not the repressive governments of man.

In short, man will control machines, not vice versa; and to

whatever extent machines are developed in the Kingdom they will foster individual, family, community, and worldwide good, all to the glory of the Eternal who created and ordered everything on the earth. No longer will a mere *one-sixth* of the total population engage in actual production,[6] but *all* of society will. Instead of only 3.5% of the "total social time" being spent on actual production,* a much greater figure may be expected, a figure which will reflect the enjoyment and might that citizens will put into their work . . . for, as Solomon said, "There is nothing better for a man than to eat and drink and enjoy himself as he does his work" (Eccl. 2:24).

The Value of Man and Family

Theoretically the amount of time spent in truly productive work, fostered by machines powered by petroleum products and electricity, could approach zero. In reality such an eventuality is impossible, since present power sources are finite, destined to run out within a few decades or centuries. Yet, why even consider such an intolerable end? Why not view children, adults, and older people as all being productive, using time, patience, and loving care to produce optimum quality goods? Why even consider entertaining the vision of a future clouded by the inhuman, faceless monster of modern technology, where mass production yields the current all-too-visible scene of violence, ecological damage, depletion of resources, and imprisonment of human development . . . when a system of "produc-

---

* This 3.5% was arrived at as follows: of the one-sixth of the total population engaged in actual production, each supports five others besides himself, of which two are gainfully employed on things other than real production and three are not gainfully employed. The fully employed person spends about one-fifth of his time on his job, allowing for sickness, holidays, and other absence. Then, productive time is about $1/5 \times 1/3 \times 1/2 = 0.35 \times 100 = 3.5\%$. The other 96.5% of the time is spent sleeping, eating, listening to radio or watching TV, doing other jobs around the home, or wasting time.[7]

tion by the masses mobilises the priceless resources which are possessed by all human beings, their clever brains and skillful hands, and supports them with first-class tools."[8]

Foremost in the physical lives of all people should be a strong family. The human family was made in the very image of the God family—the Father and the Son (Jesus Christ)—and all of society's strategies should be directed towards strengthening these ties. It is common knowledge that a nation's strength is proportional to the strength and quality of family life within that nation. Yet, family life is breaking down in America and the Western world under the strain of modern industrial life: conveniences in the home breed apathy, processed and tainted foods breed disease and weakness, and fathers working away from home dislocate the lives of lonesome wives and children.

As outlined by Wendell Berry, the modern home is destructive because it is a "generalization, a product of factory and fashion, an everyplace and a noplace. . . . They do not vary much from place to place. . . . The modern home, even more than the government and universities, has institutionalized the divisions and fragmentations of modern life."[9]

Berry continues by illustrating how the home is divorced from one's place of work, leading to some rather absurd but truthful results:

> The modern conquistador, seated in his living room in the evening in front of his TV set, many miles from his work, can easily forget where he is and what he has done. He is everywhere or nowhere. Everything around him, everything on TV, tells him of his success: *his* comfort is the redemption of the world. His home is the emblem of his status, but it is not the center of his interest or of his consciousness. The history of our time has been to a considerable extent the movement of the center of consciousness away from home.

> Once, some farmers, particularly in Europe, lived in their barns—and so were both at work and at home. Work and rest, work and pleasure, were continuous with each other, often not distinct from each other at all. Once, shopkeepers lived in, above, or behind their shops. Once, many people lived by 'cottage industries'—home production. Once, households were producers and processors of food, centers of their own maintenance, adornment, and repair, places of instruction and

amusement. People were born in these houses, and lived and worked and died in them. Such houses were not generalizations. Similar to each other in materials and design as they might have been, they nevertheless looked and felt and smelled different from each other because they were articulations of particular responses to their places and circumstances.[10]

While today's industrial "cog in the gear" does not have a clear idea of where he is or who he is, neither does he understand what his moral convictions are. The whole thrust of today's accelerating pace of industrial life seems to be tearing up the past—its friendships, family, and values—and replacing it with a new self-image which the television-viewing public is being educated in several hours each day. Modular friends, jobs, and homes result from families being uprooted. Years ago, when times and events were slower moving, five years constituted a reasonable breaking-in or acceptance period for a family moving to a new community. Today this period must be highly compressed. As Toffler puts it,

> When you move, you break all these ties . . . and you have to start all over again. . . . It is the simultaneous rupture of a whole range of existing relationships that makes relocation psychologically taxing for many. The more frequently the cycle repeats itself . . . the shorter the duration of the relationships involved. Among significant sectors of the population this process is now occurring so rapidly that it is drastically altering traditional notions of time with respect to human relationships.[11]

Today's industrial society not only tends to move a person's consciousness away from the home, but the home itself becomes a temporary haven, alternately purchased and sold as the job location changes, or whenever the right price is offered. These double-barreled forces, unless guarded against, tend to undermine the strength of families. Are they worth tolerating? Is there a better way? Thankfully there is, a way inherent through daily living in the Kingdom which will place individuals and families first in importance, for nothing is more important than human life itself . . . and little is more worthy of preservation and loving nurture than a marriage and growing children.

Chapter Seven

Millennial Changes in the Earth's Ecosphere

To enhance one's understanding of the life and setting during the Kingdom, a description of the earth's land surface and atmosphere will be attempted at this point. To become dogmatic on certain of the points to be mentioned is perhaps dangerous. Yet, certain statements in prophecy lend definite clues toward describing the earth as it will be, an earth changed to God's own millennial specifications.

At one cornerstone of an understanding of the Kingdom's environment is the following statement by Ezekiel:

> Thus says the Lord God; in the day that I shall have cleansed you from all your iniquities I will also cause you to dwell in the cities, and the wastes shall be builded. And the desolate land shall be tilled, whereas it lay desolate in the sight of all that passed by. And they shall say, This land that was desolate is *become like the garden of Eden;* and the waste and desolate and ruined cities are become fenced, and are inhabited (Ezek. 36:33-35).

Concurring with this millennial prophecy of Ezekiel is the portion of a speech made by the apostle Peter:

> Repent ye therefore, and be converted, that your sins may be blotted out, when the *times of refreshing* shall come from the presence of the Lord; and he shall send Jesus Christ [at His second coming], which before was preached unto you: whom the heaven must receive until the times of *restitution of all things,* which God has spoken by the mouth of all his holy prophets since the world began (Acts 3:19-21).

The reference here is to the setting up of the Kingdom of God under Jesus Christ's rulership at the end of this present age, with special emphasis given to a "restitution," or "time of refreshing." Though sin has brought evil upon the world and all the dismal consequences which Satan has desired, yet there was a time when the creation could be said to have been perfect . . . before disorder began to plague the Divine order of things. This time was after the six days of creation when the earth's surface was restored:

God saw all that he had made, and *very good it was* (Gen. 1:21).

The Cursing of the Land

For God to say that anything is "good" implies that there was no flaw, no sin, no error or imperfection. The environment throughout the earth was in perfect harmony with God's laws. Adam and Eve, as yet sinless, lived within the Garden of Eden wherein grew the tree of the knowledge of good and evil (symbolic of experimentation and choosing one's own course in life rather than relying upon God for direction) and the tree of life (the fruit of which would impart eternal life). The parents of all flesh, however, ate of the tree God had forbidden, and as a result sin entered into the human race and colored man's treatment of the earth's land, sea, and air ever since. Indeed, the harsh pronouncement God gave to Adam on their being expelled from the Garden underscores their future stressful life:

Cursed is the ground on your account,
You shall suffer all your life, as you win food from it;
Thorns and thistles shall it bear for you,
And you must eat plants of the field;
In the sweat of your brow you shall earn your food,
Till you return to the ground from which you were taken
(Gen. 3:17-19).

This pronouncement by God that the land *outside* the Garden of Eden would yield thorns and thistles, weeds which compete with cultivated crops, not only gives clues to the character of millennial agriculture that will be discussed later but also indicates that God knew very well the degenerative type of agriculture mankind would practice from that time forward. God oftentimes fulfills a curse through natural forces (see Ex. 23:28). Josephus stated that the ground would "not henceforth yield its fruits of its own accord, but that when it should be harassed by their labor it should bring forth some of its fruits, and refuse to bring forth others."[1]

Another viewpoint concerning the cause for this cursing of the land may be tied to vast meteoric deposits which apparently brought blight and sterility to a great portion of the earth's surface before Noah's day. Lamech, the father of Noah, alludes prophetically to the restoration of the earth's surface through his son in Genesis 5:29: "This same shall comfort us concerning our work and toil of our hands, because of the ground which the Lord hath cursed." The earth —indeed the entire solar system—has in times past been bombarded with meteors and titanic upheavals, evidenced by craters on the planets and moons and a few on the earth itself.

Satan, the author of confusion (I Cor. 14:33), was the instigator of the earth's chaotic and confused condition (Hebrew "tohu and bohu"[2]) of Genesis 1:2, prior to God's recreation of its surface. Throughout history since that time 6,000 years ago Satan and his demons have likewise instigated the chaotic and destructive activities of this world, oftentimes using men as his agents. Immanuel Velikovsky states in *Worlds in Collision* that several times during the past 6,000 years comets and planets (especially Venus and Mars) have made close passes to the earth, in a few cases even contacting it.[3] He has proposed that such titanic cosmic occurrences may have been responsible for some of the great worldwide catstrophes—earthquakes, darkening of the skies, mass deaths, and "fire and brimstone"—which the Bible and mythology have alluded to . . . and which prophecy says will occur in the near future. A meteor plague* causing a blight upon the earth could well have been

---

* Meteor displays and similar phenomena perhaps foreboding the true prophetic fulfillment of certain prophecies, are of considerable interest. The night of November 13, 1833, witnessed a tremendous shower of meteorites over the entire United States, when "the whole firmament, over all the U.S., being then, for hours, in fiery commotion. . . . During the three hours of its continuance, the day of judgement was believed by many to be

instigated by the Creator, who set the heavenly bodies into motion
with perfect precision and foresight, using them to help fulfill His
divine plan in a perfectly time-ordered sequence of events on earth
known only by Him.

The removal of the curse on the land following the Deluge (Gen.
8:21) apparently refers to God's promise to never bring another flood
upon the earth, which Noah feared might destroy all flesh each year.
Both Adam Clark[7] and Josephus[8] express this viewpoint.

Additional evidence that conditions present in the Garden of Eden
will be restored in the Kingdom of God is offered by comparing the
similarity of Genesis 1:30, referring to the original Garden, with
Isaiah 11:6-9, referring to the millennium, and comparing both of
these to present conditions within the animal kingdom:

> To every wild beast on earth, to every bird of the air, and to every liv-
> ing creature that crawls on earth, I give all the green growth for food
> (Gen. 1:30).

> The wolf shall couch then with the lamb, the leopard's lair shall be the
> kid's; wolf and lion shall graze side by side, herded by a little child;
> the *lion shall eat straw like any ox,* the cow and the bear shall be
> friends, and their young lie down together; the infant shall play at the
> hole of an asp, with the baby's feet at the nest of a viper. None shall
> injure, none shall kill, anywhere on my sacred hill; for the land shall
> be as full of the knowledge of the Eternal as the ocean-bed is full of
> water (Isa. 11:6-9).

---

only waiting for sunrise."[4] In the South, a plantation owner was suddenly
awakened by the shrieks and cries of some 600 to 800 negroes who worked
on his land: "Upward of 100 lay prostrate on the ground, some speechless,
and others uttering the bitterest moans, but with their hands raised, implor-
ing God to save the world and them. The scene was truly awful: for never
did rain fall much thicker than the meteors fell toward the earth; east, west,
north, and south, it was the same. In a word, the whole heavens seemed in
motion."[5] About 240,000 meteorites were calculated to be visible at the
same time at Boston, Massachusetts.[6] In the eyes of many observers on that
night, "the stars of the sky dropped to earth as a fig tree shaken by a gale
sheds her unripe figs" (Rev. 6:13).

Edenic and millennial conditions within the animal kingdom are pictured as being very similar. Before the Flood and after God's government is restored on earth the animals are pictured as being herbivores, a reality quite different from the present age where many are preying, carnivorous animals. The statement referring to directly *after* the Flood, that "the dread of you and terror of you shall be on every beast of the earth and every bird of the air" (Gen. 9:2), implies a radical change in the nature of animals from that before the Flood, when fearlessness of man among the animals was the rule. This fearlessness of animals will be restored in the millennium, duplicating their mild and uncompetitive nature enjoyed before the Flood.

Finally, Romans 8:19-23 speaks of the degenerative transformation experienced by the entire creation when, at the time of Adam and Eve's sin in Eden and as a result of the curse declared by God, it entered into its "thraldom of decay" from which it longs to be delivered. The freeing of the entire creation and man from this decay will occur when "God's children" will receive complete sonship (verse 23), when Edenic conditions will begin to be restored worldwide, when the entire creation will no longer "sigh and throb with pain." Complete sonship will be realized at the resurrection, the instantaneous transformation of God's saints from flesh to spirit (I Cor. 15:42-57) when Christ returns at the end of the age (compare I Cor. 15:52 with Rev. 16:18).

The Earth Before the Flood

What were conditions like on the earth's surface before the Deluge? This question has considerable bearing upon a discussion of utopian land management, for as already shown the conditions upon the earth following Christ's return will closely resemble those of the Garden of Eden (Ezek. 36:33-36). This fact is restated in Isaiah 51:3:

Even so the Eternal consoles Sion,
Consoles all her ruins,
Makes her desert *like an Eden,*
Makes her steppes like his own garden;
Joy and gladness shall be found in her,
Thanksgiving and song.

In order to have vegetative growth in the Kingdom resemble that of Eden, the climatic and other environmental conditions of the Garden must be reinstated on a global basis, which reinstatement or "period of the great Restoration" has been guaranteed (Acts 3:21).

Before the creation week began, the entire earth was covered with water (Gen. 1:2). During the second day of creation this massive body of water was separated into two parts: water upon the earth and water suspended as a canopy above the earth,

And God made the firmament, and divided the waters which were under the firmament from the waters which were above the firmament: and it was so (Gen. 1:7).

Genesis 1:8 reveals that this firmament was called the "sky," or "heaven." This mass of gases, which we call the atmosphere, originally lay between these two great masses of water. Today there is no such watery expanse above the earth, for during the Deluge it all fell during a period of 40 days and nights (Gen. 7:12). The source of this precipitation could not have been atmospheric, for the average total moisture in the air over the United States is a mere 0.75 inches.[9] Continued operation of the hydrologic cycle during the Deluge could also not account for the prodigious amounts of precipitation, since the atmosphere would have been saturated with water vapor during the rainfall, precluding further evaporation.

It is likely that this water above the atmosphere was in the form of a vapor, for alternatively, at such great altitudes, only ice crystals could exist, and in such prodigious quantities as to effectively prevent most sunlight from reaching the earth's surface. There were likely no clouds as we now know them over the earth's surface, since there was no rain; rather, "a mist used to rise from the earth and water all the surface of the ground" (Gen. 2:6). The canopy of water had been reserved for the destruction of the Deluge just as fire is reserved for the final destruction of the unrighteous during the end time (II Peter 3:5-7). Job, who may have lived prior to the Flood, likened the watery expanse above the firmament to a molten looking glass (Job 37:18). He also spoke of an open space at the North Pole through which could be seen an "empty place" (Job 26:7). Ancient Grecian astronomers have reported seeing the north polar stars revolving in a *tholos,* which signifies an opening in a vaulted enclosure.[10] Here, apparently the stars could be seen through a vaulted dome engendered by the combined forces of the earth's gravitational and magnetic fields on the water canopy.

Precisely how this canopy of water came to be stabilized above the atmosphere is a matter of conjecture. Forces had to be stupendously gigantic! It may be safely assumed that atmospheric conditions were much different during these pre-Flood days than at the present time.

Ancient Seas and Land Masses

On the third day of creation God caused the dry land to appear.

Let the waters below the heaven be gathered into one place to let dry land appear! And so it was. God called the dry land Earth, and he called the gathered waters Seas (Gen. 1:9-10).

Geographical conditions on the earth during pre-Flood days were considerably different from those found on modern maps, for during the Deluge great volcanic and seismic disturbances occurred. Since the mass of water surrounding the earth had not yet descended there must have been a much greater land mass than presently is evident. Much of the present-day sea bottom therefore must have been dry land. H. B. Rand in *Primogenesis* states,

According to the account the waters were gathered into one place, called seas. Eden might have been located upon or near the shores and the river that flowed through the garden might have emptied into the sea, but parted into four heads outside of Eden and compassed the lands of the globe.[11]

If the seas were gathered into one place the dry land would form a single mass. Such a reality is directly implied by Genesis 2:10-14:

And a river went out of Eden to water the garden; and from thence it was parted, and became into four heads.

Josephus further states,

Now the garden was watered by one river, which ran round about the whole earth, and was parted into four parts. . . .[12]

The four rivers mentioned in Genesis 2—Pison (Ganges), Euphrates, Hiddekel (Tigris), and Gihan (Nile)—according to Josephus do not correspond with their modern counterparts. A footnote by Whiston in The *Antiquities of the Jews* indicates the following:

Whence this strange notion [the garden being watered by a single river] came, which yet is not peculiar to Josephus, but, as Dr. Hudson says here, is derived from older authors, as if four of the greatest rivers in the world, running two of them [the Ganges and the Nile] at vast distances from the other two, by some means or other watered paradise, is hard to say. Only, since Josephus has already appeared to allegorize this history . . . we perhaps mistake him when we suppose he literally means those four rivers . . . though what further allegorical sense he had in view is now, I fear, impossible to be determined.[13]

Impossible? Why? With only a single land mass before the Flood there would be no great trouble interpreting this passage if one assumes that portions of this original great river system still remain and contain portions of the rivers mentioned, the rivers perhaps separated due to Flood-related tectonic movements and sedimentation. In fact, the current highly-touted theory of "continental drift," proposed by Alfred Wegener* around 1900, purports that the earth

---

* Alfred Wegner (1880-1930), a German meteorologist and student of the earth, was intrigued by the apparent relationship in form between the opposing coasts of South America and Africa. In 1912 he published a detailed account of his theory, picturing a single vast continent that he named *Pangaea* (Greek "all" and "earth").[14] This continent, he hypothesized, split asunder and drifted across the earth's face. Although he was a follower of uniformitarian theory and assumed slow land movements over millions of years, his theory could as easily apply to rapid movements as could have occurred during the Deluge. Evidence in favor of the theory includes the approximate fit of the continents (see Figures 26 and 27), paleomagnetism (polar migration suggests the continents drifted away from each other, and in some cases rotated), ancient climates (the climatic belts in ages past, varying as they do today from equator to pole, reveal different equator and pole positions than exist today), and fossils common to separate land masses.[15]

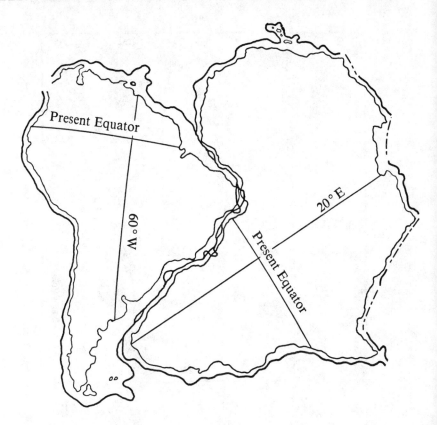

Figure 29. The fit of South America and Africa is very close, especially at 2,000 meters (6,500 foot) below sea level (see the heavy lines). Chester Longwell, a distinguished Australian geologist, found the fit so credible that he stated, "if the fit between South America and Africa is not genetic, surely it is a device of Satan for our frustration."[17]

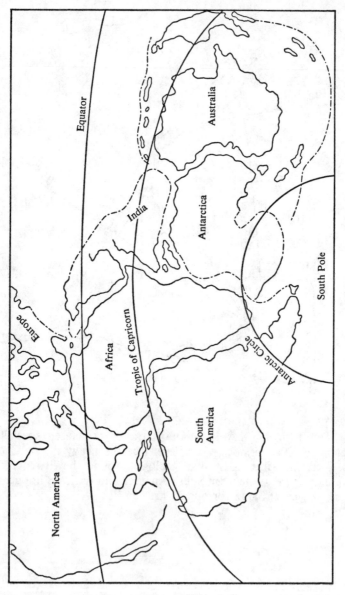

Figure 30. A suggested reassembly of a portion of Pangaea, the postulated original continent.[18]

at one time consisted of a single land mass which, over millennia, separated and moved apart.[16] Only many decades later did the proponents of plate tectonics visualize the close fit of the continents if they could be placed together at their continental shelves, much like a giant jigsaw puzzle, as shown in Figures 29 and 30.

If continental drift did indeed occur during the 150-day period when the "waters swelled over the earth" (Gen. 7:20-24), these movements of land beneath the oceanic waters could well have aided in the submergence of the land masses; the water would tend to override the continents much as the current of a stream swells over a rock. These Deluge earth crustal movements, if they did occur, of course would be on such massive scale as to defy the comprehension of current scientists.

Could a single pre-Flood land mass have split and drifted apart during the Deluge, when titanic crustal movements may have occurred? The fact that there existed four primary worldwide rivers having a common origin before the Flood, together with Wegener's hypothesis, add significant legitimacy to the idea that a single pre-Flood land mass did indeed exist.

The sea level in the antediluvian world would be the difference between todays' sea level and the amount of water which fell during the 40 day rain. Normal atmospheric pressures would also be lowered along with the reduced sea level. Today, the most ideal living conditions for humans lies in the elevation belt from sea level to about 3,000 feet;[19] this "belt of living" would also exist before the Flood, for people were physiologically the same then as now. The problem then boils down to where the antedeluvian sea level was, for once this level is established further considerations regarding the Garden of Eden and its character may be entertained.

The Pre-Flood Sea Level

A thorough review of available data relating to the antediluvian sea level has been undertaken by G. F. Carr,[20] and is recorded in part in several of the following references. The fact that six-sevenths of the earth's surface was dry land means that 14.3% of the surface was covered by seas. The sea level must then have been at a point where only 14.3% of the earth's surface was covered by water. According to *Encyclopedia Britannica,*

> The relative distribution of elevation and depth can be shown by a hysographic curve, showing two primary levels of reference, one slightly above sea level, the other at depths between 4,000 to 5,000 meters [13,120 to 16,400 feet]. Elevations of more than 6,000 meters [19,680 feet] represent only a small percentage of the earth's surface. Also, there is only a relatively small percentage of the sea bottom with depths between 200 and 3,000 meters [756 and 9,840 feet]. The mean elevation of the land is 840 meters [2,755 feet] and the mean depth of the oceans is 3,800 meters [12,464 feet].
>
> . . . detailed charts . . . have brought to light a complex topography of which the most striking features are submarine canyons which cut into the slope and sometimes across the shelf. . . . The question as to the origin of these canyons is unsettled.[21]

Next, a quote is taken from *Structural Geology* by Nevin:

> Measurements of the elevations and depressions of the crust have been made on a sufficiently close network to convince us that two levels occur most commonly, while the stages between are relatively rare. . . . The following table brings this ous clearly by showing the percentage of the earth's surface at different levels.[22]

	Percentage
Between 24,000 and 18,000 feet above sea level	0.1
Between 18,000 and 12,000 feet above sea level	0.9
Between 12,000 and 6,000 feet above sea level	1.0
At about 1,000 feet above sea level	18.0
Between 1,000 feet and sea level	5.0
Between sea level and 600 feet below (continental shelf)	5.0
Total for continents	30.0

	Percentage
Between 600 and 6,000 feet below sea level	12.0
Between 6,000 and 12,000 feet below sea level	15.0
Between 12,000 and 18,000 feet below sea level	40.0
Between 18,000 and 24,000 feet below sea level	3.0
Total for ocean basins	70.0

Using the table of frequencies of *Structural Geology,* the percentage of the earth's surface at 1,000-foot intervals between 12,000 and 18,000 feet below sea level is approximately as follows:[23]

                                                                 Percentage
Between 12,000 and 13,000 feet below sea level................7.2
Between 13,000 and 14,000 feet below sea level................7.6
Between 14,000 and 15,000 feet below sea level................7.8
Between 15,000 and 16,000 feet below sea level................7.4
Between 16,000 and 17,000 feet below sea level................6.0
Between 17,000 and 18,000 feet below sea level................4.0

Between 12,000 and 18,000 feet below sea level............40.0

Using the above information and assuming that there were no major movements in the earth's crust during the past 5,000 years, let us calculate the distance below present sea level at which the pre-Deluge sea level must have been located in order to give the pre-Deluge seas an area totalling 14.3% of the earth's surface.[24]

                                                                 Percentage
Required total percentage................................14.3
Percentage between 16,000 and 24,000 feet below sea level....13.0
Percentage between 15,000 and 16,000 feet below sea level.....1.3

At this depth (15,000 to 16,000 feet), 1.3% is equivalent to 175 feet. Subtracting 175 feet from 16,000 feet gives the required depth of 15,825 feet. Therefore, the pre-Deluge sea level stood at 15,825 feet below the present sea level. At this former level there would have been a relatively large area of the earth's surface with elevations ranging from sea level up to a point 2,000 feet above sea level. The supposition would be that the greater portion of the pre-Deluge inhabitants would have been living within 2,000 feet of this ancient sea level. This low sea level would also account for the submarine canyons. . . . It would also account for the fact that recent investigations have shown that mountain peaks are present at depths of two to three miles below the surface which are absolutely free of any sediments, for they are barren.[25]

Pre-Flood Landforms

Corroborating the evidence of G. F. Carr, that submarine canyons were formed due to erosion upon an exposed land surface, is that of

J. C. Whitcomb and H. M. Roberts. They state that these great canyons, similar in every respect to the great river canyons of the land surface, extend far out on the continental shelves, usually projecting seaward from a river valley.[26] These canyons exist in great numbers around every continent of the world. Most geologists have great difficulty explaining the greatly elevated sea level and submarine canyons, supposing that water was released from melting polar ice caps to bury the canyons, and that undersea turbidity currents aided by submarine landsliding, slumping, and creep aided their formation. However, as W. D. Thornbury has stated, "The theory . . . holds a slightly favored position, not so much because it answers all the questions connected with them, but because it encounters fewer difficulties than any other theory."[27] Yet, Thornbury admits that the submarine canyon extending out some 300 miles from the mouth of the Hudson River proceeds to nearly the exact 15,825 foot depth,[28] the antediluvian shoreline as calculated by Carr:

> The difficulties encountered in explaining the lowering of sea level necessary for the canyons to have been cut by streams seems insurmountable. . . . If Tolstoy's conclusion that Hudson Canyon extends down to a depth of 15,000 feet is correct, the magnitude of lowering of sea level to permit canyon cutting seems beyond any possibility of realization.[29]

During the past 20 years a great number of "seamounts," flat-topped submerged islands under the ocean surface, have been discovered in the ocean basins. Many are more than 6,000 feet below the ocean surface, though much evidence indicates they were at one time above the surface. According to E. L. Hamilton,

> They are fossil landforms preserved in the depth of the sea, where they are disturbed only by light currents and the slow rain of pelagic material from the waters above.[30]

The picture of the submerged ocean floor painted by W. H. Bucher, Professor of Geology at Columbia University, further elucidates Hamilton's concept:

In the summer of 1947 Ewing [Maurice Ewing of Columbia University] started a systematic mapping of the topography of the North American sea floor with modern echo-sounding devices from the research ship Atlantis. This exploration shows in precise detail what had been known before in a general way: that the surface of the sea floor is the exact opposite of what Wegener's hypothesis demands [continental-drift hypothesis]. The floor has a rugged topography. From the plain of the North American Basin at the bottom of the Atlantic more than five miles below sea level there rise large mountains ('sea mounts') which in some cases are more than 6,000 feet tall. Many of these undersea mountains have sharp peaks; others are flat-topped. From Iceland south to the Antarctic Ocean runs a complex submarine mountain belt—the Mid-Atlantic Ridge. Its central part forms a rugged highland 60 to 200 miles wide, with peaks that rise to less than a mile below the surface of the sea. . . .

Much the same picture characterizes the floor of the great central region in the Pacific, which apparently consists wholly of basalt and related rocks. Flat-topped sea mounts in large numbers have been found there. The Hawaiian Islands are the top of a great basalt range which rises above sea level from an ocean floor over three miles deep. . . . Perhaps the most significant of the young, active belts is the mighty submarine mountain belt which extends southward from Japan through the Bonins and Marianas to Palau—a range comparable in length and height to the Himalayas. Among its peaks are the islands of Iwo Jima, Saipan, Guam, and Yap. This range has the same assymetric profile, the same deep-sea trench along its steeper side and the same chain of volcanoes on its gentler back as the most active belts on the continents bordering the Pacific. . . .

Suppose there were no ocean and we were standing on the bottom lowlands of the Pacific looking westward toward this towering mountain range. Beyond it westward lies a deep sea plain that extends for more than 600 miles. There the great submarine mountain chains that form the Philippine Islands rise in precisely the same manner from the ocean deep, and behind them, covered by younger sediments, emerges the edge of the Asiatic Continent itself. From this perspective it would seem incomprehensible to us that men should ever ask: 'How did the ocean basins come to be?' Instead we might well ask: 'How did the continents come to be?'

From this point of view the very expression 'ocean basins' becomes meaningless. The continents now can be seen clearly as deformed belts of the earth's surface which have been raised at intervals through geologic time and joined together in various ways. The oceanic areas, on the other hand, must be the undisturbed portions of the earth's surface. They are underlain by the original basaltic crust, covered here and there with a blanket of diverse sediments.[31]

The foregoing discussion paints a picture of the antediluvian world quite similar to the present-day view of the Nepalese gazing northward toward the towering Himalayas. Most people, living at or near their sea level three miles below the present sea level, would view impressive mountain ranges rising many miles into the air.[32] The precise configuration of the land surface following the gathering of the waters into one place (Gen. 1:9) is difficult to determine at this time. Surely, in order for the Flood waters to cover the entire continents now above water there would need to have been titanic forces brought into play, lowering a mountain range here or elevating an ocean basin there. David directly implies this tremendous seismic activity during the Flood, when a "flattened" earth (in order for water to cover the highest mountain peaks) was resculptured into mountains and valleys, ocean basins and continents:

> Who laid the foundations of the earth,
> That it should not be removed for ever.
> Thou coveredst it with the deep as with a garment;
> The waters stood above the mountains
> At thy rebuke they fled;
> At the voice of thy thunder they hasted away
> [The mountains rose, the valleys sank down]
> Unto the place which thou hast founded for them.
> Thou hast set a bound that they may not pass over;
> That they turn not again to cover the earth (Psa. 104:5-9).

Before the Flood had ceased, great surface erosion from the torrential rainfall, turbulent rivers, tidal waves, and ocean waves and currents generated during the Deluge would have further modified vast areas of the earth's crust.

Once the millions of tons of water during the Deluge had fallen from the firmament, raising the sea level and submerging former mountain peaks, formerly inaccessible plateaus became fit for human habitation. As mentioned in Genesis 7:11, the "fountains of the great abyss [Hebrew *tehom*, or 'the deep sea'³³] all burst" on the same day the great rain began. Great volcanic explosions and eruptions are implied by this Scripture, meaning great quantities of liquids (magmas and steam), confined under great pressure within the earth's crust and triggered by some God-instigated force, burst out under the seas.

The 360 day year following Creation became a 365 day year, likely due to a transfer of the inertia of the water layer in the firmament to the earth and its atmosphere, slowing the rotational velocity. A phenomenon known as "rotary drift" may have contributed to the water's prevailing above even the highest mountains for many weeks.³⁴ These great crustal upheavals and fall of the water canopy may also have produced the 23.5° tilt of the earth's axis, for the statement of Genesis 8:22 is "while the earth remaineth, seedtime and harvest and cold and heat, and summer and winter, and day and night shall not cease." There is no indication that these seasonal conditions existed before the Flood, but rather a pre-Flood warmer and more moderate worldwide climate is implied by the presence of the poleward energy-transferring canopy. No axis tilt before the Flood would have meant no procession of the seasons, but a uniform year-long climate at any position on the globe. This tilting of the earth's axis may also have accounted for the "rotary drift" of the waters over the entire land surface during the Flood: as the earth's axis shifted from a perpendicular to the plane of revolution around the sun to point toward Polaris (the North Star), due to inertia within the fluid mass of the oceans, coupled with the Coriolus force of the earth's rotation, the waters would override the land masses. If a single pre-Flood land mass also drifted apart to create the continents, as described earlier, further overriding of the land by oceanic waters would have occurred. These land masses already could easily have been temporarily lowered to some degree through tectonic forces.

The seasons added a curse upon man's labors, necessitating that he fight the elements of nature in order to exist on the earth:³⁵ the cold of winter, periodic drought, the storms of temperate and arctic regions, and the hurricanes and monsoon rains of tropical rain-forest regions. The rainbow signaled changed atmospheric conditions, which appeared to Noah and his family with the first rainshower

(Gen. 9:11-13). Now sunlight could be refracted and dispersed into the spectral colors through raindrops under the proper conditions following a rain, quite unlike the situation with a mist which watered the earth before the Flood.

The "quick frozen" hulks of countless mammoths, now found perfectly preserved in northern Siberia, were very likely almost instantaneously interred during the sudden downrush of freezing precipitation in the polar zones of the earth, just as water suddenly downrushed in temperate and tropical regions. In fact, the two to three mile original thicknesses of the Antarctic and Greenland ice caps, according to geologists, closely approximates the presumed depth of precipitation which fell upon the earth during the Deluge.

As already mentioned, the Garden of Eden would have been located near sea level. After the Flood it would have been covered by nearly three miles of ocean water *unless* the site was elevated due to tectonic forces during the subsiding of the waters (Gen. 8:3-14). Even if the site of the Garden was elevated above water its present state would be utterly obscured by erosion or sedimentation, eliminating the need for cherubims with flaming swords to guard the way to the tree of life in the midst of the Garden (Gen. 3:24) . . . for that tree would no longer be found.

Chapter Eight

Millennial Climate, Soils, and Productivity

The Climate and Soils of the Garden of Eden

Speculation concerning climate and soils in the original Garden may indeed be risky. Yet, it is clear that the plants of the Garden of Eden were growing on the third day of creation on soils formerly sea bottom earlier that day: " 'Let the waters below the heaven be gathered into one place, to let dry land appear.' And so it was" (Gen. 1:9). It is also quite clear that God created everything in a state of maturity, i.e., every plant appeared fully grown and bearing fruit, which was necessary for man's survival when he was created—also fully grown—on the sixth day.

And God said, 'Let the earth put out verdure, plants that bear seed and trees yielding fruit of every kind, fruit with seed in it.' And so it was; the earth brought forth verdure, plants bearing seed of every kind and trees yielding fruit of every kind, fruit with seed in it (Gen. 1:11-12).

Genesis 2:4-5 restates the fact that plants were fully formed at creation. A special park, the Garden of Eden, was planted by God Himself where man was placed, a garden where "the Eternal made all sorts of trees to grow that were delightful to see and good to eat, with the tree of life and the tree that yields knowledge of good and evil in the centre of the park" (Gen. 2:9). The food for man included "every plant that bears seed all over the earth, and every tree with seed in its fruit" (Gen. 1:29). This entire creation was "very good," surely a sign that God's mighty hand assured the highest quality of abundant yields for all crops raised both within and outside the Garden of Eden.

As mentioned above, the land worldwide had been covered with sea water the day before God caused the plants to appear. The superb growing conditions of soils derived from the sea floor is underscored by E. W. Russell, author of *Soil Conditions and Plant Growth,*[1] a widely-used soils text in the English-speaking world. He cites a report by T. S. Dymond and F. Hughes of a case when flooding from seawater caused the formation of a sodium clay along the English coast.[2] From 1897 to 1899 they observed that the first effect of flooding was to kill the vegetation by direct salt effects. When the flood subsided and rainwater began to dissolve and leach out the salt, however, an interesting sequence of events was observed. The soil was at first "in remarkably good condition, plowing well and forming a capital seedbed." However, when more salts were removed through further leaching "this condition gradually altered until the soil became difficult to work and in dry weather [became] hard and cindery."[3] Dymond and Hughes correctly theorized that the sodium displaced calcium and magnesium from the clay, leading to deflocculation of the clay and unfavorable physical conditions; the original excellent condition of the soil was due to some calcium and magnesium yet remaining on the soil exchange sites.[4]

The Dutch, according to Russell, have had similar experiences while reclaiming land from the sea (see Figure 31). The soil starts out very sticky and wet, but after a drainage system has been installed and some salts have been washed out the surface soil acquires excellent tilth. At this stage barley and mangolds grow and yield well. Trouble arises during following years when more salts are removed by rain so the clay becomes deflocculated. In time the calcium normally present in these soils will replace the sodium and improve the structure once again; however, cultivation must be very shallow so the poorly structured soil remains below.[5]

These results point lucidly toward the remarkably prolific vegetative growth prophesied for the millennium and experienced in the Garden of Eden. Once the canopy of water is replaced in the firmament there will be no rain as we now know it, but rather, as in

Figure 31. A Dutch polder.

Eden (Gen. 2:6), a "mist" will water the soil. Once the land masses have been raised above the ocean floors a condition similar to that experienced by the English and Dutch may be experienced . . . not for one or two years, but continuously thereafter. There will be no rain showers to leach away the salts, resulting in no soil deterioration after the first year or two. The "remarkably good condition," as Dymond and Hughes related,[6] will remain indefinitely! Experiments using sea water or sea salts as fertilizers, or sea water as an irrigation water source, have been extensive in recent years. Some soils may tolerate up to 3 quarts of sea water per cubic foot, or 3,000 pounds of sea solids (deposits of evaporated sea salts) per acre and produce excellent crops, both in yield and quality.[7] Sodium in combination with the other elements found in sea water, within certain limits of concentration, is not toxic to plants.[8] In recent years an entire technology has grown up around the use of sea water *directly* for irrigation, especially in arid regions of the world such as the Middle East and North Africa. High yields of many important field and orchard crops have been obtained despite the high salt content of these irrigation waters.[8]

Specific pre-Deluge climatic characteristics have already been mentioned. As stated in Genesis 2:6, a mist arose from the earth and watered the soil surface. In addition, Genesis 2:5 states "no plant had sprung up, for God the Eternal had not sent rain on earth." What is likely implied here is daytime evaporation from plants, soils, and water sources, with subsequent condensation of this atmospheric moisture during the cooler nighttime hours, creating a fog or mist. A heavy condensation of moisture on plants and soils within an atmosphere perpetually near the saturation point for water vapor— maintained by the water canopy surrounding the earth—would supply vegetation each day with water sufficient for continued florid growth, not greatly unlike conditions within a well-maintained terrarium. Plant growth would be profuse without a drop of rainwater! With the elimination of the harmful effects of desiccation on plant growth—an effect which plants readily adapt to but at the expense of the plant expressing its full growth potential (some energy is diverted toward life-saving changes in plant structure and metabolism)—untold rates of growth and abundance of vegetation would be realized.

The presence of the water canopy, besides helping to maintain atmospheric humidity levels, would tend to limit seasonal and diurnal temperature variations around the earth. Heat would be trapped in the water vapor and moved on a massive scale as the canopy would circulate.* Global circulation of the canopy would transport heat trapped in equatorial regions to polar regions where the energy would be reradiated, greatly expanding the belt of comfortable year-round temperatures much closer to the poles than presently experienced. It is doubtful that antediluvian polar icecaps even existed, though the abundance of woolly mammoth remains in Arctic regions, presumably living just before the Flood, indicates fairly cold conditions existed in northern Alaska and Siberia; some "quick-frozen" specimens had unmasticated leaves from trees now native to southern Siberia in their mouths.[11] Other species of animals common to northern regions have been uncovered in the presently uninhabited polar regions:

> The extensive salty alluvium, now frozen, in central Alaska contains a numerous mammal fauna. . . . Freezing has preserved the skin and tissue of some of the animals. The formal list includes two bears, dire wolf, wolf, fox, badger, wolverine, saber-tooth cat, jaguar, lynx, wooly mammoth, mastodon, two horses, camel, saiga antelope, four bisons, caribou, moose, stag-moose, elk, two sheep, musk-ox and yak types, ground sloth, and several rodents.[12]

An interesting explanation for these frozen animals has been proposed by I. T. Sanderson which ties in beautifully with the cascading snow, rain, volcanism, and crustal movements associated with the Deluge in polar regions.

---

* Water has a very high heat capacity compared to the other gases present in the atmosphere. At 25 °C water has a specific heat (the ratio of a substance's thermal capacity to that of water at 15 °C; it takes 1 calorie of heat to raise 1 gram of water from 14 to 15 °C) of 1.000; nitrogen (N_2), which comprises about 78% of dry air, has a specific heat of only 0.249, while oxygen (O_2), which constitutes about 21% of the air, has a specific heat of 0.219.[9] Water vapor thus can transmit 4 to 5 times as much heat energy as can the two major gases in air, although its content in the air seldom exceeds 5% by volume when temperatures are high and maximum moisture is available.[10]

A sudden mass extrusion of dust and gases . . . might even be so heavy as to cut out sunlight altogether for days, weeks, months, or even years if the crustal movements continued. Winds beyond anything known today would be whipped up, and cold fronts of vast lengths would build up with violent extremes of temperature on either side. There would be forty days and nights of snow in one place, continent-wide floods in another, and roaring hurricanes, seaquakes, and earthquakes bringing on landslides and tidal waves in others, and many other disturbances.[13]

Sanderson claims that the mammoths found quick-frozen in Alaska and elsewhere were frozen due to the descent of great masses of chilled volcanic gases, first expelled into the stratosphere and then rapidly falling until a downburst occurred on the ground. Violent winds and floods overcame hosts of other animals. As Sanderson continues,

. . . mammoths and other animals were all literally torn to pieces while still fresh. Young and old alike were cast about, mangled and then frozen. There are also, however, other areas where the animals are mingled but had time to decompose before being frozen; and still others where they decomposed down to bones and were then either frozen or not. Beyond these again, there are similar vast masses of animals, including whole families or herds, all piled together into gulleys and riverbeds and other holes, but where only bones remain.[14]

Utopian Climate and Productivity

Since God has declared that the earth will become a veritable Garden of Eden after Christ's return to establish the Kingdom (Joel 2:3), then Scriptures relating to the Kingdom should verify this fact. Indeed they do! A pivotal reference in this regard is recorded in Isaiah 35:

The wilderness and the solitary place shall be glad for them; and the desert [arabah] shall rejoice, and blossom as the rose. It shall blossom abundantly, and rejoice even with joy and singing: the joy of Lebanon shall be given unto it, the excellency of Carmel and Sharon, they shall see the glory of the Lord, and the excellency of our God. . . . Then the eyes of the blind shall be opened, and the ears of the deaf shall be unstopped. Then shall the lame man leap as an hart, and the tongue of the dumb sing: for in the wilderness shall waters break out, and streams in the desert. And the parched ground shall become a pool, and the thirsty land springs of water: in the habitation of dragons, where each lay, shall be grass with reeds and rushes (Isa. 35:1-2, 5-7).

Here the desert and desolate places, today parched and unproductive, are pictured as being lush with vegetation and bringing forth springs of water. This requires a worldwide revolution of climate to enable moisture-yielding atmospheric mechanisms to water nearly the entire face of the earth. Such a change is reminiscent of Genesis 2:6, where a mist watered the earth in pre-Flood days. Since the earth will become a Garden of Eden in the Kingdom, one may directly assume that the water canopy which fell to earth during the 40 consecutive days of rainfall during the Flood will somehow become reinstated. This would lower sea levels to expose perhaps six-sevenths of the earth's surface as before the Deluge;[15] but coupled with a lowering of mountain ranges and raising of valleys the arable land within the zone of living (less than about 3,000 feet elevation) would likely be greatly expanded compared to pre-Flood days.

The mechanism needed to place such a tremendous volume of water from the oceans back into position above the earth's atmosphere may be alluded to in prophecy. Christ spoke of certain events to occur during the end time:

Immediately after the misery of those days, the sun will be darkened, and the moon will not yield her light, the stars will drop from heaven and the orbs of the heavens will be shaken (Matt. 24:29).

In addition, Christ states that

And just as it was in the days of Noah, so will it be in the days of the Son of man; they were eating, drinking, marrying, and being married, till the day Noah entered the ark—then came the deluge and destroyed them all. Or just as it was in the days of Lot; they were eating, drinking, buying, selling, planting, and building, but on the day that Lot left Sodom it rained fire and brimstone from heaven and destroyed them all. So will it be on the day that the Son of man is revealed (Luke 17:26-30).

Both of these events, the Flood and the destruction of Sodom, may
have been tied closely to the close approach of a comet or planet[16]
(God oftentimes uses natural phenomena to fulfill His will). They
were prophesied events, i.e., the area of the earth in question was
known well ahead of time, and the righteous people in areas so affected by the cataclysms were warned and protected . . . in Noah's
case by an ark, and in Lot's case by leaving the vicinity. The coming
worldwide cataclysms are similarly pictured through John's writings:

> The first [trumpet] blew, and there came hail and fire mixed with
> blood, falling on the earth. . . . The second angel blew, and what
> looked like a huge mountain on fire was hurled into the sea. . . . The
> third angel blew, and a huge star blazing like a torch dropped out of
> the sky. . . . The fourth angel blew; and a stroke fell on a third of the
> sun, a third of the moon, and a third of the stars, so as to darken one
> third of them, withdrawing light from a third of the day and likewise
> of the night (Rev. 8:7-8; 10, 12).
>
> The second [angel] poured out his bowl upon the sea; it turned blood
> like the blood of a corpse, and every living thing within the sea
> perished. The third poured out his bowl upon the rivers and fountains
> of water, and they turned blood. . . . The fourth angel poured out his
> bowl upon the sun; and the sun was allowed to scorch men with fire,
> till men, scorched by the fierce heat, blasphemed the name of the God
> who had control of these plagues. . . . The fifth poured out his bowl
> upon the throne of the Beast; his realm was darkened, and men
> gnawed their tongues in anguish. . . . The sixth poured out his bowl
> on the great river Euphrates, and its waters were dried up . . . (Rev.
> 16:3-4, 8-12).

"Fiery hail," a "mountain of fire," or a "star blazing like a
torch" sound very much like heavenly bodies—meteorites, comets,
or others—which are destined to strike the earth. A great deal of attention is focused, in the Scripture cited above, on occurrences which
involve water: heavenly bodies hurled into the ocean, waters of the
sea, rivers, and fountains turned to the color of blood, and rivers of
water dried up. Also, powerful sources of heat and light are dealt
with in these prophecies: heat of the heavenly bodies, the sun and
other heavenly bodies partially darkened, a fiercely burning sun
scorching men, and darkness over the land of the Beast.

The titanic energy sources and heavenly bodies will likely somehow combine to elevate the water canopy once more above the earth, providing the solar shield that enabled men to live many centuries, and which will enable crop yields and quality to reach unheard of proportions within a mild and uniformly pleasant worldwide climate. Even so, seasons will continue to exist as guaranteed in Genesis 8:22, indicating the earth will maintain some degree of tilt to its axis. Without this tilt there would be no annual procession of the seasons.

Many of these events are analogous to the miracles surrounding the release of the Israelites from Egyptian captivity. Likewise, the righteous firstfruits of the present age will be released from this present sinful world of slavery to Satan's repressive government.

Will a comet suddenly appear out of nowhere in the next few years and race toward a collision with the earth? Many comets come and go, some predictably and some not. According to Velikovsky, more than 60 comets are known to definitely belong to the solar system, having short periods (less than 80 years) that revolve in stretched ellipses within the orbit of Neptune (except for one comet).[17] Astronomers have estimated, however, that hundreds of thousands of other comets at times may visit our solar system; they are seen at a rate of about 500 per century.[18] It is not known if they return periodically. Also, comets are thought to be born under certain circumstances.

Whatever cosmic occurrences will fulfill the end-time prophecies mentioned, one may be sure that God has already set such bodies into His ordained trajectory within the universe. Man, with his limited knowledge and capabilities, may view only those bodies visible to his telescopes. Were he to somehow grasp the entire cosmic pattern being worked out, he would surely, upon seeing the earth's plight in the light of prophecy, bow down in awe to the Designer and Creator of this celestial masterpiece of beauty, order, timing, and perfection.

It is not known whether some desert areas will remain, for beautiful desert plants are perfectly designed to survive within their environment. Would God remove this portion of His creation from the earth by removing the desert environment supporting these arid region plants?

A further summary of the fruitful results of this worldwide revolution in climate is recorded by Joel:

Fear not, O land; be glad and rejoice: for the Lord will do great things. Be not afraid, ye beasts of the field: for the pastures of the wilderness do spring, for the tree beareth her fruit, the fig tree and the vine do yield their strength. Be glad then, ye children of Zion, and rejoice in the Lord your God: for he hath given you the former rain moderately [according to righteousness], and he will cause to come down for you the rain, the former rain, and the latter rain in the first month. And the floors shall be full of wheat, and the vats shall overflow with wine and oil. And I will restore to you the years that the locust hath eaten, the cankerworm, and the caterpillar, and the palmerworm, my great army which I sent among you. And ye shall eat in plenty, and be satisfied . . . (Joel 2:21-26).

Alongside improved climatic conditions must come enhanced soil fertility, for the soil provides the true basis of real national wealth.[19] Just as the land immediately following the Creation was lush with vegetation—grown on land previously inundated by seawater—so after the Deluge the land had been covered and renewed through the action of seawater. One may say that the fertility of the soil was largely replenished by the sea, its dissolved minerals and sedimentary activities, during each of these momentous turning points of man's history on the earth, just as much of the land to be reclaimed by a retreating sea at the inception of the millennium will be likewise renewed. The characteristic lush growth observed through fertilization of soils with seawater and sea salts, as well as the results of reclaimed sea-flooded land, has already been described.

The vastly improved millennial weather conditions and plant growth are tied directly to in verse 23 of Joel 2, to righteous behavior of individuals a reflection of the automatic rewards for obedience and the punishment for disobedience to God's commandments:

If ye walk in my statutes, and keep my commandments, and do them; then I will give you rain in due season, and the land shall yield her increase, and the trees of the field shall yield their fruit. . . . But if ye will not hearken unto me, and will not do all these commandments . . . ye shall sow your seed in vain, for your enemies shall eat it . . . and I will make your heaven as iron, and your earth as brass: and your strength shall be spent in vain: for your land shall not yield her increase, neither shall the trees of the land yield their fruits (Lev. 26:3-4, 14, 16, 19-20).

Since, in the Kingdom, the Spirit of God will be poured out among all mankind (Joel 2:28), and will fill the entire earth, man will learn obedience to God and be blessed by abundant production from the soils beneath his feet, blessed by a climate unbelievably moderate and life-giving.

The Millennial Landscape

Along with the vegetation being lush and productive as in the Garden of Eden, the entire earth will experience a topographic revolution at the time of Christ's return. Isaiah makes this clear in the following verse:

> Every valley shall be exalted, and every mountain and hill shall be made low: and the crooked shall be made straight, and the rough places plain [a plain place] (Isa. 40:4).

The meaning of this prophecy is dual, referring first of all to the pompous individuals and governments (mountains) of the present Babylonian world system being eliminated (lowered; Rev. 18; Prov. 16:18) and those individuals who are meek and humble (valleys) being lifted up to positions of rulership (Matt. 5:5; Rev. 5:10). Secondly, this prophecy literally will be fulfilled in the Kingdom when the valleys and mountains will be smoothed, perhaps during the last mighty earthquake during the end time (Rev. 16:18) for as John reveals,

> . . . and there was a great earthquake, such as was not since men were upon the earth, so mighty an earthquake and so great. And the great city was divided into three parts, and the cities of the nations fell. . . . And every island fled away, and *the mountains were not found* (Rev. 16:18, 20).

Thus, the topography of the millennium will likely be one of rather broad, highly fruitful plains bathed within a climate optimal for the livelihood of plants, animals, and man. This picture differs substantially from the Adamic period, when mountains and valleys existed presumably as they do today. The Garden of Eden, however, readily pictures the God-plane, perfectly structured system of pastoral beauty and perfection prevalent across the entire face of the earth. With seabeds raised and the continents relatively flat most of the earth will be habitable, bringing most elevations within the range of sea level and 3,000 feet. Whether *all* mountains and valleys will be eliminated is an unanswerable question, for most people familiar with the awesome beauty of a majestic peak or a flowering, fertile valley—or even an austere but flowering desert—would question if God could improve upon such untainted masterpieces. The potential for high population within an environment breathtakingly beautiful and fruitful, having in large part been just reclaimed from the sea in all of its restored fertility, is beyond belief; yet, the entire earth will be in perfect reinstituted compliance with the harmonious laws of nature initiated during the creation week. Eden will become a reality worldwide!

Chapter Nine

Millennial Soil Management

Dressing and Keeping—Plowing and Tilling

A dam and Eve were given the responsibility to "dress and keep" the Garden of Eden. This word "dress" comes from the Hebrew *abad,* meaning "to serve, labor, or work,"[1] and is usually translated "till" or "tiller" (Gen. 2:15; 3:23; 4:2; 4:12; II Sam. 9:10; I Chron. 27:26; Neh. 10:37; Prov. 28:19; Jer. 27:11; Ezek. 36:9; 36:34). "Keep" (Gen 2:15) comes from the Hebrew *shamar* meaning "to keep, observe, or take heed."[2]

In all of these references there is no indication they were to till the soil by inverting or fracturing the surface, but rather they were to work with the natural productivity of the soil, keeping the Garden properly ordered through their labors. Fruit of the trees and herbs bearing seed which grew in the Garden could be freely eaten (Gen. 1:29; 2:15). No great personal effort was apparently involved with tending the plants and animals before sin entered the picture, for it was not until after they had eaten of the tree of the knowledge of good and evil that they were told, "In the sweat of your face shall you eat bread."

They were expelled from the Garden of Eden to live in a land apparently not as harmonious, well-planned, and tended as the Garden itself "which God had planted" (Gen. 2:8). The implication is that man would plan the earth's crop culture from then on through a system swayed by Satan, resulting in the curse upon the ground and harvests reduced by weeds (thorns and thistles) and other environmental limitations (Gen. 3:17-18).

As shown earlier, and as stated by Josephus,[3] Cain was a tiller of the soil who forced the land beyond its normal capacity, and whose offering to God was not accepted (Gen. 4:2-5). His attitude was that of getting. To force the land he probably plowed or disturbed the soil in some manner, thereby accelerating the rate of organic matter oxidation and the concomitant release of nutrients. Abel, on the other hand, was a keeper of sheep whose sacrifice was acceptable to God. He grazed his animals upon grass, a practice involving no tillage.

If Cain did evil by fracturing and/or inverting the soil surface, what then is meant by "tillage" or "plowing" in order that a farmer might properly grow a crop without forcing the soil beyond its natural potential? An understanding of Hebrew cultivation techniques may partially answer this question. The instrument anciently used to "plow" the soil was, interestingly, quite similar to a sword, and could reasonably be fabricated from one to literally fulfill the prophecy, "they shall beat their swords into plowshares . . ." (Micah 4:3). The intent of the prophecy is perhaps more poetic than literal, however, for the last half of the same verse states "they shall beat their spears into pruninghooks," symbolizing that weapons of war will no longer be made. Rather, industry will fabricate agricultural instruments from metals and wood and war will no longer be a sordid part of world affairs (Micah 4:3).

Most references dealing with the word "plow" and its derivations (Deut. 22:10; Judg. 14:18; I Kings 19:19; Jer. 26:18; Job 1:14, 4:8; Psa. 129:3; Prov. 20:4; Isa. 28:24; Hos. 10:11, 13; Amos 6:12; 9:13; Micah 3:12) come from the Hebrew *charash,* meaning "to plow."[5] In two cases (Isa. 61:5; Jer. 14:4) the Hebrew *ikkar* is used, meaning "plowman" or "husbandman."[6] In yet three other cases "plowshare" comes from the Hebrew *eth,* meaning "coulter" or "plowshare"[7] (Isa. 2:4; Joel 3:10; Micah 4:3), and once the Hebrew *nir* is translated as "plowing," meaning "tillage"[8] (Prov. 21:4).

The instrument termed a plow means a ground-breaking or furrow-making implement pulled by an ox. A "plowman," as in Amos 9:13, is one who makes a furrow in the ground, literally "to make an indentation." The plowman (*charash*) would guide the furrow-making instrument, hooked to the oxen, across the field (see Figure 32). Typically another person would follow the plowman and drop seeds into the furrow, covering them as he went.[9]

The literal meaning of Amos 9:13 is couched closely in rich Hebrew poetic language, very typical of Old Testament Scripture. Figuratively, the produce of the land will be so abundant that the reapers, attempting to harvest the great abundance, will yet be bringing in the crop as the plowman and his oxen begin to seed the following crop; poetically, crop production will exceed the wildest imagination of today's agriculturalists. As verse 13 continues, the poetic meaning of the words become more apparent, for a "treader of grapes" cannot logically overtake the "sower of seed," for their operations are carried on in different locations (in a *time* reference this overtaking perhaps could occur). Also, mountains dripping wine and hills flowing with milk cannot literally occur, but the sheer, uplifting agricultural abundance of the land can imaginatively be pictured as such.

The Meaning of the Land Sabbath

Every seventh year in ancient Israel a Land Sabbath was to be observed.

> When you enter the land I give you, the land shall enjoy a sabbath rest for the Eternal. For six years you may sow your field, for six years you may prune your vineyard, and gather in the produce; but the seventh year shall be a sabbath of entire rest for the land, a sabbath in honour of the Eternal, on which you must neither sow a field nor prune a vineyard . . . it shall be a year of entire rest for the land (Lev. 25:2-5).

As mentioned earlier, the parallel with the seven-day Sabbath is quite obvious:

> Six days you may labour . . . but the seventh day is the sabbath in honour of the Eternal, your God, on it you must do no business (Ex. 29:9-10).

As for the seventh year land rest, the seventh day weekly rest was "a sabbath of *entire rest* . . . for all time" (Lev. 16:31). Whereas the weekly Sabbath pictures the seventh 1,000 year rest period of man's history on earth (Heb. 4:9)—each day equalling 1,000 years (II Pet. 3:8)—the seventh year land rest must picture this same 1,000 years of the land's rest.

Figure 32. New John Deere 3600 Drawn Plows are available in sizes up to 8 bottoms (16 when two plows are linked in tandem). Wide choice of sizes, adjustable cutting widths, two types of coulters and standards, and on-land or in-furrow hitches allow matching to tractor horsepower and field conditions.

How may land be rested for 1,000 years? Is the land not to be sown nor fruit trees pruned for 1,000 years, and are the people to rely on the natural production of the land for their sustenance (Lev. 25:6)? One cannot carry an analogy too far. True, the land is to prophetically "rest" from its 6,000-year abuse for 1,000 years, just as mankind and his carnal, inhuman nature is to rest from history of war, unrest, and self-inflicted misery for this same 1,000 years. One cannot, however, expect that the sixth 1,000-year period, within which we are now living, is providing food plentiful enough so "that the land shall yield a three years' crop" (Lev. 25:21); the literal fulfillment of providing food for 3,000 years of living for all of mankind from the stored produce of the previous 1,000 years is impossible!

Neither can one expect that the Land Sabbath will be done away with during the Kingdom, the very time pictured by the Sabbatical year, any more than one can expect that the weekly Sabbath will be disbanded. God has guaranteed that "the Sabbath is a token between me and you *throughout all ages*" (Ex. 31:13). The Land Sabbath will be kept during the Kingdom! This makes clear the fact that the Sabbatical year is designed for the good of man (Mark 2:27) and the land, a year of rest and rejuvenation, meshing with God's great spiritual principles.

Two Views Concerning Millennial Crop Culture

Many questions have already been raised regarding the manner in which food crops and animals will be raised during the Kingdom. What will be the worldwide system of crop culture? At least two major possible systems emerge: (1) no tillage or pruning and minimum labor in tending plants and soil, or (2) minimum tillage and pruning, and moderate labor in tending plants and soil. These possibilities are discussed below.

No-till Farming

(1) No tillage or pruning. The millennium is pictured as a literal Garden of Eden, a land fruitful and beautiful, restored to the original natural productivity of that first abode of mankind on the earth. In the original Garden Adam and Eve were placed to "serve,

labor, work, and keep" the land. The original Garden was planted by
God (Gen. 2:8) and was in perfect harmony with His perfect laws of
nature. When the millennium begins Christ will have undisputed
rulership over the earth for the first time since Satan's kingship
began, having qualified to replace Lucifer during the temptation in
the wilderness (Matt. 4:1-11; Luke 4:1-13). Will not the entire earth
then be a "Garden planted by God," and not just a restricted area as
in Genesis 2:8, in complete harmony with His perfect ways, even as
Christ pleaded that the Father's will be done "on earth [today among
God's people, and in the future in the Kingdom] as in heaven"
(Matt. 6:11)?

Josephus (*Antiquities of the Jews* I, I, 4) adds that God had intended that man

> might lead a happy life, without any affliction, and care, and vexation
> of soul; and that all things which might contribute to your enjoyment
> and pleasure should grow up by my providence, of their own accord,
> without your own labor and painstaking; which state of labor and
> painstaking would soon bring on old age. . . .[10]

This adds credence to the fact that no tillage was performed in the
Garden, nor will be performed in the Kingdom. Rather, "every plant
that bears seed all over the earth, and every tree with seed in its fruit"
(Gen. 1:30) was food for man. Cain, a tiller of the soil, who
"forced" the soil, was disapproved of God, while Abel, a shepherd
and not a tiller, was approved.

Christ, the master agriculturalist (for He was the Word who
created the earth; John 1:1-14), in a parable described that, rather
than prune a fig tree in order for it to produce fruit, the tree should
be manured and dug around (Luke 13:6-9). This short excursion into
the realm of agricultural advising may signal a foretaste of the millennial reign as prefigured by the Land Sabbath . . . when no pruning is
to be done.

Experiments performed in various parts of the world have shown
that tillage does not need to be performed in order to achieve yields
equal to or exceeding those achieved through conventional farming
methods. Masanobu Fukuoka, in southern Japan, has developed a
double-cropping system of culturing barley and rice using four basic
principles:[11]

1. No cultivation: the earth cultivates itself naturally by means of the penetration of plant roots and the activity of microorganisms, small animals, and earthworms.

2. No chemical fertilizer or prepared compost: if left to itself the soil maintains its fertility naturally, in accordance with the orderly cycle of plant and animal life; only plant residues (straw, green manure crops, etc.), animal wastes, and other nonsynthetic materials should be added to soils, and then in the proper amount and at the proper time as in a natural system.

3. No weeding by tillage or herbicides: weeds should be controlled but not eliminated, as by straw mulching, temporary flooding of rice fields, and timely management practices.

4. No dependence on chemicals: nature, left alone, is in perfect balance; harmful insects and plant diseases are always present, but do not occur in nature to an extent which requires the use of poisonous chemicals.

He developed these points over years of trial and error while seeking a means of applying nature's methods of growing things to his own fields, such as scattering seeds on *top* of the soil. His methods involve hand power and simple machine power on a small acreage. Barley and rice yields approach an average of 80 bushels per acre per year for each crop.[12] Mandarin oranges are grown without pruning, requiring little care but yielding excellent yields and high quality fruit. Vegetables are grown in clearings in the orange orchard without cultivation: seeds are scattered haphazardly over the soil, and weeds are cut back if they present too vigorous competition with the vegetables.[13] Old standard, open-pollinated varieties of vegetables and grains are used, which still outyield most neighboring fields that use hybrid seed and conventional culture methods.[14] Mr. Fukuoka's system of growing crops takes work averaging about one hour per day during the entire year, though providing food crops far exceeding a family's needs . . . all on only 1¼ acres of grain land and 12½ acres of orange orchards.[15]

The tribes of North American Indians which raised maize during the days before the European settlement apparently practiced no tillage. In some notes regarding Kansan Indians, Don Juan De Oñate, a Spanish explorer who journeyed through parts of the Southwest in 1601, wrote the following:

We remained here [on the banks of the Rio de San Francisco] for one day in this pleasant spot surrounded on all sides by fields of maize and crops of the Indians. The stalks of the maize were as high as that of New Spain and in many places even higher. The land was so rich that, having harvested the maize, a new growth of a span [nine inches] in height had sprung up over a large portion of the same ground, without any cultivation or labor other than the removal of the weeds and the making of holes where they planted the maize.[16]

Several studies are in operation nationwide to investigate the potential for no-till systems for raising small grains. In North Dakota, Dr. Edward Deibert has found that yields and nutrients uptake of spring wheat under no-till are comparable to conventional tillage systems.[17] Success with the no-till systems depends on soil type, stubble management, weed control, and adequate fertilizer, and may vary with climatic conditions. As expected, soil nitrogen mineralization (release from organic matter) and plant uptake are reduced due to less oxidation of the organic matter in an undisturbed soil.[18]

A major exponent of no-till agriculture during the past century is Edward H. Faulkner, author of *Plowman's Folly*.[19] He has distilled from his studies and experience the following statement: "The fact is that no one has ever advanced a scientific reason for plowing."[20] For generations farmers' and researchers' reasoning has rested upon the use of moldboard plow. Yet, Mr. Faulkner has shown that "soil impoverishment, erosion, decreasing crop yields, and many of the adverse effects following droughts or periods of excessive rainfall could be traced directly to the practice of plowing natural fertilizers deep into the soil."[21] He succeeded in emulating nature's way of prairie and forest culture through use of the disk harrow, oftentimes transforming ordinary or inferior soils into extremely productive cropland.

In a *Scientific American* article entitled "Agriculture Without Tillage," scientists Glover Triplett, Jr., and David Van Doren, Jr., cited a 1975 prediction by the U.S. Department of Agriculture that by the year 2010 more than 90% of the crop acreage in the U.S. will be grown with reduced-tillage systems, and that on more than half of the acreage some form of no-tillage farming will be practiced.[22] The control of weeds, they state, is a primary objective of tillage, which in the case of no-till systems is achieved mainly by the application of herbicides but partly by mulch provided by the old crop residues, stifling the growth of unwanted plants.[23] They lucidly pictured the story of excessive tillage during past decades:

Tillage as it was practiced 40 or 50 years ago entailed, for a farmer growing corn in the U.S. Middle West, some 10 trips over the field by harvesttime. Plowing came first and was followed immediately by dragging or harrowing operations that broke up clods and made a fine, firm seedbed. Just before the crop emerged the field was lightly tilled again to destroy weeds that were emerging simultaneously. While the crop was growing the field would be cultivated two to four times more, mainly to control weeds. Eventually the corn plants grew high enough to keep the weeds suppressed by cutting them off from sunlight, but if the field was particularly weedy, it might be tilled again with a small cultivator pulled by a horse or a mule, even when the corn was as much as shoulder high. Hand labor was often required to pull out or attack with hoes the weeds that survived the successive cultivations.[24]

The elimination of much of the usual tillage reduces power and labor requirements, especially during the limited planting season. Besides, soil erosion is reduced due to the protective residue of the previous crop, and water evaporation and runoff are reduced compared to bare soil, resulting in more water for crop growth.[25]

Crop culture using no tillage would require practices akin to natural wooded or prairie environments. Perennial plants are common in such landscapes. Much current interest is being focused among plant breeders toward the development of perennial species of wheat, corn, barley, and other grain or fiber crops. Erosion would be greatly reduced or eliminated by eliminating the need to till the soil each spring or fall when planting annual or winter annual crops. However, the methods presently envisioned to fertilize, weed, cultivate, and harvest these proposed perennial varieties are still deeply entrenched within today's standardized dogmas based on fossil fuel technology: herbicides, pesticides, commercial fertilizers, and engine-powered field operations. Despite these operations, weeds, insects, and plant diseases remain as thorny problems even yet; " . . . for the country of my people is overgrown with thorny weeds" (Isa. 32:13), "What the lopping locust left, the swarming locust ate . . . " (Joel 1:4), and "The fields are blasted: the land is woebegone, for the corn is wasted . . . " (Joel 1:10). True to this prophecy, today weeds continue to plague farmers with increasing vigor, insects eat as much as 40% of the world's food supply,[26] and plant diseases threaten to devastate the narrow genetic base of many world crops.[27]

If a no-tillage system of agriculture is to be practiced during the Kingdom it is essential that the prophecies relating to tillage (*abad,* or "serve, labor, and work") be interpreted in terms of man's complementing natural systems already established since creation, not in terms of ignoring and blatantly opposing them. Tillage cannot, in this case, imply disturbing the soil. Man would only plant the seeds and God would give the increase (I Cor. 3:6). Moreover, God's wisdom would dictate what crops or trees would be grown in any particular environment. Grasses would grow within a prairie area, and only those designed for the specific soil and climatic conditions unique to that area, not as today when one variety of hybrid corn is planted over millions of acres regardless of soil characteristics. Adapted trees and forest plants would grow within forested areas.

Apparently in the millennium the many forested areas will be replaced by fruit trees. Isaiah clearly comments on this point:

> Soon, very soon, shall forests turn to orchards, and orchards be like woods (Isa. 29:17).

> Yet one day from the heights of heaven a spirit shall breathe into us, till the downs grow like an orchard, and the orchard like a forest (Isa. 32:15).

Since this changeover from nonfruiting trees or rather barren pasture land (downs) to an orchard takes time, the implication here is that the full utopian setting will not materialize for many years. When it does, untold abundance of incredibly fruitful lands will greet the surviving families that begin to repopulate an earth transformed to complete harmony with God's laws.

When the settlers first arrived in America and moved on west they found a land replete with forests having seemingly unending stands of superb timber, as well as a full complement of food crops: wild plums, hickory nuts, chestnuts, walnuts, chokecherries, wild carrots and parsnips, and a host of other plants and trees. It is possible that originally all the food crops needed to sustain life throughout the years could be found in the immediate vicinity of most locales. Bluestem grass reached past the shoulders of oxen as wagons and families rolled into the Plains provinces of the newly-opened western lands. Rather than utilize and skillfully manage the high nutritional value of these native grasses—which had sustained millions of buffalo, deer, elk, and other prairie birds and animals throughout the centuries—man felt a need to "progress." What God had originally placed within an environment was not good enough. Within this vacuum of values among a people bent upon exploiting the incredibly rich, virgin land, another set of values came to the fore: lawlessness, disorder, greed, and destruction of a beautiful, fruitful land.

This new value system introduced by man, displacing quality in favor of quantity, demanded that the somewhat lower-yielding but highly nutritious plants, perfectly designed for each specific environment, be eliminated—plowed under, stamped out! In their place came the highly-bred, higher yielding but nutritionally inferior plants: brome, fescue, bluegrass, wheatgrass, canarygrass, timothy, alfalfa, and clover, all being plants native to a specific range of environments themselves, but usually not to the environments to which they were introduced. Each of these plants, once procured from other environments in Asia, Europe, Africa, or the Middle East, has been selectively bred for yield and little else to complement the perverted economic dictate of profit maximization.

Another major point which needs to be resolved to justify entertaining the no tillage or pruning concept during the millennium is the true meaning behind the prophecies of Isaiah 2:4 and Micah 4:3, which state,

> . . . they shall beat their swords into plowshares, and their spears into pruninghooks.

If this prophecy is to be taken literally, that plowshares and pruninghooks will be fashioned from these instruments of war, then the use of the seed furrow plowshare is compatible with no-till agriculture;

the use of pruninghooks presents a somewhat more difficult problem to resolve. However, it must be remembered that no swords or spears will likely be used in the coming conflicts. Our weaponry now consists of tanks, guns, armored personel carriers, trucks, battleships, aircraft, missiles, and rocket launchers from which plowshares and pruninghooks cannot easily be directly fashioned. They must first be melted down and then cast or "beaten."

The true meaning behind the prophecy of Isaiah 2:4 could be metaphorical, i.e., the weapons of war (swords and spears in ancient times, or tanks and airplanes today) will be literally converted into agricultural instruments to be used during the millennium, yet not necessarily plowshares and pruninghooks, which were two very common implements used during days past. These comments also may be applied to Amos 9:13, which describes the super-abundance of millennial agriculture where "the plowman shall overtake the reaper."

Although plowing (the making of a furrow into which seeds may be dropped) and pruning were practiced by the ancient Israelites under God's system of government, their use of these practices does not automatically condone their use in the Kingdom . . .any more than divorce, which was allowed and legislated for, is not condoned by God and will surely not be a part of God's perfect millennial system. One thus reads in Deuteronomy 24:1-4 of God's regulations regarding divorce, but in Matthew 19:8 Christ is quoted as saying, "Moses permitted you to divorce your wives, on account of the hardness of your hearts, but it was not so from the beginning." If Cain's Satanic agricultural system began abuse of the soil through forcing it beyond its natural productivity—and this abuse involved primarily inverting or fracturing the entire surface of the soil—then Israel, living within the world's system, inherited much of the world's system. Because of His promise to Abraham, God still remained true to His word to make of Abraham and his descendants a great people "as plentiful as the stars of heaven."

The sons of Jacob (Israel) received this blessing as well, with Joseph's sons receiving the birthright blessing of supreme wealth and worldly prominence. The Israelites were to eventually receive all of the promises God made to them despite some of their practices being tied into the world's Satanic system of exploitation, selfishness, and jealousy acquired by living within the world's spiritual Babylon. If God had pressed them to adjust their agricultural methods to those of the millennial reign they might well have totally rebelled, for even without much pressure to change their ways (God is a perfect leader, never forcing men to follow His ways), and in spite of the many miracles they witnessed to illuminate God's stupendous power and perfect leadership, they still proved to be rebellious and stubborn (Ps. 78:8; Ezek. 2:3). God adjured them to seek totally after His ways (Ex. 20). Had they truthfully pursued after God's righteous foundation of life—the Ten Commandments—and not hardened their hearts throughout the 40 years' wandering in the wilderness (when no agricultural operations except grazing were performed) they could conceivably have appeared after the 40 years ready to establish a millennial agricultural setting. Yet, God's plan was not to instruct His chosen nation as yet in millennial agriculture; that instruction was to begin nearly 3,500 years later.

One additional point which might add credence to the prospect of no tillage during the millennium is the fact that essentially no soil erosion will be tolerated. The native forest floor and prairie carpet hold erosion in check much like an untilled field does. Plant roots, alive or decaying, permeate and stabilize the surface as in a prairie. No soil is loosened, whereas with conventional plowing a bare soil surface allows the splash action of raindrops and consequent erosive forces of concentrated rivulets of water to operate.

Minimum Tillage Farming

This method of tillage involves the use of implements such as hoes, plows, cultivators, and harrows which disturb the soil only enough to grow a crop.

(2) Minimum tillage and pruning. If one is to accept the agricultural system of ancient Israel as the model upon which God will base millennial agriculture, then the narrow-shanked plow used to make a small furrow in the soil for planting seeds may well become a major tillage tool in the Kingdom. As explained above, there is little reason to believe that Israel possessed full knowledge of utopian agriculture.

The principles of minimum tillage (a minimum of soil disturbance in order to grow a crop) however, are one step closer to the no-till ideas already mentioned. Power requirements are greatly reduced during tillage operations while yields are usually as high as with conventional plowing. A major benefit of minimum tillage is the rapid infiltration of rainfall and reduced runoff and erosion. One example of this benefit is given in the following table:[28]

The effect of minimum and conventional tillage on runoff and erosion from Fayette silt loam on 15° slope*

Kind of tillage	Runoff water (inches)		Erosion soil (tons)	
	1959	1955-59	1959	1955-59
Conventional	2.50	0.81	7.6	2.9
Minimum	1.13	0.35	1.5	0.7

* Rotation is corn, grain, hay. In both treatments the land is spring plowed. On conventionally tilled plots the soil is double disked and worked with a field cultivator prior to seeding. There is no seedbed preparation after plowing on the minimum tilled plots. Corn is wheel-track planted.

Erosion is greatly reduced under minimum tillage systems as compared to conventional culture. Yet, significant erosion does occur, enough to pollute streams and lakes and hasten the removal of soil minerals. This may be due to improper tillage. God's system of agriculture requires that erosion be reduced to essentially zero. Also, herbicides are oftentimes used for weed control to complement modern minimum tillage practices; herbicide use will not be allowed under a system of pure agriculture dictated by God's perfect laws.

If the meaning of Isaiah 2:4 and Micah 4:3 is literal, that "swords will be beaten into plowshares and spears into pruninghooks," then a certain amount of tillage is essential in God's millennial plan.

What of Abraham's Wanderings?

The discussion so far has been based upon families living upon permanent homesteads that would never pass from the family. Generation after generation would possess and build upon the home estate. As children would marry and the family would expand, so would the area of land possessed.

What about Abraham's (Abram's) example? Abram was born and raised in Ur of the Chaldees, and at an appointed time the Eternal commanded him, "Leave your country, leave your kindred, leave your father's house, for a land that I will show to you" (Gen. 12:1), the land of Canaan where both he and his nephew Lot dwelled in tents (Gen. 13:5). His own life, the life of his son Isaac, and of his grandson Jacob were replete with wandering over the land his descendants were eventually to inherit. When asked by the Pharaoh how long he had lived, Jacob replied,

> For a hundred and thirty years I have had a wandering life of it; few and hard have been the years I lived, fewer then the years my fathers lived and wandered (Gen. 47:9).

Now, those who are Christ's are called "Abraham's offspring," and "heirs according to the promise" (Gal. 3:29). These same individuals "have no certain dwelling place" (I Cor. 4:11) in the present age. Is it possible that millennial life will entail some form of wandering within territorial limits for separate families or clans, much like in the case of Abraham and many of the patriarchs? Indeed, Christ Himself during His 3½ years' ministry lived a wandering life of sorts, typified by His statement, "Foxes have holes, wild birds have nests, but the Son of Man has nowhere to lay His head" (Matt. 8:20).

Many of the American Indians lived a wandering type of life, and in the meantime maintained the ecosphere of America in a pristine condition. They considered land to be of no private possession—they often could not comprehend treaties designed to "sell" land to the white man, for such treatment of land was foreign to them—but rather the property of the supreme ruler of the earth. Don Juan De Oñate, writing about an expedition through New Mexico, Texas, and Kansas in 1601, stated:

> In some places we came across camps of people of the Apache nation, who are the ones who possess these plains, and who, having neither

fixed place nor site of their own, go from place to place with the cattle [buffalo] always following them.[29]

The wandering of clans within territorial limits may well be another factor in millennial life. Although the lives of the Hebrew patriarchs were difficult, and the Indians experienced multitudes of hardships, yet this type of idyllic lifestyle envisioned in a millennial atmosphere where man lives in absolute harmony with a perfectly harmonious ecosphere may indeed be part of what God has in mind for man. The Feast of Tabernacles, the annual festival period examplary of the millennial reign of Jesus Christ, also pictures God's people living in temporary dwellings made of tree branches (Lev. 23:39-43); hence the alternative name, Feast of Booths. Tillage would be eliminated and people would eat of the natural produce from the land as pictured for the Sabbatical land rest (Lev. 25:6).

Nutrient Cycling a Primary Concern

Mentioned earlier in this text is the fact that the cycling of plant nutrients is primary overall concept operating within a properly structured system of agriculture. Nitrogen (preserved mostly in the organic matter), plant minerals, carbon and oxygen (from the air), and water are used from the environment and must subsequently be replaced, recycled from the dead waste products of the land to yield new life. Life itself is thus cycled from death, just as Christ was dead three days and three nights in the heart of the earth, only to be given new life on a higher plane (Mark 16:6).

In order for the cycling of nutrients from soil, to plants, to animals and man and back to the soil to be complete, a "closed community" must exist, as described earlier. Plant and animal products must be consumed near their point of production, and waste materials (manure and straw) must be returned to the soil from which the original elements came. This would be analogous to a forest populated by squirrels, rabbits, bears, and deer: each eats of the acorns, leaves, beetles, grubs, berries, and grass while depositing the waste products of these foods upon the soil. At death the carcass of the animal decomposes into soil, or is eaten by other animals and returned as waste products.

In a forest, leaves, decaying wood, and soil animals and micro-organisms return to the soil from which they came, completing the nutrient cycle without the intervention of animals or man. A prairie environment produces a similar picture. Transport of foods from farms to cities to rivers and oceans prevents nutrient cycling (see Figure 33) and will not be general practice within a world intent on building up the fertility of its soil resources. How easily this problem could be resolved by having people living on the land itself instead of in crowded cities, each man living "underneath his vine and underneath his fig tree" (Micah 4:4).

Millennial Fertilization Practices

Methods of soil fertilization in the Kingdom flow naturally from the preceding section. Residues (straw, leaves, etc.) from the previous crop will provide the majority of replenishment the soil requires to maintain its organic matter and mineral contents. Christ in a parable spoke of a vinedresser who prescribed digging in manure around a fruitless fig tree in order that it might bear fruit (Luke 13:8). Without tillage, or with only a minimum of tillage, organic matter oxidation rates will be significantly reduced from rates experienced under conventional tillage methods. This will allow the organic matter content of the soil to remain high, similar to the virgin state under prairie or forest conditions, maximizing favorable soil structure, water infiltration and percolation rates, water-holding capacity, microbiological activity, nutrient holding capacity, and natural soil nutrient release rates. The perpetual downward trend in soil nitrogen (virtually synonymous with organic matter in natural systems)* content in nearly every cultural scheme of today's farmers is revealed in Figure 34; after even 30 years of cultivation the equilibrium organic matter level has not been reached but continues to drop, even when

---

* Organic matter contains a large part of the total reserves of boron and molybdenum, 5 to 60% of the phosphorus reserves, up to 80% of the sulfur, and practically all of the nitrogen.[32]

Figure 33. The structure of food production channels today directs plant nutrients from the land to the oceans, an "open-ended" cycle which needs to be closed through the return of waste products back to the land.[30]

nitrogen-fixing legumes are used in a crop rotation.**

The removal of crops as grain, forages, roots, fruit, vegetables, or nuts will result in a net overall depletion of the soil nutrient reservoirs. However, by having "closed communities," where nutrients are replaced as waste products at or near their point of origin in the environment, the overall impact of man upon his environment will be negligible, with no net efflux of soil wealth from the soil as experienced today. Man will fit into the overall scheme of nature much as deer in the forest or a horned lark on the prairie: life is fulfilled by complementing nature, not conflicting with her. What is given by nature is returned in full. Nature and her laws are respected, not trampled upon, her resources not pictured as objects of exploitation. *Use* of her products according to *need,* the very basis by which God provides for His people (Matt. 6:25-34), becomes the foremost concern . . . and whoever in his right mind has considered pummeling and stealing from one's mother (nature) the objects which ought to be freely and lovingly given for one's proper use?

The addition of synthetic, crushed rock, or other imported fertilizers will become unnecessary once the initial fertility level of the soil is restored to the superb richness of the Garden of Eden. A modern curse resulting from the current use of agricultural chemicals is nitrate contamination of groundwater supplies. Such contamination was virtually unknown until synthetic nitrogen fertilizers began to be added to cropland. Coupled with intense tillage of soils containing high organic matter levels, much nitrate has been released in soils over the years and carried, in humid regions, with percolating rainwater to the water table.[34] Unlike most mineral ions, nitrate is not easily held by the clay and organic matter, and readily moves with water.[35] Poorly designed feedlots and other livestock concentrations

---

** The magnitude of annual organic matter changes tends to decrease with additional years of cultivation. On Missouri soils organic matter declined 20% from the virgin conditions during the first 20 years of cultivation. A second 20 years of cultivation reduced organic matter another 10%, and a third 20 years a further 7%. At this rate of decline an equilibrium organic matter level of about 50 to 60% of the amount present in virgin soil would eventually be reached; the change would be about 80% complete in 60 years.[33]

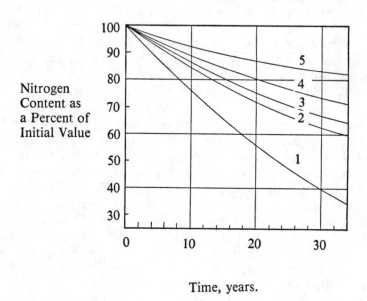

Nitrogen Content as a Percent of Initial Value

Time, years.

Figure 34. The reduction of soil organic nitrogen content under different systems of land utilization: 1. Continuous maize; 2. Continuous wheat; 3. Continuous oats; 4. Five-course rotation: maize, oats, wheat, clover, and timothy; 5. Three-course rotation: maize, wheat, and clover.[31]

with their high levels of released nitrates also add to the problem of contaminated water supplies of both wells and streams.

The current heavy usage of commercial fertilizers and lime is depicted in Figure 35. Especially noticeable is the skyrocketing use of fertilizers since 1940, when war industries were shifted from manufacturing munitions to producing commercial fertilizers. As revealed in Figure 36, wheat production has skyrocketed as a result of using these fertilizers, and also because of the development and widespread planting of high-yielding wheat varieties and favorable weather conditions; other crops have responded similarly to these recent agricultural innovations.

How is a restoration of Edenic soil fertility possible? As explained earlier, there will be a total revolution in the earth's climate and topography at the inception of the Kingdom: ocean levels will be lowered, mountains lowered, and valleys raised to allow the habitation of much of the earth's surface. Much of the new land will be exposed ocean beds, replete with a superb fertility which the Dutch and English have already attested to in their sealand drainage projects. Only the land presently cultivated may need plant nutrient additions, though for a considerable period of time following the destruction of civilization the land will have a chance to recover on its own through natural soil building processes.* Speaking of the end time Isaiah wrote the following:

> Behold, the Lord maketh the earth empty, and maketh it waste, and turneth it upside down, and scattereth abroad the inhabitants thereof. . . . The land shall be utterly emptied, and utterly spoiled . . . the inhabitants of the earth are burned, and few men are left (Isa. 24:1, 3, 6).

---

* Estimates of the rate of soil formation are extremely varied depending on local conditions of parent material, climate, vegetation, topography, and time. Although some researchers claim at least 100 years are needed to form an inch of topsoil, a study on recently deposited glacial till in southeastern Alaska, in an area quite cold with minimal biological activity, found that in 100 years a distinct six-inch A horizon had formed that contained as much organic matter as in many soils of the eastern United States.[38]

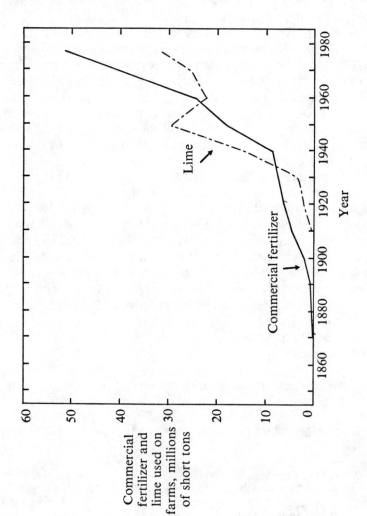

Figure 35. Commercial fertilizer and lime usage on U. S. farms from 1850 to 1977.[36]

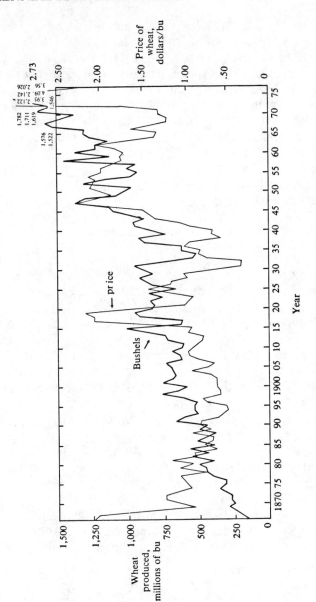

Figure 36. Wheat production and average price received by farmers in the U. S. from 1866 to 1977.[17]

Because of man's disregard for God's eternal precepts and holy judgments, he is to be removed from the land: "Therefore my people are gone into captivity, because they have no knowledge . . . " (Isa. 5:13). During this time the land will lie idle, enjoying the Sabbaths it ought to have enjoyed from the time man first set foot on it. Instead he has pummeled and beaten it through disregard and greed, through ignorance of the Creator who set the laws of nature into motion which demanded that a Sabbatical year be kept each seventh year.

> The land also shall be left of them, and shall enjoy her sabbaths, while she lieth desolate without them: and they shall accept of the punishment of their iniquity: because, even because they despised my judgments, and because their soul abhorred my statutes (Lev. 26:43).

When no one tills a field it immediately becomes overtaken with weeds which check soil erosion. As years pass a flora suited to the particular environment becomes established, and either a native prairie or forest landscape replaces the tilled fields. Soil building proceeds at a rapid pace, for there is no tillage and crop removal to retard its progress. One might even envision a future reclaiming of the land similar to that of the great westward trek during the 1800s in the United States, when millions of brilliant, optimistic immigrants rolled westward toward the setting sun, spurred on by the lure of private land and a prosperous living . . . only this time the land will be given forever, never to be removed from the family. Never again will harsh winters, drought, grasshopper plagues, overwork, malnutrition, or disease stalk the future pioneers as they did those of the nineteenth century. Only success will reign, success through laws kept, and through knowledge unending.

With so much undersea land and previously arid land now bathed by the life-giving mists (Gen. 2:6), nutrient leaching will be very limited, enough only to maintain optimum, lush, beautiful growth as in the Garden of Eden. Irrigation will apparently not be necessary, since according to Isaiah 32:20, "Oh, happy folk, to sow land watered everywhere. . . . " It is likely that the initial excellent soil tilth and fertility conditions experienced by the Dutch polders are a foretaste of future luxuriant growth conditions for most exposed sea floor areas. Coupled with optimum climatic conditions, the sustained worldwide production of agricultural goods in the millennium will certainly exceed anything dreamed of today. What is even more amazing is that this production will be undertaken by virtually all citizens of the world on their own homesteads ("they shall sit every man under his vine and under his fig tree;" Micah 4:4) without credit and usury, without the need for imports from more prosperous nations, and without an agribusiness community pushing sales for profit maximization. Independent landholders will wake up refreshed each day to an enjoyable, harmonious, peaceful world, full of the knowledge of man's purpose and design on earth which God will soon spread abroad to all men (Joel 2:28). As Isaiah stated centuries ago, " . . . then justice fills the very downs, and honesty the orchards, and justice brings us welfare, honesty renders us secure; my people shall have homes in peace, resting in houses undisturbed" (Isa. 32:16-18).

Soil Erosion Eliminated

Within any agricultural system in which food quality and quantity are to be optimized it is necessary for the soil components to remain in place. This necessitates a total elimination of soil erosion which, as described earlier, removes a much greater amount of plant nutrients annually than is removed by crops. Natural stabilized forest or prairie environments achieve zero erosion even with today's unpredictable climate, when heavy thunderstorms at times unleash unmerciful, torrential downpours upon the land.

In the Kingdom streams everywhere will be crystal clear (Rev. 22:1), drinkable, and teeming with fish. Forseeing anything less would be denying the power of the Almighty God to recreate the face of the earth to one in total harmony with His laws, just as the Garden of Eden was in perfect harmony with the laws of nature.

A major deterrent to soil erosion in the Kingdom will likely be a lack of rainfall as we now know it. Instead, when conditions resembling the Garden of Eden are reestablished over the earth, a mist will water the soil and plants (Gen. 2:6). Without pelting rains, which now are responsible for the erosion farmers experience, no runoff may be expected from a landscape richly fertile and continuously stabilized by plant roots and leaf cover.

What a stark contrast this renewed soil environment will be compared to today's unchecked erosion. A 1953 report by W. C. Lowdermilk, former Assistant Chief of the U. S. Soil Conservation Service, revealed that more than 300 million acres of our 400 million acres of farm fields were eroding faster than soil was being formed.[39] Based on North Carolina experiments, land continuously cropped to cotton lost an average of 10% of the rainfall and 22 tons of soil per acre annually. At this rate, only 44 years would be needed to erode away seven inches of soil. Crop rotations reduced the erosion so those seven inches would be lost in 109 years, a very short time on nature's scale of reckoning time. However, when the land was kept in grass it lost less than one percent of incipient rainfall and so little soil that it would take 96,000 years to wash away seven inches . . . a rate far slower than soil formation.[40]

Just as amazing is the tenacity of the forest floor to eliminate erosion and runoff. Less than 0.3% of rainfall is lost, and so little soil that more than 500,000 years would be required to wash away seven inches of soil![41]

Lowdermilk succinctly summarized his viewpoints with the following words:

> In doing this [exposing our sloping lands by cultivation] we enter upon a regime of self-destructive agriculture. The direful results of this suicidal agriculture have in the past been escaped by migration to new land or, where this was not feasible, by terracing slopes with rock walls as was done in ancient Phoenicia, Peru, and China.
>
> Escape to new land is no longer a way out. We are brought face to face today with the necessity of finding out how to establish permanent agriculture on our farms under cultivation before they are damaged beyond reclamation, and before the food supply of a growing population becomes deficient.[42]

Lowdermilk also wrote what he termed an "Eleventh Commandment:"

> Thou shalt inherit the Holy Earth as a faithful steward, conserving its resources and productivity from generation to generation. Thou shall safeguard thy fields from soil erosion, thy living waters from

drying up, thy forests from desolation, and protect thy hills from overgrazing by thy herds, that thy descendants may have abundance forever. If any shall fail in this stewardship of the land thy fruitful fields shall become sterile stony ground and wasting gullies, and thy descendants shall decrease and live in poverty or perish from off the face of the earth.[43]

Millennial Cropping Patterns

The unimaginable abundance of crops visualized prophetically in Amos 9:13 raises a number of questions. It may be quite readily understood that land holdings and fields will be relatively small, with energy sources being efficient and down to earth. Yet, how will a particular land tract be used? What crops will be raised?

As discussed earlier, land will be used according to its natural potential, not restructured to fit man's petroleum-based agribusiness concepts bent upon profit maximization. Sloping prairie lands will remain in grasses, and only the nonerosive, level bottomlands will likely be used for crop culture. Perhaps cropping patterns as we now envision them will not even exist in some areas should the nomadic existence typified by Abraham and the patriarchs be implemented; food crops and animals growing naturally and profusely would be harvested freely from the land according to current need. Swamps and potholes will likely remain undrained,* retaining runoff water and maintaining niches for waterfowl and other wildlife which will be universally tame and serving to mankind, their nature having been changed (Isa. 65:25). Forests will be carefully harvested only as building materials and firewood are required, without clear-cutting and disregard for beauty of the forest. Mosquitos, gnats, ticks, and other preying insects and animals will no longer harass people during

---

* Slough and pothole drainage, especially in the glaciated prairie pothole region of the Upper Midwest, did not really commence in earnest until the advent of the tractor. Previous to the "tractor age" fields tended to be smaller, and horses or oxen would easily saunter around potholes (they would balk at traversing soils too wet to till); but tractors had no minds and would easily become mired down in wet areas. It is in large part due to the intensive use of engine-powered farm machinery that land drainage commenced.[44]

invigorating, mild summer days, nor will frigid Arctic winds chill one's bones during much more moderate winters of the higher latitudes.

Double or triple cropping or some other type of continuous cropping is implied in Amos 9:13, where the "plowman overtakes the reaper." Since nature's method of culture is essentially a mixed monoculture—the same crops growing year after year on the same soil over massive areas—there appears to be no essential error with continuously growing the same crops well adapted to an area if the law of return is obeyed. Barley or wheat grown continuously in an area, interplanted or rotated perhaps with a legume or cover crop, could provide unending abundance with predictably superb weather, and with crop residues and animal and human wastes returned to the soil. The use of synthetic purchased nitrogen fertilizers, according to E. H. Faulkner, is a sheer waste of money, since nature is perfectly organized to supply the correct level of nitrogen for plants in each soil environment.

The extent of the earth able to be multiple-cropped each year appears to be extensive, considering that a much greater total and cultivatable land surface will exist and the cold Arctic climates will be replaced by temperate climates far to the north. The parade of seasons is to persist as long as the earth exists (Gen. 8:22), so if the inclination of the axis remains at 23.5° then belts of climate will undoubtedly exist from the equator and poleward, the seasons becoming more pronounced toward the poles, though quite mild in contrast to today's extremes. The polar tundra, desert barrenness, and mountainous wastelands will no longer hold sway over the earth (Isa. 35:1; 40:4), unless a few such areas are maintained as vestiges of the past for man to view.

Modern man finds such sparsely-populated locations beautiful, peaceful, and comforting, probably because they remain relatively untouched by greedy entrepreneurs who find little wealth to rape from the landscape. Man, whose senses are preordained to appreciate beauty when he sees it, has seldom in this generation seen the untainted bounty of naturally rich prairies and forests now overtaken by cities, industries, roads, and field upon monstrous field. He must look where he can to find that purity and harmony in the trees, grass, flowers, birds, insects, and other plants and wildlife that his senses crave. Those places are few and usually remote from his urban habitat, but to maintain spiritual and mental equilibrium so many sense-starved citizens drive hundreds of miles just to glimpse the pristine, wooded peaks of the Rockies, or the stark serenity of the Mojave desert where there is little for man to debauch. These settings have remained pristine due to their poverty and seclusion.

Man has ignored the charm and beauty he could have maintained and nurtured at his very doorstep from Maine to California, but, no . . . greed has held sway; now he eulogizes in sobbing agony over the wealth of beauty our land possessed in days past. He sets up national and state parks and forests to recapture perhaps a bit of the joy he yearns for . . . but then in remote areas. He seeks but doesn't know how to gain oneness of his own spirit with the beauty and prosperity of the land. Soon it is too late to even try.

The extent to which the much more simplistic millennial life stands in contrast to present-day methods is underscored by E. H. Faulkner:

> One of the persistent puzzles has been the fact that an ignorant, poverty-stricken Egyptian who stirs his land with the ancient crooked stick can produce more per acre than his British neighbor whose equipment is right up to the minute.[46]

When full knowledge covers the land, erasing ignorance of this Egyptian farmer but maintaining and building upon his native wisdom,* surely land use and cropping patterns will blend into a landscape so productive and beautiful that our eyes would today be unable to believe its bounty.

---

* According to Wendell Berry,[47] the veracity of native wisdom in matters of agriculture has been underscored by the Peruvian Andes peasants. The average family in Uchucmarca "needs" less than $100 yearly (not "has only" $100 as modern anthropologists might say; these peasants are concerned with *enough*, not profit or affluence). Like most farmers, these Peruvians must cope with the hazards of erosion, frost, too much or too little rain, pests, and diseases, which they do very effectively without recourse to industrial technology of machines and chemicals. They cope with erosion by

using small fields (usually less than an acre) which are hand cultivated by four or five family members, and surround the fields by hedgerows, rocks, brush, and living plants; on steeper, more erosive slopes potatoes are cultivated two or three years, and then the land is fallowed for five or more years to allow organic matter to accumulate. Climatic variations are dealt with by planting several crops in different climatic zones, or planting several fields of the same crop in the hope that some of the fields will produce well should others not. To combat insects and diseases the peasants utilize genetic diversity: adapted varieties are grown for each ecological niche (fast growing types to avoid late blight, or frost resistant types on float bottomlands).[48] The farmer is teacher-researcher, student, extension agent, and client, with culture and agriculture firmly wedded. Thus, as Berry puts it, in this truly healthy agriculture where the Uchucmarca farmers produce 2,700 calories and 80 grams of vegetable protein per capita per day (a good diet for a well fed populace), "our land-grant college complex may be seen less as a symbol of our agricultural success than as a symptom of our failure."[49]

Chapter Ten

Plant Varieties in a Renewed World

The natural system of plant species selection was initiated by God from creation. Each environment on earth—tropical rainforest, desert, prairie, temperate or boreal forest, and tundra—possesses its own unique array of annual and perennial trees, shrubs, and other plants as well as algae, bacteria, fungi, earthworms, millipedes, and a host of other large and small animals and plants. These plants were originally adapted to their locales since creation and represented, within an undisturbed natural system, God's basic order of things. Bluestem, buffalo grass, needle grass, and other grasses of the Plains supported huge populations of buffalo, elk, antelope, and deer, but man has considered progress to be the destruction of both the animals and the grasses, replacing both with species he has introduced while possessing only partial knowledge of their merit. Man was directed to "be fruitful, multiply, fill the earth and *subdue it,* mastering the fish in the sea, the birds of the air, and every living creature that crawls on earth" (Gen. 1:28). He was not, however, directed to reorder either the plant or animal kingdoms, replacing the species God established for each environment with others he considered in his own imagination to be "superior." Rather,

In the land of Eden . . . God the Eternal then planted a park. . . .
And from the ground God the Eternal made all sorts of trees to grow
. . . (Gen. 2:8-9).

149

The Hebrew word translated "subdue" in Genesis 1:28 is *kabash,* meaning "to subdue."[1] Subdue means to "conquer and bring into subjection," or "bring under control as by execution of the will,"[2] it does not mean to reorder what has already been placed at one's command. Subduing the earth may surely be visualized as bringing into control both the plant and animal kingdoms—just as God ordered Adam and Eve to dress [*abad,* or "to do service, labor, or work"[3]] the Garden through their labor—but just as surely not restructuring the creation after the directions of man. God created the plant and animal kingdoms, and they were *very good* (Gen. 2:31). Can man improve upon what God considers to be very good?

Natural Plant Selection

The natural system of plant selection, offering the optimum combination of quality and quantity attainable (for God is the author of this system), stands in stark contrast to the current system of plant breeding that demands the expenditure of thousands of work hours and tens of thousands of dollars to produce only one variety within a land grant university or seed corporation.* Rather than inbreeding single lines of cross-pollinated crops and then crossing the parent lines to produce a hybrid (as for hybrid maize; see Figure 37), or painstakingly removing the stamens from self-pollinated crops and then equally painstakingly adding pollen from another plant (as for hybrid wheat)—procedures not performed within a natural system—the natural system of crop selection is extremely simple. It encourages the selection of plants best adapted to a particular environment. At the same time superior yields are encouraged without sacrificing nutritional quality (the effect of the crop on the growth, health, and energy levels of the consumer) of the resultant crop. This quality is the crop's foremost attribute.

---

* During 1969 a total of 370.0 scientific man-years (SMY) were assigned to plant breeding research for major agronomic crops. Corn breeding received the most attention: 65.1 SMY. Major horticultural crops received 117.4 SMY[5].

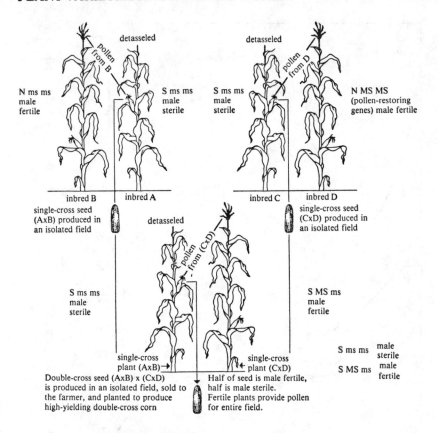

Figure 37. To produce single- and double-cross hybrid corn, oftentimes
detasseling can be reduced by manipulating male sterility determined by an
interaction between a cytoplasmic factor S and a double recessive gene ms.
Only the combination Sms is male sterile. Only plants with N (normal)
cytoplasm, or which contain the Ms gene, produce viable pollen. Although
corn yield is increased through hybridization the use of male sterility may
produce plants highly susceptible to certain plant diseases, such as Southern
corn leaf blight.

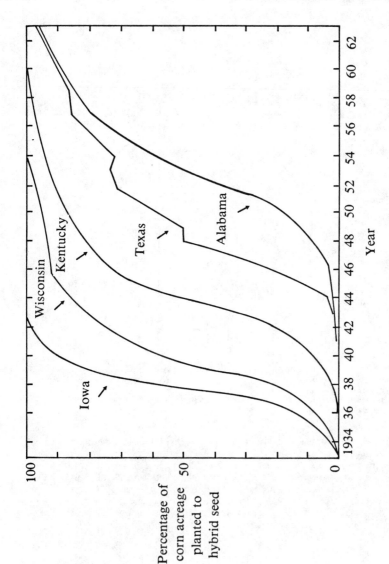

Figure 38. Percentage of all corn acreage in five states planted to hybrid seed from 1934 to 1960.[10]

Until the early twentieth century seedstocks were usually selected by the farmer from his own field. He would walk through his field and choose the best-looking ears of corn from the strongest plants for next year's planting. Since many farmers possessed their own varieties, this diverse genetic pool would seldom permit the devastating strike of a single crop disease to wipe out a significant portion of the nation's crop, such as occurred in 1970 when corn yields dropped an estimated 50% or more in some Southern states due to Southern corn leaf blight; losses to the blight were 15% nationwide.[7] That year 90% of all hybrid corn was of the blight-susceptible T-cytoplasm strain.[8] The extent to which hybrid corn has replaced open-pollinated varieties in several states since 1933 is illustrated in Figure 38.

A study in Iceland by B. Sigurbjoernsson, related in an article entitled "Evolution of Agronomically Superior Genotypes in Natural Habitats,"[11] revealed that just as genotypes resistant to a given disease will not be selected naturally or artificially unless the disease is present (so a distinction can be made), so "genotypes efficient in the uptake and utilization of nutrients will not be preferred naturally and cannot be selected artificially unless conditions of ample nutrient supply prevail."[12] He showed that a native population of a certain pasture grass which evolved under conditions of high fertilty was superior in both yield and nutritional value to other native populations which evolved under conditions of reduced soil fertility. This native variety outperformed even varieties developed by man when tested at different sites in Iceland. Mr. Sigurbjoernsson concluded,

This evidence has an important bearing on the role of induced mutations in plant breeding when one is considering the relative merits of using breeding material from collections of wild plants and the induction of desired characters [through modern plant breeding techniques] in established crop varieties. Variability in nature occurs as a result of interactions in the long course of evolution between newly appearing spontaneous mutations and their recombination products, on one hand, and the particular natural environment present at the time, on the other. A spontaneous mutation giving rise to an attribute of value in modern agriculture is not necessarily preferred under natural conditions in the absence of positive or deliberate selection. On the contrary, characters which can contribute to the high performance of modern varieties do not usually improve the plant's ability to survive and compete under natural conditions.[13]

One is reminded at this point of the Peruvian mountain farmers of Uchucmarca who do not possess modern hybrid plant breeding techniques. Their genetic program is based upon *diversity,* such diversity that in single villages like Uchucmarca about 50 potato varieties may be identified, each one associated with a particular ecological niche.[14] Botanists estimate that in Peru alone there are well over 2,000 potato varieties.[15] According to Berry,

> . . . here we arrive at the greatest complexity, versatility, and responsiveness of this agriculture, as well as its most intense sensitivity to place. For these varieties are not used at random, but are delicately fitted into their appropriate ecological niches. . . . In their understanding [of diversity] and use of this principle, they have developed an agriculture much more sophisticated, efficient, and conservative of the soil than our own—and one that is also much more likely to survive a crisis.[16]

Recent attempts to introduce the standardized industrial technology of the West and "improved" potato varieties have failed in this Andean community. Western agriculture requires gross simplification of agricultural processes and drastic complication of the economy which requires a cash economy and credit, favors large producers, and "threatens to destroy the human community and the ecological viability of a farming system that is the result of thousands of years of natural and human selection."[17]

These Peruvian farmers typify the adaptation of natural plant selection processes as envisioned by Sigurbjoernsson for the development of nutritionally superior crops. In addition, disease resistance, climatic adaptation, and optimum yields compatible with these other plant requirements are maintained. Berry continues,

> The 50 potato varieties used in Uchucmarca are not a stable quantity, but rather a sort of genetic vocabulary in a state of continuous revision . . . new varieties are constantly being created through cross-pollination between cultivated, wild, and semidomesticated (weedy) species. . . . These wild and semidomesticated species thrive in the hedgerows around fields, and birds and insects living there assist

cross-pollination. Thus, if an Andean farmer loses a crop because of an extremity of the weather or an infestation of insects or disease, he may find a plant of a new variety that has survived the calamity and produced in spite of it. If he finds such a plant, he may add it to his collection of domesticated varieties or substitute it for the one that has failed.[18]

Before the age of experiment stations and seed corporations this system of variety selection was practiced out of necessity. Failure of a barley crop in fifteen century Bavaria due to a new strain of rust meant a naturally selected resistant strain had to be found. This usually meant harvesting what few hardy plants did survive in the fields for planting the next year's crop. Farmers had no choice but to work with natural systems, since modern plant breeding techniques had not been devised. Not until the Industrial Revolution was well underway, backed by a petrochemical industry producing fertilizers, pesticides, and herbicides could such techniques even be considered.

Crop Species Selected for Optimum Health

In summary, a system of crop selection continually operates within a natural environment. The direction is God-oriented, initiated at creation for the maximization of crop nutritional quality commensurate with optimum yield.* The array of variables contributing to nutritional quality is far too complex for man to investigate through his system of examining one or a few variables at a time, then putting the puzzle back together again in hopes the proper conclusions may be reached. Sir Albert Howard, the eminent English agriculturalist of the early- and mid-1900s who strongly professed the values of organic soil fertility, came to the same conclusions.[20] Only by in-

---

* The prime importance of crop nutritional quality, or "the properties of the crop in terms of growth response of an organism," is underlined by a recent doctoral study entitled *The Influence of Fertilization on the Nutritional Value of Two Hard Red Spring Wheat Cultivars.* In it, the author stated that "Agriculture has as its central goal the production of food, fuel, and fiber for optimum health of the consumers through supplying several life-essential food components."[19]

vestigating the entire array of factors as they vary together, and viewing how their totality affects mankind within a certain environment for generations, can any ultimate answers regarding crop nutritional quality be found.

Such investigations would take lifetimes to perform, and would require separating out the effects of other factors affecting health: rest, air quality, mental attitudes, exercise, and so forth. Of course, such an investigation, using a proper control population and statistical methods, could never be done with people. The best one can do is view certain isolated groups of people around the world whose lives are healthy, long, and fulfilling, whose attitudes are robust and optimistic, and whose living conditions are agrarian and in tune with nature. Such populations do exist today in isolated areas of the Caucasus in Russia, the Hunza Valley in Kashmir, and the Sacred Valley of Ecuador. In common to all three areas is a simple, peaceful, unencumbered lifestyle, natural foods grown without conventional Western soil and plant amendments, an understanding of the "meaning of life" (to their own satisfaction), relative freedom from disease (colds, cancer, influenza, measles, and others), and a lifespan oftentimes exceeding 100 years! More on this subject will be discussed in chapter twelve.

As a final note in this section on plant breeding, one must be aware of the fact that the *kinds* of plants and animals created at the beginning of this age, as mentioned in Genesis 1, are incapable of converting to other kinds. The theory of evolution as expounded by Haeckel, Darwin, Morgan, Howells, and others, which purports that man ascended from a single cell and progressed through many stages of change to reach his present state, is totally erroneous. It is a science based upon faith as admitted by evolutionists themselves, such as Professor Louis T. More of the University of Cincinnati:

> When we examine the cause of our belief [in evolution] we find that, excepting our desire to eliminate special creation and, generally, what we call the miraculous, most of them can be considered only as secondary proofs to confirm a theory already advanced.[21]

According to Byron C. Nelson author, of *After Its Kind,* the *species* we now observe fit the qualifications of the *kinds* represented at creation, for each possesses marked characteristics of its own and breeds true to form.[22] The Bible allows for new *varieties* to have arisen since the days of creation, but denies any new *species* (kinds) have arisen. Two original dogs have given rise to the Chihuahua and the St. Bernard, two horses have produced the thoroughbred and the Clydesdale, two chickens gave rise to the bantam and the Cornish Rock, and Adam and Eve have given rise to the Australian aborigines and the ruddy Scots. Intra-species evolution, which occurs in nature and is accelerated through man's breeding techniques, has produced a plethora of individual variations within species known as varieties: as produced in nature (God's system of plant breeding) the varieties selected are those most able to live and thrive within a certain set of environmental conditions (light, temperature, soil fertility, rainfall, drainage, and the like); as produced by man's breeding programs varieties selected are those best complementing his machine-oriented agri-business system of profit maximization (high yield, uniform maturity, uniform height, ease of harvesting, etc.).

In nature's system, where soil fertility is maximized through the operation of soil building processes, a population of plants will naturally be selected for superior nutritional value and yield. In man's system of variety selection, an unnatural, man-determined system of soil fertility prevails (sometimes using *infertile* soils). As B. Sigurbjoernsson has stated, characteristics of varieties which contribute to high performance in modern varieties do not usually improve the plant's ability to survive and compete under natural conditions. Neither is the nutritional value of the crop maximized; rather, it tends to be diminished under modern crop breeding programs.[23]

Ominous Current Trends in Plant Breeding

Seed control by the agri-business complex in the West through hybridization has already been discussed. Farmers are not able to plant the seed from the crop they grow and obtain a reasonable yield, meaning they must purchase seed from a company year after year.

More recently, attempts to corner the seed market have taken the legislative route. A proposed amendment (HR 999) to the Plant Variety Protection Act would outlaw the growing of plant varieties which are not patented. This would greatly reduce the size of the germ plasm pool in America, as will soon occur in Europe under the enforcement of a similar law enacted there recently. On June 30, 1980, 2,126 vegetable varieties are scheduled to become illegal in Europe.[24] The USDA has admitted that the conservation of plant genetic resources has become a problem in Europe with this forced system of illegal vegetables, but has denied a similar situation would occur in the U.S.[25]

Even without patenting laws in force the nation's commercial seed varieties have been reduced to a pitiful few for many major crops. As the National Academy of Sciences has stated in its monumental work, *Genetic Vulnerability of Major Crops,* " . . . most crops are impressively uniform genetically and impressively vulnerable. This uniformity derives from powerful economic and legislative forces."[26]

Acreage and farm value of major U. S. crops, and the extent to which small numbers of varieties dominate crop acerage (1969 figures).[27]

Crop	Acreage	Value	Total varieties	Major varieties	Acreage
	millions	millions of $			%
Beans, dry	1.4	143	25	2	60
Beans, snap	0.3	99	70	3	76
Cotton	11.2	1,200	50	3	53
Corn*	66.3	5,200	197**	6	71
Millet	2.0	?	?	3	100
Peanut	1.4	312	15	9	95
Peas	0.4	80	50	2	96
Potato	1.4	616	82	4	72
Rice	1.8	449	14	4	65
Sorghum	15.8	795	?	?	?
Soybean	42.4	2,500	62	6	56
Sugar beet	1.4	367	16	2	42
Sweet potato	0.13	63	48	1	69
Wheat	44.3	1,800	269	9	50

* Corn includes seeds, forage, and silage.
** Released public inbreds only.

The driving force behind the Plant Variety Protection Act is supposedly the preservation of plant breeder's "rights." In reality, the purpose of the Act is to protect the investment of companies active in plant breeding and insure their control over the marketing of new varieties. This reality is driven home by the following table which reveals some recent takeovers of old, family-owned seed companies by corporate giants.

Some recent North American seed company takeovers.[28]

New owner	Seed company	New owner	Seed company
Cargill	Dorman Seeds Kroeker Seeds PAG	NAPB (Olin and Royal Dutch Shell)	Agripro, Inc. Tekseed Hybrid
Ciba-Geigy	Funk Seeds Intern Louisiana Seed Stewarts Seeds	Occidental Petroleum	Ring Around Products
FMC Corp.	Seed Research Assoc.	Pfizer	Clemens Seed Farms Jordan Wholesale Co.
General Foods (Burpee sold to ITT)	Burpee Seeds		Trojan Seed Co. Warwick Seeds
International Multifoods	Baird, Inc. Lynk Brothers	Purex	Advanced Seeds Ferry-Morse Seeds Hulting Hybrids
I.T.T.	Burpee Seeds O. M. Scott and Sons	Union Carbide	Keystone Seed Co
Monsanto	Farmers' Hybrid Co.	Upjohn	Asgrow Seeds Associated Seeds

Dr. Jack Harlan, an outspoken proponent of genetic diversity, has stated recently,

Genetic erosion is already well advanced in much of Europe, the United States, Canada, Japan, Australia, and New Zealand, where active plant breeding programs have been underway for some decades. . . . The speed with which enormous crop diversity can be essentially wiped out is astonishing.

These [genetic] resources stand between us and catastrophic starvation on a scale we cannot imagine. In a very real sense, the future of the human race rides on these materials. . . . A pure line mentality, convinced that variation was bad, uniformity was good, and off-types in the field somehow immoral, developed. Symptoms of the mental climate could be found in crop judging contests, ribbons awarded at county and state fairs, crop improvement associations, seed certifying agencies, and in some provisions of state and federal seed acts. . . . The Mexican wheats have washed over Asia with astonishing speed, replacing major centers of diversity almost overnight. . . . In many areas it is already too late to salvage anything. . . . The line between abundance and disaster is becoming thinner and thinner, and the public is unaware and unconcerned. Must we wait for disaster to be real before we are heard? Will people listen only after it is too late?[29]

Dr. Garrison Wilkes of the University of Massachusetts reiterates how rapidly a few new varieties have overwhelmed the earth:

The extinction of these local land forms and primitive races by the introduction of improved varieties is analogous to taking stones from the foundation to repair the roof. . . . Up to the present time, we have been able to return to areas of genetic diversity, usually located in Third World nations, to collect germplasm for further breeding programs. Suddenly in the 1970s we are discovering Mexican farmers planting hybrid corn from a midwestern seed firm, Tibetan farmers planting barley from a Scandinavian plant breeding station, and Turkish farmers planting wheat from the Mexican wheat program. Each of these classic areas of crop-specific genetic diversity is rapidly becoming an area of seed uniformity.[30]

Coming back to legislative deliberations over HR 999, Mr. Cary Fowler of the National Science Foundation presented testimony of an in-depth study on genetic uniformity to a congressional committee. This testimony strongly parallels the conclusions already reached in this chapter:

Human efforts and natural selection processes resulted in different varieties of food crops becoming adapted to different niches in the ecosystem. . . . With the breeding and marketing of new 'improved' varieties, traditional varieties are being replaced. Farmers and gardeners stop growing them. Field after field is planted with one variety. Where thousands of varieties of wheat once grew, only a few can now be seen. When these traditional plant varieties are lost, their genetic material is lost forever. Herein lies the danger. Each variety of wheat, for example, is genetically unique. It contains genetic 'material' not found in other varieties. If, because of genetic limitations which result from in-breeding, new varieties are no longer resistant to certain insects or diseases . . . then real catastrophe could strike. Without existing seeds which carry specific genes conferring resistance, it may not be possible to breed resistance back into wheat, corn, tomatoes, or any other crop.[31]

Another current trend in plant breeding which is assured to reduce the nutritional value of crops is the breeding of high-yielding varieties under conditions of reduced soil fertility. Actually, this trend has been operating ever since experiment stations began their plant breeding work: yield was the goal, and nutritional quality has seldom been the objective.[32] The three primary nutrients—nitrogen, phosphorus, and potassium—are applied to soils in prolific amounts to achieve the desired high yields; the other required nutrients for plant growth, however, are seldom applied unless their absence is found to limit yields. Raising crops with the objective of yield maximization alone has oftentimes reduced the nutritional value of the grain, leaf, root, or fruit due to one or more of the following reasons:

(1) High-yielding hybrid cultivars are often inferior nutritionally compared to open pollinated cultivars.[33]

(2) Since the sum of the cations calcium, magnesium, potassium, and sodium (expressed as milliequivalents per unit weight of dry matter) tends to remain constant for any plant variety, then increasing one of these nutrients through high soil applications may decrease the sum of the other cations.[34] This principle also tends to operate for mineral anions, such as phosphate.[35]

(3) Due to the "dilution effect," as the yield is increased through the application of one soil nutrient the concentration of one or more plant nutrients may decrease. This may be caused by a high water

content (distended cells) of plant tissues due to heavy nitrogen applications,[36] or an increased carbohydrate content compared to other plant components.[37]

(4) High levels of one nutrient within the plant due to soil additions may increase or decrease the content of another plant nutrient (these are called "nutrient interactions").[38]

(5) A nutrient imbalance created within the plant from any cause may detract from its nutritional quality. For example, osteomalacia (bone disease) may develop in animals grazing over calcium-poor soils.[39]

(6) As crop yield is increased through environmental (especially climate and fertilization) or genetic effects the nutritional value may not be maintained for several plant components, e.g., the nutritional value of wheat protein usually decreases as nitrogen fertilization increases.[40]

Norman E. Borlaug, father of the "Green Revolution," has emphasized that modern hybrids are custom designed to respond maximally to fertilizer inputs, insecticides, and herbicides,[41] though plant quality does not fit into the production equation. A current push is also being made to develop plant types which will yield well on soils deficient in certain micronutrients or too saline to grow normal varieties. One such example is breeding soybean varieties resistant to iron chlorosis.[42] The trend in nutritional value of these deficiency-tolerant plants is unclear, but more than likely it will be negative, another example of modern plant breeders denying the precept expounded by several agronomists[43] that plant cultivars and other agronomic investigations should be developed on highly fertile soils. As expounded by Sigurbjoernsson,

> These plants [from overgrazed and unfertilized pastures], although possessing a high degree of endurance under conditions of low fertility and abuse, do not possess genotypes capable of utilizing the high levels of soil fertility necessary for the production of large quantities of green matter; nor do they perform well under managed pasture systems.[44]

Few people will deny that the positive nutritional attributes of a food crop are more important than the sheer volume of production.

With crop nutritional value being so complex and difficult to investigate one must rely upon the Creator of plants, animals, and humans alike—the Designer of the complete soil-plant-human food chain—to have built into that Creation the natural laws which, if obeyed and complemented by man in his God-ordained commission to "subdue the earth," will result in optimum yields of the most nutritious food crops possible.

Chapter Eleven

Millennial Livestock Management

G od chose for His own nation a shepherd people, grazers of livestock. Righteous Abel was a shepherd (Gen. 4:2). Abram was "very rich in cattle, silver, and gold" (Gen. 13:2), as were his descendants on down to Jacob and his sons: "Your servants [the Israelites] have bred cattle ever since we were young, both we and our fathers" (Gen. 46:34). During the Exodus from Egypt and during the wilderness wanderings, livestock always traveled with the Israelites. Even the Ten Commandments (Ex. 20) make mention of resting cattle on the seventh day, and not coveting another's livestock. Many laws and statutes of ancient Israel involved livestock: oxen prone to goring people, stolen animals, and the many sacrifices requiring the killing of cattle, sheep, goats, or doves.

In times of old, riches were usually equated with an abundance of livestock, such as in Job's case:

In the end, then, the Eternal made Eyob [Job] more prosperous than he had been at first; he had 14,000 sheep and goats, 6,000 camels, 1,000 pair of oxen, and 1,000 she-asses . . . (Job 42:12).

Jacob also grew very rich in the land of his brother-in-law Laban:

In this way, the weaker lambs fell to Laban, the stronger to Jacob, who grew extremely rich, with large flocks, male and female slaves, camels, and asses (Gen. 30:42-43).

Dietary Principles Regarding the Eating of Flesh

There is every reason to believe that livestock in the millennium will be a major enterprise, representing a great portion of the real wealth available to all nations, providing both food and labor. God outlines animals which are "clean," or edible, for man to eat in Leviticus 11 and Deuteronomy 14. Although some vegetarians have contended that this allowance for eating meat was only a compromise, the lesser of two evils, with only the less harmful animals permissible to eat, yet Abel's raising of livestock shortly after the Creation (Gen. 4:2) and Paul's New Covenant condoning of eating meat (I Cor. 8), reaffirm the veracity of Old Testament dietary precepts. Also, Noah and his sons took on the Ark seven pairs of every clean beast, whereas only a single pair of unclean animals was taken (Gen. 7:2), the implication being that some of those clean animals would be used as food.

Nowhere does the New Testament discard the Old Covenant dietary laws as some have claimed, using the vision of Peter in Acts 10:9-17 as evidence. This thrice-repeated vision, "like a huge sheet lowered by the four corners to the earth, which contained all quadrupeds and creeping things . . . and wild birds," coupled with the plea, "Rise, Peter, kill and eat," prompted Peter to deny he had eaten anything unclean. In Acts 10:28-29 and 35, however, it is clear that the meaning of the vision is that no man must be called common or unclean, but that "whoever reverences God and lives a good life in any nation is welcomed by Him."

The instructions for proper food to eat as given in Genesis 1 and 2 are only partial.

> See, I give you every plant that bears seed all over the earth, and every tree with seed in its fruit; be that your food. To every wild beast on earth, to every bird of the air, to every creature that crawls on earth, I give all the green growth for food (Gen. 1:29-30).

> 'You are free to eat from any tree in the park,' he said, 'but you must not eat from the tree that yields knowledge of good and evil . . . ' (Gen. 2:16-17).

Is it possible that before the Flood man was intended to live only on fruits and vegetables? Genesis 9:3-4 lends interesting evidence that this may be the case:

> Every moving thing that is alive is to be food for you; I give you them all, as once I gave you the green growth. Only, you must never eat flesh with the life (that is, the blood) in it.

This Scripture seems to imply that the eating of meat did not commence until the Flood, notwithstanding the fact that Abel was a shepherd (and presumably ate of his flock, though he could have used the animals for wool, skins, and for sacrifices) as were many other pre-Flood patriarchs. Were the removal of the water canopy above the earth, attendant climatic changes, the commencement of leaching and eroding rains (a mist watered the earth before the Flood; Gen. 2:6), and cosmic radiation such negative influences on man's health and nutritional status that rich foods such as meat would henceforth be required . . . at least until the reinstitution of the water canopy, a mist watering the earth, and conditions resembling the Garden of Eden throughout the earth during the Kingdom? Adam Clarke comments as follows on Genesis 9:3:

> There is no positive evidence that *animal* food was ever used *before* the flood. Noah had the first grant of this kind, and it has been continued to all his posterity ever since. It is not likely that this grant would have been now made if some extraordinary alteration had not taken place in the vegetable kingdom, so as to render its productions less nutritive than they were before; and probably such a change in the constitution of man as to render a grosser and higher diet necessary. We may therefore safely infer that the earth was less productive *after* the flood than it was before, and that the human constitution was greatly impaired by the alterations which had taken place through the whole economy of nature. Morbid debility, induced by an often unfriendly state of the atmosphere, with sore and long-continued labor, would necessarily require a higher nutriment than vegetables could supply. That this was the case appears sufficiently clear from the grant of animal food, which, had it not been indispensably necessary, had not been made. That the constitution of man was then much altered appears in the greatly contracted lives of the postdiluvians; yet from the

deluge to the days of Abraham the lives of several of the patriarchs amounted to some hundreds of years; but this was the effect of a *peculiar providence,* that the new world might be the more speedily repeopled.[1]

Free-Ranging Livestock

When each family is placed on its permanent, essentially self-sufficient homestead there will be no concentration of livestock in feedlots as we so often see in modern America. Individual family flocks of sheep and goats or herds of cattle may be envisioned, but a much different concept of livestock management may well be in operation during the Kingdom. As Isaiah wrote concerning the millennium, "Ah, happy folk, to sow land watered everywhere, and let your ass and ox range free" (Isa. 32:20). Within a world where beauty and luxuriant vegetative growth is likened to the Garden of Eden, few fences will exist, except perhaps on private property, around a garden plot, vineyard, or orchard to keep out animals,* and then likely using barriers constructed of natural materials such as stone, timbers, or living hedges. In a totally natural system of

---

* The history of grasslands settlement in the U. S. reveals patterns of utilization determined largely by the relationship between the supply of grassland and population. *Stage one:* In most newly settled communities the livestock were turned loose to graze on grasses and vegetation found in natural clearings and woods. Owners of the livestock may have first cleared their fields for corn and garden crops, but there was nothing even approximating systematic crop farming. A community might hire one or more herders to watch their livestock. *Stage two:* Large numbers of stock were combined with crop production. The crops rather than the livestock were enclosed by fences of some sort. *Stage three:* When range grass became scarce, livestock raising had to be integrated with general farming, giving rise to systematic animal husbandry. In some communities, stock raising became subordinate to staple crop production and was continued largely for domestic needs. In other communities, especially in the Corn Belt, most grains were fed to livestock destined for slaughter or milk production. Laws that forced the fencing in of crops were later reversed to force the fencing of pastures. Care had to be given to natural or renovated grassland production and the storage of hay for winter feed as the third cycle became extant in an area.[2]

agriculture it is possible that manicured gardens, vineyards, or orchards will not exist as they now do. Lawnmowers may be unheard of, a historic novelty of the erroneous days in ages past. Vegetables, fruit trees, nut trees, and grapevines will grow everywhere, the whole countryside lush with the growth of all foods essential to man . . . and free for the taking from a generous God who has restored the entire earth to the sinless vitality of the Garden of Eden.

Without a need for fences animals of all sorts will roam over the grasslands, much like the buffalo, antelope, elk, and deer did in the forests and on the Plains of virgin America; perhaps these species will even constitute the breeds of livestock used in the new age. Since God's economic system entails free giving of His increase from the land according to individual need, animals within this system of management would be available to anyone who is in need, much as in the case of the Indians. God would provide the vegetation for feed and the trees for shelter, all of which originates with the rain, soils, and photosynthetic plants that convert sunlight to useful energy.

The idea of common pasturage for the livestock of a community is not new. In New England and in other locations of the East where New Englanders developed the land, a community would often have a cowherd who would go through the village street every morning, sounding his horn and gathering the livestock for their daily trek to the pasture. Everett Edwards wrote in the 1948 Yearbook of Agriculture,

> If the farmers of the community had enough sheep to justify segregation they were handled separately by a shepherd during the grazing season. Swine were especially troublesome and became the subject of more legislation than any other single agricultural matter. Circumstances soon compelled the registering of livestock brands and earmarks with the town authorities.[3]

The Dutch in the new Netherland had common pastures, the practice being legally recognized when the colony was taken over by the English. However, further south in the Middle Colonies each farmer generally cared for his own stock; these settlements were made by individuals rather than groups.[4]

The Nature of Animals Changed

The animals will not endanger man but will be his friends, for their nature will be changed to that extant in the Garden, and perhaps during the entire period before the Flood. Moses indicated that after the Flood

> The *dread* of you and *terror* of you shall be on every beast of the earth and every bird of the air; for they are now in your power, with every reptile of the land and every fish within the sea (Gen. 9:2).

This Scripture implies that before the Flood there was no such "dread" (Hebrew *mora,* or "fear, reverence"[5]) and "terror" (Hebrew *chath,* or "terror, fright"[6]) of man implanted in the brains of the animals. When the animals came to Adam to be named none devoured him (Gen. 2:19-20). God later divinely placed this fear into the animal world. When the millennial reign of Jesus Christ begins on this earth a harmony between man, animals, and the total environment is predicted such as has never before been experienced.

> The wolf shall couch then with the lamb, the leopard's lair shall be the kid's; the lion shall eat straw like any ox, wolf and lion shall graze side by side, herded by a little child; the cow and the bear shall be friends, and their young lie down together; the infant shall play at the hole of an asp, with the baby's feet at the nest of a viper. None shall injure, none shall kill, anywhere on my sacred hill; for the land shall be as full of the knowledge of the Eternal as the ocean-bed is full of water (Isa. 11:6-9).

The mediating force renewing the face of all nature is once again the Spirit of God "which shall be poured out on all man" (Joel 2:28). The nature of the animal kingdom—and all creation by implication—will no longer be one of predation and the "law of the jungle" but of "love, joy, peace, good temper, kindliness, fidelity, gentleness, and self-control" (Gal. 5:22-23), contrasted to the present Satanic nature of all creation (which "sighs and throbs in pain" until the resurrection and commencement of the Kingdom; Rom. 8:22-23) of anger, rivalry, jealousy, revelry, competition, and the like (Gal. 5:19-21). A wolf and lamb peacefully coexisting demonstrates an utter about-face in character.

In order that the lion and wolf may eat straw (grass or other forages) like an ox and survive, a physical as well as a mental change must come over these animals . . . a change reflecting what must have been the state of these predator animals, birds, and fish prior to the Flood:

> To every wild beast on earth, to every bird of the air, and to every living creature that crawls on earth, I give all the green growth for food (Gen. 1:30).

For a physical change to remain permanent, a change in the genetic composition of these predatory animals must occur, i.e., the DNA and chromatin itself must be altered to provide these creatures with a chewing mechanism and digestive tract capable of thriving on this vegetation. Oxen, sheep and other cud chewers have four stomachs in which bacteria live to break down cellulose in forages to simple sugars. Horses have a caecum and/or colon which is greatly enlarged that serves as the principal site for the bacterial breakdown of roughages. The relative percent fiber digestion of alfalfa hay by various animals is as follows: cattle, 44%; sheep, 45%; horse, 39%; elephant, 34%; swine, 27%.[7] Will the lion, tiger, bear, and other sharp-toothed predators be given crushing and grinding teeth like the cow or horse, and a rumen or caecum as well? If God created the animals on earth and changed their nature at the Flood, He can surely once again intervene to change His creation again. God clearly changed the serpent from a limbed creature to one possessing none: "on your belly shall you crawl and eat dust all your days" (Gen. 3:14). Also, the structure of Eve's body was changed in such a way that childbirth would be more difficult (Gen. 3:16).

Not to be overlooked will be the changed nature of noxious insects and common pests such as mosquitos, gnats, biting flies, ticks, spiders, scorpions, tape worms, and liver flukes.* Their continual harassment of man will be forgotten, their natures changed from Satan's to God's.

What of the Balance of Nature?

How is one to envision a world—the entire creation—existing without the current reality? Some have claimed that no other "balance of nature" than the present one can be imagined, for it is necessary that certain creatures be devoured by others to prevent the earth from being overpopulated.

So far as we can see now, the existence of carnivorous beasts (including insect-eating birds) is necessary to preserve the 'balance of nature.' Without insectivorous birds, insect life would soon destroy vegetation, and even apparently harmless little animals like rabbits may become a scourge if there are no foxes and other carnivores to keep their numbers in check, as was abundantly illustrated in Australia some years ago. This 'balance of nature' is essential to the perfection of God's creation and we are not to reckon it a blemish or an afterthought.[8]

Despite these human thoughts can one limit God to only the present scheme of things, which Paul states "sighs and throbs with pain" (Rom. 8:23) and is to be replaced? Cannot God prevent the overpopulation of the earth with insects, fish, and other animals

---

* At the present time these pests seem to bother only susceptible individuals, or those not practicing sanitary living habits. The increasing abundance of mosquitoes as one proceeds into the more undisturbed northern environments, however, raises some interesting questions which at this point cannot be answered. Species of mosquitoes are present in all climatic zones of the earth. They tend to proliferate the most in areas of stagnant water, such as in commonly found on the saturated tundra during the short growing season. The essence of the Kingdom indicates that fresh, running water will be the rule, the type of water which favors an abundant population of clean fish and discourages insects like mosquitos that require stagnant waters (see also John 7:38 and Rev. 22:1).

through a means different than by mutual extermination? Uniformitarian* philosophers such as Thomas Aquinas, Leibnitz and other Germans, the Stoics, and Edward Hitchcock state that the present world is the best possible one, and that the present "balance of nature" is essential for the perfection of God's creation. Yet, a few authors, including Monsma, have considered alternatives to the present chaotic world:

> . . . the original creation is considered as having been free from sin and its effects. There were no destructive forces at work; no disease, no sudden death, no animals preying upon others, no violent storms or destructive floods. The destructive forces which we see in nature are in the Bible traced back to the fall of Adam. It is because of the sin of man that nature has become disruptive. Any other view has its source in the rationalism of modern thinking which considers pain and suffering, death and destruction as natural aspects of creation.[10]

A dramatic alteration of the nature and structure of many creatures of nature is soon to be in the offing when Christ establishes His kingship on the earth. Along with the supernatural modification of existing creatures, what is to prevent God from recreating the species of birds, animals, fish, insects, and even microorganisms whch once existed on the earth, but since the time of the Garden have disappeared? Man has been an especially virile force in causing the extinction of animals, prompting scientist Kai Curry-Lindahl to say, "Never in the realm of nature have so many been exterminated by so few in so short a time."[11] In the last 400 years more than 200 kinds of animals have become extinct.[12] In America alone nearly 40 different mammals and birds have disappeared since 1820, nearly half since about 1900.[13] In the United States today no fewer than 78 different species of mammals, birds, reptiles, and fish are in immediate danger of extinction.[14] Extinct animals include the passenger pigeon, eastern bison, eastern elk, heath hen, and Stellar's sea cow.

** "The present is the key to the past," or that "the processes now operating to modify the earth's surface have also operated in the geologic past,"[9] in line with II Peter 3:4 which states, "Where is His promised advent? Since the day our fathers fell asleep, things remain exactly as they were from the beginning of creation."

When the creation is renewed and the earth comes into harmony with God's perfect laws, will these extinct creatures be recreated? Will the original array of land, sea, and air creatures, as in Eden, be again assembled?

Grassland Management a Key to Livestock Production

Farmers and ranchers today are beset with the laborious task of maintaining, planting, or renovating pasture land for their livestock. Ranchers of the Plains may maintain the native grass species, but often feel pressed economically to such an extent that overgrazing of the range is the result. In the eastern half of the country the native grasses were virtually all plowed up, and introduced grasses and forage crops have been used. The wisdom of this two-pronged abrogation of natural principles—the replacement of native range plants with introduced species, and overgrazing of pasture land—is highly suspect, and has brought a number of resultant evils to the cattlemen of America: increased soil erosion, reduced production from overtaxed pastures, and inferior nutritional quality of many high yielding introduced plants. In addition, the continual removal of cattle from the range means a drain of soil nutrients from pasture to city, and thence down to the ocean . . . an "open circle" of nutrient flow.

The superiority of the native prairie environment to pastures developed according to conventional pasture theory was illuminated by J. E. Weaver. Using only a few wild acres he discovered that the prairie flora is more drought-resistant than the agronomic flora. Prairie species practice "team work" underground by distributing their root systems to cover all soil levels down to several feet, whereas "the species comprising the agronomic rotation overdraw one level and neglect another, thus building up cumulative deficits."[15] Aldo Leopold reiterated how paleontology offers abundant evidence that "wilderness [including grasslands] maintained itself for immensely long periods; that its component species were rarely lost, neither did they get out of hand; that weather and water built soil as fast or faster than it was carried away."[16]

Modern agronomists cannot claim the same benefits of their "industrialized" environments geared around agri-business. We have already seen how erosion of land in crop rotations is excessive, and overgrazed pastures are acknowledged by all authorities to contribute heavily to both water and wind erosion. Species differences in nutritional quality may also be profound, even beyond the fact that a modern cultured pasture may contain only relatively few species of plants which the livestock may choose from to balance their diets. Compounding the problem of lack of different species is the problem of the fenced prairie, which Beeson and Matrone have emphasized is a major cause of nutrient deficiencies:[17] soil differences that give rise to differences in plant quality are much more limited within a localized fenced-in area.

A comparison of the nutritional content of two common native prairie grasses and two common grasses used to replace them is given below.

The comparative nutritional value of two native prairie grasses and two grasses often used to replace them in pastures or grazing areas (aerial part, mid-bloom, fresh*)[18]

Plant component	Native grasses		Introduced grasses	
	Buffalo-grass	Big bluestem	Kentucky Bluegrass	Smooth Bromegrass
Dry matter, %	54.5	67.2	31.7	27.1
Ash, %	6.3	4.4	2.4	1.9
Crude fiber, %	15.8	23.0	9.2!8.3	
Ether extract, %	0.6	1.5	1.2	0.9
N-free extract, %	26.5	33.7	14.6	13.2
Protein (Nx6.25) %	5.3	4.4	4.2	2.8
Digestible protein				
Cattle, %	3.4	2.4	2.9	1.8
Sheep, %	3.3	2.1	2.9	1.8
Energy**				
Cattle, DE	1.25	1.63	0.84	0.79
Sheep, DE	1.35	1.69	0.89	0.78
Cattle, ME	1.03	1.33	0.69	0.65
Sheep, ME	1.11	1.39	0.73	0.64
Cattle, TDN	18.4	37.0	19.1	17.9
Sheep, TDN	30.6	38.4	20.2	17.8

Calcium		0.22	0.10	0.09
Phosphorus		0.07	0.10	0.08
Carotene, mg/kg	40.4	55.3		
Vitamin A				
equivalent, IU/g	67.3	92.1		

* The fresh tissue is used for comparisons here, since this is what the animal eats while grazing.

** DE = digestible energy in M cal/kg; ME = metabolizeable energy in M cal/kg; TDN = total digestible nutrients in %.

It is quite obvious that the bluestem and buffalograss, which often tend to appear less lush in the field and are not as adaptable to machine field operations, contain about double the energy and mineral matter and are somewhat higher in protein as well compared to the introduced, agronomic types. Moreover, these wild grasses are well adapted to the annual life cycles and nutritional needs of the native Plains and prairie animals—buffalo, elk, pronghorn antelope, and deer—which require succulent, high protein grass in the spring for the rapidly growing calves and drier, more concentrated, high energy feed in the fall and winter to maintain body heat and nourish gestating calves. The buffalo gained much flesh by late fall eating the native grasses and other prairie plants. The grass seeds were their grain, which ripened at the time of the year they were most needed, giving an extra high fat, high carbohydrate, high mineral thrust for adding fat to weather the winter.

Free-ranging livestock provide even another advantage for men and agiculture: energy consumption is greatly reduced. The animals themselves harvest the forage, eliminating the need for expensive harvesting equipment and storage facilities. The waste manure is returned immediately to the land, in the vicinity of its point of consumption by the animal; the organic wastes of humans who have harvested any of these animals has also been pictured earlier as being returned to the land from which the original grass was eaten. Fencing and its need for posts, wire, and continued maintenance is eliminated.

Should Cattle Be Confinement Fed?

Furthermore, confinement grain feeding is eliminated. The vast majority of the livestock sold on today's markets are confinement fed for at least part of their lives. Yet, the question may be asked, "Is it good economically, nutritionally (for both man and beast), and ecologically for animals to be grain-fed in confinement?" Answers to these questions are quite startling!

Economically speaking, the question of importance boils down to whether the land produces more nutritional value under grass or grain. An in-depth study by Dr. K. L. Blaxter, director of the Rowett Research Institute at Aberdeen, Scotland, provided the following results:[19]

Human food output per hectare (2.47 acres)	Milk production*	Cereal production*
Dry matter, kg	1,420 milk solids	3,557.5 flour
Calories, M cal	8,512.5 14,585	
Protein, kg	397.5	460
Lipids, kg	455	42.5
Lysine, kg	31.8	10
Threonine, kg	18.8	9.3
Thiamine, g	4	2.8
Riboflavin, g	17	2.5
Nicotinic acid, g	107.5	5
Calcium, kg	107.5	5
Phosphorus, kg	85	35

* Milk production figures are based on grassland yielding 11,045 lb. dry matter converted to 9,312 lb. milk per acre. Cereal production is based on wheat yielding 40.5 cwt (75 bu) per acre (15% moisture).

Based on this data Dr. Blaxter stated the following:

The results show that the calorific yield is much greater when good land is used to grow bread grains rather than to produce milk. At least 50% more biologically useful calories can be obtained from the cereal crop in terms of flour yield than from the milk produced. This is the *only* major nutrient however, in which the cereal crop excels. Intensive milk production and wheat growing produce similar amounts of protein. These proteins, however, differ markedly in nutritive value for man. Direct experiment with man shows that the biological value of wheat flour proteins is 41, while that of milk proteins is 74. The difference stems from the deficiency of wheat proteins, and indeed all cereal grain proteins, in the amino acids lysine and to a lesser extent threonine. The yields per hectare from dairy production of lysine and threonine are three times and twice those from cereal production. With the exception of nicotinic acid, yields of the vitamins of the B complex group are greater for dairy production than for cereal production and so, quite obviously are yields of calcium and phosphorus (vital for strong bones and health).[20]

If a yield typical of the United States, say 40 bushels per acre, was used instead of the 75 bushels per acre utilized in this study the nutritional value of foods would be even more heavily favored toward grasslands.

A study in the United States by H. W. Staten revealed the shocking fact that "cattle fed on good pastures will produce milk or beef at about one fourth to one fifth of the cost of dry-feeding."[21] Besides that,

> Total digestible nutrients produced by green pastures cost about one fifth as much as those produced by general grain crops. Kansas reports that the cost of producing corn and oats [is] six to seven times that of producing pastures, and other states find comparable feeding costs. . . . Cows turned onto good pastures from the best dry-lot feeding maintain or increase their milk flow.[22]

Besides being superior economically, pasture feeding of livestock also results in superior health for both man and beast. Confinement feeding severely restricts exercise of the animal, an important factor in its overall health status. In the natural state animals find ready space to run and sometimes migrate hundreds of miles each year, giving leaner, more muscular bodies. Reduced exercise combined with high carbohydrate and fatty feeds (grains and concentrates) yields fatty carcasses and fatty steaks, unhealthful not only to the animals but also the people who eat them. The Eternal forbids the eating of fat (Lev. 3:17); people who do may expect a greater risk of heart attacks, atherosclerosis, and other circulatory ailments.*

For the animal, life is not so rosy when grains constitute the majority of its diet: the pH of the digestive tract may become 100 times more acidic than if grass was eaten, leading to liver abscesses and other problems. Also, most confinement feeders add antibiotics and growth stimulants** to the feed or to the animal itself in an effort to coax out every last ounce of profit. The DES (diethylstilbestrol) scandal recently pointed toward the potential harmful effects of such synthetic hormones on people: rare vaginal cancer of the daughters of mothers who took DES during pregnancy, effeminization of males, and other effects.[25] Already mentioned is the fact that confinement feeding, or grazing on restricted pasturage, drastically limits the instinctive nature of an animal to balance its diet by feeding on a variety of species (each unique in nutritional value) and over a variety of soil types, often leading to nutritional problems. A cow, if given enough choices of plant species and soil variations, will instinctively balance her own diet. As general agriculture increased in the semiarid regions of the West, and as grazing animals were increasingly restricted by fenced rangeland, the occurrence of animal nutritional diseases such as osteomalacia (bone disease) was more frequently noted in that region. According to K. C. Beeson and G. Matrone, noted soil and nutrition researchers,

> On native range, selective grazing by cattle markedly affects their intake of phosphorus because of the differences in phosphorus concentration in the species comprising the flora. To acquire a balanced

---

* A recent study by Dr. Kaare Norum of the University of Oslo showed that 97% of the experts in the field of cardiovascular disease, worldwide, agree that dietary cholesterol raises the blood serum cholesterol level and with it the risk of heart disease. Eating high-cholesterol foods such as fatty meats may raise blood cholesterol 15 to 30%. Low dietary cholesterol levels pose no problem since the body manufactures what cholesterol it needs.[23]

** By 1971 it was estimated that close to 90% of the 40 million cattle slaughtered in the United States were being raised on feed containing diethylstilbestrol.[24]

diet, therefore, there should be ample opportunity for the animal to cover an area encompassing many soil conditions. Restrictions to small fenced areas often have led to nutritional problems.[26]

Ecologically speaking, the maintenance of native pastures and the livestock God originally designed to live there is of crucial value. The natural balance between the buffalo, the prairie wolves, and the grass supply assured that overgrazing would be avoided, and with it the soil erosion which swiftly accompanies this abominable practice. The bison would never chew the bluestem or buffalo grass entirely to the ground year after year. They would eat their fill of the more palatable leaves and stems in one area and then move on, always leaving enough seed heads to mature and reseed the area the next year, and assuring that less desirable species able to survive heavy grazing pressure would never take over. Today's severe grazing pressure has all but eliminated the native grasses in most pastures, allowing the lower-growing, finer-bladed grasses such as bluegrass to outcompete the nutritionally superior and more productive native species. Grazing large numbers of sheep and goats after cattle have taken all they can get is another practice which has removed prairie plants from all but fence rows and wastelands. Areas of the Middle East and Mediterranean have been virtually denuded to barren wastelands because of rapacious goats that graze down every accessible living plant[27] (see Figure 39).

The wisdom of utilizing and building upon the patterns in nature originally established in the environment may thus be seen to be extremely useful to livestock raisers. In stark contrast to the natural system stands the system of range management employed by the American pioneers. As Everett Edwards of the U. S. Department of Agriculture stated in 1948,

> As long as the grass of the public domain was the main reliance for the grazing of stock, whether cattle, sheep, or horse, no thought was given by the owners to range conservation. The prevailing principle was first come, first served. Besides, the stockmen were unaware of the rudiments of forage growth and requirements of plants.[28]

In a short time the indigenous forage plants were being gnawed to the ground and so weakened that much less palatable and worthless

Figure 39. The grazing of goats has reduced many areas of the Middle East to a barren, foresaken wasteland.

plants took over. Shrubs along streams were devoured and the meadows dried out, resulting in considerable erosion when heavy thunderstorms poured down their rain. Damage was accentuated over the entire Plains and West during periods of drought.[29]

The invention of barbed wire in 1874 greatly aided the confinement of livestock on the Plains, for it provided a cheap, quick way to enclose a pasture in the face of the high cost of timber and smooth wire fences, or the high labor and time requirements for building sod or rock fences or planting Osage orange hedges.[30] Cattle enclosed by fences could forage only within their confined areas; they often grazed it to the ground.

About 1880 a boom element began to enter the cattle industry. Financed by capital mostly from Europe, cattle numbers increased sharply and fully stocked the ranges. At this point the land was still largely in the public domain and unfenced. Edwards summed up the sad plight which followed:

> Without regulated grazing the supply of tall grass was soon exhausted, leaving only buffalo grass and grama grass, and shortly these also were threatened in many places.
>
> The lack of adequate provision for winter feed spelled widespread and terrific disaster when the unusually severe winter of 1886-87 came. The decreased grass supply of the summer range, due to the prolonged drought of 1886-95, brought further losses to the cattle companies, and the inroads of homesteaders on the range contributed other difficulties. Because of these circumstances, large-scale cattle ranching was gradually replaced by smaller operations.[31]

Farmers and ranchers of America's grasslands *could* renew the natural habitat if they wished, and bring back the natural grasses and buffalo. At the National Bison Refuge near Moiese, Montana, nearly 500 bison live on a grassland which is gradually approaching its former splendor. The original buffalo grass no longer grows there, but wheat grass and other native grasses are abundant. Predators such as prairie falcons, goshawks, horned owls, coyotes, and bobcats have moved into the refuge,[32] reminding an observer of the days of old before man's rapine allowed a scene of pristine wonder to degenerate over a few short years into typical overgrazed ranchland still commonly observed in America's grasslands.

Animal Breeding—Whose System?

In nature a supreme law prevails which affects the fate of every species: it is called "survival of the fittest." Within a particular "kind,"* or species, animals may vary over time to encourage more favorable adaptations to the environment. Thus, a beaver which has a slightly greater acuity of hearing will be encouraged to outwit its predators, and will be more likely to survive, breed, and leave progeny having this same improved survival technique. The beaver is still a beaver, however, not a badger or a muskrat. The great cardinal law of biology—kind reproduces after its own kind—has not been broken.

There is little if any inbreeding among animals in nature, though in the plant kingdom several species, such as wheat, rye, and many grasses, are naturally "selfed," i.e., the pollen from the plant fertilizes the ovum from the same plant due to the proximity of the stamens and pistil. A female lion, however, once its male cub is old enough to fend for itself, refuses to admit him back into her fold, requiring the young lion to find a new mate outside the immediate

---

* The "kinds" of Genesis 1 must refer to species. Taxonomists have no difficulty defining what a species is, while no line of demarcation exists, logically or biologically, between genera, families, orders, classes, phyla, sub-kingdoms, or kingdoms.[33] Variations within species, known as "varieties," exist for nearly all species, giving rise to types of dogs, cattle, wheat, or cabbage-like plants that are unique but yet can be crossed with any other variety within the species. Similar but distinct species of animals or plants may be crossed at times, but the offspring will be sterile; examples are the horse and donkey, producing the mule, or cattle and bison, producing "cattalo." Nearly 150 years ago cattle raisers in the northwestern states tried crossing cattle and bison, but nearly all bison male and cattle female matings produced dead progeny; mortality was less when a bison female was crossed with a cattle male. Male hybrids are always sterile, and only a few of the female hybrids are fertile. This sterility of the male continues to the fifth and sixth generation before signs of fertility in the male hybrids are noted, and by that time the animals have lost all traces of one or the other of the original parent's nature, both in outward appearance and in breeding ability.[34]

family and eliminating the potentially destructive effects of inbreeding.

Is there anything inherently wrong with this natural system of animal breeding? Obviously not, since God established the system, setting it in array at the time of the creation, calling all that He had made "very good" (Gen. 1:31). At that time inbreeding was practiced out of necessity for presumably a relatively short period of time immediately following the creation. Yet, the first male and female of each species were in a state of physical perfection, having no trace of physical malformation or genetic defect, meaning that any inbreeding would carry with it no negative side effects for the progeny as may occur today. Inbreeding, or "selfing," tends to accentuate the negative traits of animals, a fact confirmed by A. M. Winchester in his text on genetics:

> Animal breeders have long recognized the effects of inbreeding. Hog breeders, for instance, know that they get smaller litters from crosses between litter mates than if they outbreed their hogs. Also, they get more abnormal and deformed pigs, because recessive genes for such abnormalities are more likely to become homozygous. Since natural selection tends to eliminate dominate genes for such abnormalities rather quickly, most genes for these abnormalities in the population are recessive.[36]

How do these "errors" among the chromosomes occur? It is now well known that certain forms of radiation are prime causes of mutations (most of which are destructive) in animal, human, and plant cells. Normal forms of radiation which reach the earth's surface—visible light, ultraviolet rays, infrared rays, and radio waves—do not penetrate much beyond the skin and do little harm to the chromosomes of the germ cells. However, gamma rays (X-rays) from radioactive elements and cosmic rays* easily penetrate flesh and

---

* Primary cosmic radiation reaches the earth's upper atmosphere as nuclei of certain elements (carbon, oxygen, etc.). Few of these ever reach the earth's surface, however, since the atmosphere acts as a shield which is the equivalent of three feet of lead. We receive only secondary cosmic radiation, caused by primary cosmic particles colliding with the nuclei of molecules and atoms in the upper atmosphere. This gives rise to a shower of particulate and electromagnetic radiation that is highly penetrating but, fortunately, very minor in amount.[37]

can cause breaks in chromosomes, often causing a terminal deletion. Such deletions are usually lethal and the cell dies because a block of genes is lost from one end of the chromosome. Many cells survive these single breaks, however, by rejoining. When several breaks on the chromosome occur an aberration may result when the broken ends become improperly attached.[38]

These abnormalities are not too serious with normal body cells, when the death of a cell may be compensated for by the multiplication of surrounding cells to replace it. With generative cells in the ovaries or testes, however, chromosomal aberrations take on added importance because these abnormalities may be passed on to future progeny and lead to defects, most of which will be lethal to the new life but some of which may cause partial debilities within the animal: dwarfism, cleft palate, hairlessness, or reduced function of various body organs. Fortunately, most of these mutants are sterile, so the debility cannot be passed on to the future animal population.

Other environmental factors besides radiation may cause chromosomes to break. These include many drugs, feed additives, pesticides and herbicides, and certain viruses.[39] However, for animals living within the preindustrial society before the Flood, radiation would cause most of the problems . . . *if* there would be a significant amount of destructive radiation that would reach the earth's surface. It is highly likely that the water canopy above the atmosphere would filter out virtually all of the destructive rays which might potentially damage the delicate mechanisms of heredity of all creatures on the earth. Gamma rays, cosmic rays, and ultraviolet radiation would all tend to be greatly reduced, and so would be the tendency for man to harbor destructive mutations as a result; the perfection of the race from creation would tend to be preserved indefinitely, and the aging process would be greatly diminished.

Perhaps God's requirement for no inbreeding after the Flood was a necessary decree following the precipitation of the water canopy, one that was not essential before the Flood when genetic aberrations would have been few or nonexistent. However, it is difficult to visualize a natural environment replete with herds of bison, caribou, and antelope that did not practice random matings within a group as occurs today. The current practice of inbreeding to accentuate certain characteristics is a manmade innovation.

The God-given principle of animal breeding appears to find its closest analogy to the people of God themselves. Noah was a man "perfect in his generations" (Gen. 6:9). Abraham, Isaac, and Jacob and their families maintained racial purity by marrying within the clan centered in Ur of Chaldea, both Isaac and Jacob traveling great distances merely to procure their wives from this locale. In addition, God admonished Isaac, and later all Israel, to marry only a kinswoman, never to marry a Canaanite (Gen. 24:3), the principle being expressed in Numbers 36:8: " . . . any heiress in Israel must marry one of her father's clan, so that the clans of Israel might each preserve their own property." Surely the necessity of discouraging the worship of foreign gods and of keeping property within the clan were behind certain of these statutes. Yet, a common thread among so many of these orders results in the maintenance of racial integrity.

May not the same be said for animal breeding principles? The buffalo would breed within their restricted "clan" of this particular species which roamed the prairies from Mexico into Canada. In this polygamous natural system only the strongest bulls would mate with the females, assuring maximum vitality for coming generations within the oftentimes hostile Plains climate. This mating system is similar for many other animals and birds, though not universal, since geese, wolves, and certain other animals and birds usually have one mate for a lifetime.

The admonition of Leviticus 19:19, which states one must "never let any cattle breed with a different kind," apparently is dealing with the highly unnatural circumstance of a horse and an ass mating; both are separate kinds, and the progeny are sterile. Even more unnatural is the mating of a he-ass with a cow, though in some Eastern countries the allowance of such unusual circumstances is not unusual.[40] Surely God intended kind to breed only with the same kind of creature, and direct contravention of this sacred principle is grounds for severe recrimination by the Creator of all life.

The Masai tribe in Africa determines the value of a cow for retaining in their herd by the length of time it takes her calf to stand on its feet and run after it is born, which is usually only a few minutes.[41] Their system of livestock breeding is very close to a natural system, and is in sharp contrast to the practice of modern dairymen who are chiefly concerned with the quantity of milk and butterfat rather than with its value as a source of nutrients. According to the famous dental researcher Dr. Weston Price,

Many of the calves of the modern high-production cows of civilized countries are not able to stand for many hours after birth, frequently twenty-four [some dairy farmers make assisting these 'factory selected' cows during birth a standard procedure]. This ability to stand is very important in a country infected with predatory animals, such as lions, leopards, hyenas, jackals, and vultures.

This reminded me of my experience in Alaska in studying the reindeer of the Eskimos. I was told that a reindeer calf could be dropped in a foot of snow and almost immediately it could run with such speed that the predatory animals, including wolves, could not catch it. And, moreover, that these fawns would go almost immediately after their birth with a herd on a stampede and never be knocked down.[42]

Selective Breeding and Artificial Insemination

An important consequence of livestock breeding over the past centuries is the evolution of grain-fed, confined cattle possessing considerably more fat within their muscle tissues than their wild counterparts, such as wild buffalo or deer.[43] Just as a bulldog may differ from a Chihuahua in external appearance, so internal characteristics of a particular variety of one kind of animal may vary from another variety—fat within the muscles, size of the head, shape of the kidneys, or average weight. Along this same vein of thought it is of interest that the hog, an unclean animal, contains about *four* times the amount of polyunsaturated fatty acids in its muscle tissue than in domestic cattle, the former fed largely on grains and the latter on forages as well as grain . . . though differences are probably more genetic (due to heredity) than environmental (due to what the animal ate). According to T. L. Cleave, retired Surgeon-Captain of the British Royal Navy, the modern breeds of cattle and sheep themselves account for differences in the fat, or "marbling," within the muscle tissues:

. . . Crawford [an animal researcher], having been at great pains to demonstrate that domestic animals, like cattle and sheep fed on grass, have much more fat between the muscle fibers . . . than in the case of wild counterparts, has suggested that eating the meat of these grass-fed animals may hold danger for us, since it may be akin to taking into the body pathological material, or 'eating obesity,' as he has called it.[44]

Fattening wild cattle on grass will not give the same fat content within the muscles as for domestic cattle, any more than it would be possible to fatten up a wild rabbit on grass as compared with various breeds in a rabbit hutch. Cleave continues,

> . . . it has taken very long periods of selective breeding to evolve animals that will behave in this manner. The situation is even better seen in the case of domestic ducks, most of which cannot fly off the ground. This is true, from the Aylesbury duck in this country to the flocks of domestic ducks seen along the rivers of China, each flock attended by a small boy. *Thousand of years of selective breeding have been needed to replace muscle by fat to this extent.* . . . We must, therefore, very sharply distinguish this *evolved* fat . . . from any fat that is remotely pathological. . . . And it should be added that it is the above 'marbling' with fat that is partly responsible for the taste in lean meat; without it there is a tendency for lean meat to have a watery taste.[45]

The acquired taste for fatty meat mentioned above is largely a product of growing up, a taste intertwined with the total experiences that shape the individual within the home. In the same way people acquire a perverted preference for sweet or salty foods.

The animal researcher Crawford claims that not only the quantity of fat is greater in the muscles of modern livestock breeds than in similar wild animals, but the *quality* differs. He points out that the fat of domestic cattle is more saturated (contains a higher proportion of saturated fatty acids to unsaturated fatty acids) than the fat of wild African cattle feeding on a more varied diet; only the Kob of Uganda, a plains dweller, possesses a fatty acid composition similar to the milk, meat, and butter of typical modern cattle.[46]

The ultimate digression from the ordained order of nature is the widespread use of artificial insemination. In this way a single bull may impregnate thousands of cows via the tools of modern science: a tank of liquid nitrogen (in which the semen, obtained from a breeding association, is kept frozen at -196 °C) and a plastic or glass tube. The physiological consequences of such an intrusion into the natural means of breeding are an increased number of calf abnormalities and a decreased genetic base of the cattle themselves: brothers and sisters may be scattered from one end of the country to the other.

The psychological consequences of having no bull mingling with the cows are increased listlessness and odd—even homosexual—behavior within the herd. Surely God knew what He was doing when He created them male and female, a system that man is attempting to reform merely for the sake of quantity production. High production of beef or milk cannot assure maximum quality of the product under a system intent upon making a factory of an organic being, a faceless assembly line of vibrant flesh and blood. Whose system of animal breeding will operate within the Kingdom, God's or man's? The answer is obvious, and the fruits of this future abundance lie far beyond the images of present-day imaginations.

The Land and the Animals—a Final View

A landscape replete with all creatures adapted to each particular environment will freely roam the unfenced, florid, fertile pastures and woodlands of the Kingdom. Animals, birds, and fish will abundantly populate the earth, streams, lakes, oceans, and air, unafraid of man, their natures changed from fear and violence to peacefulness and gentleness. If man is to eat animal flesh he will probably have no problem capturing and bleeding the beasts; they will likely more or less offer themselves up for food, as a living, loving sacrifice for the sustenance of life. In fact, the sacrifices will be reinstituted during the Kingdom (Isa. 56:7; Zech. 14:21), a direct proof that livestock will be used by man in the coming era.

Because a new standard of "balance in nature" will be established within an unfenced countryside, it is hard to imagine any system of livestock confinement and tending as man now practices. The buffalo—about 60 million of them—roamed over the grasslands of North America, most of them living in the Mississippi River Basin.[47] Some herds covered an area 25 miles wide by 50 miles long! They survived wonderfully well until the white man nearly exterminated their numbers by 1900. Had man populated America having full knowledge of the laws of nature and worked fully to complement them he would have found a land superbly prepared to provide him all the meat and clothing he would ever desire from animals perfectly adapted to the full array of America's diverse lands and climates.

Chapter Twelve

Health and Nutrition in the Millennial Age

I t is not the purpose of this chapter to provide a detailed discourse on health problems of the present age. Such a task would fill many volumes and would serve little to fulfill the intent of this section. Instead, an overview of what state of health is in store for the millennium will be expounded upon, including the major laws of health and some current serious problems of nutrition experienced by a great many people. Also included will be a different view toward the nature of disease than medical science currently recognizes, a view that is currently emerging to explain the cause for most ills which are of organic origin. A discussion of millennial agriculture without touching upon the subject of health would be a great injustice, for diet is perhaps the overriding factor influencing health; one may break his health by neglecting rest, proper hygiene, a positive mental attitude, or breathing fresh air, but if he eats "garbage" he will most quickly observe his health go "down the drain." Without a proper diet the cause is lost; with it there is yet hope.

Jesus Christ—the Author of Health

Few people will challenge the statement that "life without good health is not life at all." People from all walks of life have spent fortunes in order to be healed, oftentimes suffering greatly while degenerating even further. It is the asset all people value most highly: freedom from disease, vitality and energy to accomplish, and a positive, joyous outlook toward the future.

191

One is reminded of the woman whom Christ met who had experienced a hemorrhage for 12 years, "suffering much under a number of doctors, and had spent all her means, but was none the better; in fact she was rather worse" (Mark 5:25-26). Christ miraculously healed this woman of her ailment through the mighty healing power of His Spirit, just as He healed countless other suffering men and women during His three and one-half years of ministry on earth.

Since those days during the first century A.D. His spiritual power has also healed many (James 5:14-16); in the Kingdom, when His Spirit is poured out to the entire world (Joel 2:28), He will heal *all* men and women of their afflictions. Speaking of the time when the "desert and dry land are glad, and the steppes rejoice and flower . . . seeing thus the Eternal's living power [in the Kingdom]," God says through Isaiah,

And then the blind shall see, the deaf shall hear; then shall the lame leap like a deer, and dumb tongues sing for joy (Isa. 35:5-6).

Then the eyes that see shall not be closed, and ears that hear shall listen; the hasty shall learn how to judge, and stammerers shall speak clearly (Isa. 32:3-4).

This freedom of lives which had been shadowed by blindness, deafness, lameness, dumbness, or other debilities, is to be of body, mind, and spirit—the whole being! When God stated that He came "to open the eyes that are blind, to free captives from their bondage, darkened lives from prison" (Isa. 42:7), He was referring to not only healing of bodily infirmities but also the wiping away of the evil influences of Satan who is the author of physical and mental ailments, blindness to truth, and every other problem and sin ever perpetrated within the universe:

Even if my gospel is veiled, it is only veiled in the case of the perishing; there the god of this world [Satan; see Luke 4:6] has blinded the minds of unbelievers, to prevent their seeing the light thrown by the gospel of the glory of Christ, who is the likeness of God (II Cor. 4:3-4).

This blindness to the light of the gospel refers not only to an ignorance of the stupendously rich hope and life of those called by God (John 6:44; Gal. 5:22-23), but also an ignorance of the healing power Christ possesses for mankind in spirit and body as revealed during His entire New Testament ministry as well as the healing of disorder within the entire creation brought about by man's choosing to follow Satan-directed human reasoning. This *gospel* ("good news")[1] refers to a Kingdom in which perfect health, enthusiasm to live, and incentive to work constructively within a gorgeous agrarian environment will be present everywhere. The gospel also means life and health to the Church (Greek *ekklesia,* or "called out ones")[2] in this age, those called out of this present Babylonian system (Rev. 18:1-5) who obey the laws of health rooted within God's immutabale ways.

What are these ways—now accessible to God's people as a guide to proper living habits (the *cause*)—yielding vibrant, positive health (the *effect*)? Scientists and laymen alike recognize that proper diet, rest, exercise, cleanliness, sunshine and fresh air, avoidance of accidents, and proper mental attitude[3] contribute to superb health, provided a person is not debilitated by some genetic disease over which he has no control. What does God have to say about these influences upon health—especially food, the products of agriculture—which operate today and which will just as surely operate in the Kingdom?

Millennial Diet

In previous sections several discussions have considered the use of vegetables, fruits, and animal products for food. All edible herbs which bear seeds and every tree bearing fruit having seeds is designed as food for both man and beast (Gen. 1:29-30; 2:16-17). This instruction was given to Adam and Eve in the Garden of Eden (which God planted) and surely has applied to all men upon the entire earth ever since.

Regarding the use of animals and their products, an earlier in-depth discussion has pointed to the question of whether or not animals were part of the pre-Flood diet (compare Gen. 9:3 with Gen. 1:29-30). As discussed earlier, Abel was a shepherd and may have used these animals for food as well as for sacrifices and wool. Also, the taking of seven pairs of clean animals into the ark may have revealed that Noah knew of, and regularly partook of, clean meats in his diet; or it could have been merely the beginning of the use of animals in the diets of men corresponding to the great post-Flood change of climate and soil conditions (the commencement of rainfall and subsequent leaching of soil nutrients). Moses' mentioning of "clean" (edible) and "unclean" (inedible) animals in Genesis 6 for the first time, just prior to the Flood, does not necessarily imply they were being used yet for food at that time; rather, it signifies that a distinction was now being made by God, the purpose for which later became very clear.

Following the Flood, animal products definitely were condoned as food. When God mentioned that "every moving thing that is alive is to be food for you" (Gen. 9:3), He obviously could not mean *everything,* for to His chosen nation Israel He clearly distinguished between clean and unclean animals (Lev. 11, Deut. 14). Among four-footed beasts, clean animals included those that were both ruminants and possessed a split hoof (sheep, cattle, goats, deer, moose, etc.). Clean fish were those having both fins and scales (bass, perch, pike, mackerel, cod, etc.), while clean birds included mostly seed eaters, grass and forage eaters and song birds (ducks, geese, quail, chickens, etc.). Among the insects only grasshoppers and locusts were edible. Any preying animal or bird was not to be eaten. Neither were other insects or creatures of the sea or land which did not fit the assigned specifications.

The Mystery of Clean and Unclean Meats

Scientists and nutritionists have recently come to observe the negative health effects of several of these forbidden creatures. It has long been known that pork is a meat difficult to digest, one of the first foods omitted from diets of the sick. One reason for its not being included in the list of clean animals may be the high amount of polyunsaturated fatty acids in its fat, much higher than in beef fat; its consumption may lead to heart and arterial diseases.[4] The transmission of trichinosis by eating swine, bear, or certain other forbidden meats is well-known. Shark meat is high in uric acid, an undesirable waste product of the human body, and eels and related species tend to have fatty meats.

Perhaps less well understood in God's instructions regarding unclean animals is that man, besides being forbidden to eat them, is also forbidden to *touch* their dead bodies (Lev. 11:24); this includes touching a dead human body, since humans are classified as unclean creatures (Num. 5:2). If contact was made with the carcass of an unclean creature the person was to remain unclean until evening. Moreover, "anything on which their dead bodies fall shall be unclean, any article of wood or dress, any skin or sack, any vessel in use—it must be put into water, it remains unclean till evening, and then is clean again" (Lev. 12:32). An earthen jar into which the dead body of an unclean animal fell had to be broken, and the contents were declared unfit to consume. An oven or chafing pot had to likewise be broken and disposed of, though a nonporous utensil in contact with a dead unclean creature was merely declared unclean until evening (Lev. 12:33-35). Presumably these utensils were washed in running water.

Interestingly, a well containing running water was declared clean if the carcass of an unclean beast fell into it, though anything used to lift out the dead body became unclean (Lev. 12:36). The cleansing properties of soil also rendered dry seeds clean if they were ready to be planted but had contacted an unclean carcass; if the seeds were wet when contact was made with the carcass they remained unclean (Lev. 12:37-38). In addition, a clean animal which died would render a person unclean until evening if he touched the carcass; his clothes which contacted the carcass were also unclean and needed to be washed (Lev. 12:39-40).

The apparent meaning behind all of these rituals is far more than ceremonial. It is obvious that microorganisms of some sort are being dealt with here, too miniscule for the Israelites to see but which the Creator knew had to be dealt with. It is also obvious that these organisms were potentially harmful and had to be avoided and purged from the body, and provision was made to prevent transmission of these microbes to other humans by the isolation technique of being "unclean until evening." This segregation of potentially infectious individuals, articles, or even houses was the same system rigorously enforced for the highly contagious disease of leprosy. Touching a dead carcass would transmit potentially disease-causing microorganisms to the person, necessitating segregation until their effects would be washed off and neutralized by the body. Clothes, articles of wood, skins, and other cleanable items, washed in running water, would have the microbes removed. Porous articles such as earthenware, ovens, and chafing pots, however, might still harbor the organisms even after being washed, so the only effective means of eliminating the organisms was eliminating the article.

The logical question to ask at this point is what is inherently wrong with the microorganisms of unclean animals? Of course, a dead animal, be it clean or unclean, usually has died of some sort of disease unless killed by beasts (one is warned against eating the flesh of a clean animal torn by beasts, though penalties for touching this torn carcass were not apparently imposed; see Ex. 22:31). If the organisms within the animal caused its death, may they not also adversely affect a susceptible person?

Large numbers of specific microorganisms and enzymes are contained within an animal's tissues which decompose the cells after death. If meat or organs from an unclean or dead animal are ingested by a person, or even contacted by the person (with the microbes finding their way into his body), their potentially harmful microflora will multiply within the individual and directly or indirectly lead to disease—if he is susceptible.[5] Perhaps a species of bacteria foreign to the body proliferates and manufactures toxic materials within the digestive tract that are then absorbed by the bloodstream, the toxins manifesting themselves as disease symptoms.* The microbes

---

* The presence of a proper microorganism population within the body is essential for life. Without it vitamin K, so essential for the proper clotting of blood, could not be manufactured in the large intestine. The long transit times of fecal matter within the bowels, associated with the ingestion of a low fiber, high refined carbohydrate diet (the intestines go into "slow motion") is related directly to an abnormal microflora which produces toxins thought to be associated with bowel cancer and other ailments. With modern food technologists intent upon manufacturing a totally synthetic diet, Eugene Rabinowitch, editor-in-chief of the *Bulletin of Atomic Scientists,* said the following: "The only animals whose disappearance may threaten the biological viability of man on earth are the bacteria normally inhabiting our bodies. For the rest there is no convincing proof that mankind could not survive even as the only species on earth! If economical ways could be developed for synthesizing food from inorganic raw

themselves could also spill over into the bloodstream and attack weakened tissues elsewhere in the body. The fact that a type of flesh ("unclean meat") is present within the digestive system that ought not to be there may be the key to the problem: the decomposition products of this flesh are likely to be inherently debilitating to the human body.

In time it is likely that human investigators, if somehow directed to search for unbiased truth, would end up classifying animals in the same manner God has. God, the master nutritionist of all time, has a gigantic advantage over man, however: He created the human body and knows precisely how to best feed it for optimum health. Man says, "As long as it has some vitamins, minerals, protein, or energy in it eat it!" Man reacts to partial knowledge, and a little knowledge is said to be dangerous. God acts and instructs out of full knowledge in all things. It is to Him and His Word we ought to look for answers!

Other dietary prohibitions include the eating of blood (Lev. 17:14) or fat (Lev. 7:23). Adam Clarke outlines a number of reasons, aside from the moral reason of blood picturing the life of the flesh (Lev. 17:14), why blood is an abominable food:

> 1. Blood, being highly *alkalescent,* especially in hot climates, is subject to speedy putrefaction. 2. It affords a gross nutriment, being very difficult of digestion, so much so that *bull's blood* was used in ancient times as poison, 'its extreme viscosity rendering it totally indigestible by the powers of the human stomach.' 3. It is allowed that when blood

---

materials—which is likely to happen sooner or later—man may even be able to become independent of plants, on which he now depends as sources of his food. . . . I personally—and, I suspect, a vast majority of mankind—would shudder at the idea [of a habitat without animals and plants]. But millions of inhabitants of 'city jungles' of New York, Chicago, London, or Tokyo have grown up and spent their whole lives in a practically 'azoic' habitat [leaving out rats, mice, cockroaches, and other such abnoxious species] and have survived."[6] Rabinowitch, of course, takes the view of a pure scientist isolated from the real world, not recognizing that nature on the outside, as well as within man, will rebel before such a travesty of natural laws becomes established.

was used in this country in great quantities, the *scurvy* was more frequent than at other times. 4. It appears from history that those nations who lived most on it were very fierce, savage, and barbarous, such as the Scythians, Tartars, Arabs of the desert, the Scandinavians, etc., some of whom drank the blood of their enemies, making cups of their skulls.[7]

Our Unhealthy American Diet

A high fat content in meats and foods in general has recently been recognized as a partial reason that Americans are disease-prone. In a document entitled *Eating in America: Dietary Goals for the United States,* released in 1977 by the U.S. Senate Select Committee on Nutrition and Human Needs, a significant reduction was urged in the intake of fat, sugar, and salt.* More fresh and frozen fruits and vegetables, whole grains, poultry, and fish were recommended, justifying its recommendation by the link of diet with six of the 10 leading causes of death: heart disease, cancer, cerebrovascular disease (stroke), diabetes, arteriosclerosis (hardening of the arteries), and cirrhosis of the liver.[9] Fat consumption accounts for nearly 43% of total calorie intake, up 11% since 1900. Sugar and alcohol make up a greater part of carbohydrate calories than ever before, increasingly replacing wheat and potatoes since 1900.

From 1960 to 1975 the consumption of soft drinks more than doubled, displacing milk as the second most consumed beverage. In 1975 Americans drank, on the average, 295 twelve-ounce cans of soda.[10] In 1976 every man, woman, and child in the U.S. consumed 125 pounds of fat and 100 pounds of sugar, both formidable amounts.[11] In the early 1900s, almost 40% of our calorie intake came from fruit, vegetables, and grain products; today only slightly more than 20% of our calories came from these sources.[12]

The modern change in dietary regime is thought by many medical

---

* The Goals report recommended a reduction in overall fat consumption from approximately 40% of energy intake or total calories to 30%; this recommendation was to be met by a greater use of lean meats, fish, and poultry.[8]

authorities to contribute to a number of diseases, from tooth decay to mental illness. Indeed, our entire livestock feeding industry is geared toward heavy grain feeding of animals designed to consume fibrous grasses. The resultant fatty animals become all the more unhealthy to eat, another example of Satan's system in operation to turn around the God-ordained order of nature. Animals normally ranging far and wide over an open range can instinctively balance their diets, and exercise maintains leanness of body, whereas modern confinement feeding leads to lethargic and fatty animals, subject to any deficiencies their feed may provide them. These dietary deficiencies, despite the boastful claims of meat advertisers, are directly reflected in the nutritional quality of the meat, liver, or other portion of the animal.

It was pointed out earlier that high dietary cholesterol (associated with high-fat diets) may raise blood cholesterol 15 to 30% above blood levels from individuals having low cholesterol diets.[13] With this increase comes an increased risk of heart and vascular disease. The reality of our present morbid state of circulatory health—a reflection of our refined diets, high intake of food additives, and tense lifestyle—is dramatized by a study performed by Dr. W. F. Enos and colleagues in 1953.[14] He studied the coronary arteries of 300 American soldiers killed in action in Korea. The average age in 200 cases was 22 years; in the entire series the youngest recorded age was 18 and the oldest 48. In 77.3% of the hearts examined there was gross evidence of arteriosclerosis,* and in 15% more than half of the openings of the coronary arteries were plugged. The people constituting this age group are now middle-aged, and are particularly prone to sudden heart attacks. A similar study done on Vietnam casualties some 20 years later indicates a significant increase in

---

* Atherosclerosis, a form of arteriosclerosis, meaning a disease where a "sack is filled with something," is a circulatory disease affecting arteries throughout the body. It begins with lesions forming on the inner walls of the vessels. These increase in size and build up large amounts of fatty materials, including cholesterol. As the disease increases in severity the "atheromas," or bulbous, protruding areas on arteries such as the aorta, increase in size and total fatty acid content. Other changes in lipid fractions occur with age, and in advanced stages calcium deposits give the fatty structures a rigidity (i.e., "hardening of the arteries").[15]

atherosclerosis.[16] Ross Hume Hall and several other prominent workers do not claim that the higher fat consumption of recent years is precipitating this circulatory degeneracy among Westerners, but rather he points the finger directly at refined sugar and flour.[17] He states that:

> Sugar, if free, consisted of a mixture of fructose, glucose, lactose, sucrose, and other simple molecules. Man's digestive tract was designed to handle the complex carbohydrates, and even when sugar molecules were ingested they were eaten together with starch and other complex molecules of natural foods, as in fruit. Only in recent years has the major source of starch in the Western diet, flour, been almost completely separated from bran and germ, and sugar (sucrose) sold in a chemically pure state.[18]

Animal fat alone cannot be implicated as the underlying culprit in the diets of people, for Eskimos in their original cultural state subsisted almost totally on an animal diet high in protein and fat; yet, diseases of the cardiovascular system were uncommon.[19] One cannot ignore the Biblical admonition to abstain from eating fat of an animal, however. The physical effects of ingesting these concentrated fats obviously are negative or Scripture would not have repeated this law to the Israelites (and modern civilization) several times. Perhaps the placement of total blame for circulatory diseases upon fats—especially unsaturated fatty acids and cholesterol—by modern medicine can be viewed as a smokescreen, one clouded by dollar bills because the revelation of the primary culprit would mean reduced sugar consumption and few trips to the hospital. "The love of money is the root (or, *a* root, Greek) of all evil" (I Tim. 6:10).

The scientific paradigm (the official hypothesis that medical science promotes to explain cardiovascular disease) states that dietary fat is the problem; research by many others has proved otherwise. Why cannot the medical establishment turn around its theory and face the full, enlightening truth which would herald improved health for millions of people? Hall points his finger directly to the problem:

> For Western society there can be no turning back—technological society demands that the technologic diet be eaten; any difficulties

man's basic biology has in adapting will be compensated for by technical progress in treating the side effects. This fundamental belief is one reason why research on cardiovascular problems has taken the direction it has. Medical scientists recognize that dietary factors are important, but *they seek a solution to heart disease that does not disturb the basic technologic dietary pattern,* a solution that conforms to the objectives of the technologic food system. . . . The gap between the capacity of man's biology and the demands technologic society places on it is also widening at an ever increasing rate.[20]

Thus, meat itself—especially from lean, range-fed animals of wild species—is not the primary cause of circulatory problems. Clean animals themselves cannot be implicated as causes of disease when eaten in moderation, but rather are prime sources of health through high quality protein, vitamins, and minerals.

The Medicine of Scriptural Directives

Foods condoned by God include salt (Mark 9:50), milk (Gen. 49:12; Prov. 27:27), butter (Deut. 32:14; II Sam. 17:29), cheese (I Sam. 17:18; Job 10:10), bread (Gen. 18:5; I Sam. 17:17), parched corn (Ruth 2:14; I Sam. 17:17), herbs (Prov. 15:17; Rom. 14:2), dried fruit (I Sam. 25:18; 30:12), honey (Song 5:1, Isa. 7:15), oil (Deut. 12:17; Prov. 21:17), vinegar (Num. 6:3; Ruth 2:14), and wine (II Sam. 6:19; John 2:3, 10). In all cases moderate consumption is urged (Gal. 6:23; Phil. 4:5). Even though Christ was called "a glutton and a drunkard" (Matt. 11:19), these rash statements were merely hollow accusations by detractors intending to deride and persecute the Master of moderation and perfect, wholesome, abundant living. He set the perfect working example of Solomon's admonition to "eat, drink, and enjoy your work" (Eccl. 3:13).

Drunkenness (the excessive use of alcoholic beverages) is expressly forbidden (Deut. 20:20-21; Prov. 20:1, 23:20-35; Gal. 5:18, 21; I Thess. 5:7-8), not only among ancient Israelites but also in the Church . . . for a drunkard would have no inheritance in the Kingdom (Gal. 5:21).

Although *wine* (Greek "oinos"[21]), the fermented, alcoholic juice of grapes, is oftentimes mentioned as a drink used by Christ, and also used as an antiseptic (Luke 10:34), nowhere are distilled liquors such as brandy, whiskey, vodka, or the like mentioned clearly. Some have thought that the biblical references to "strong drink" refer to such distilled beverages. However, the Hebrew word used for "strong drink" in all 21 Old Testament references is *shekar*, meaning "sweet drink, that which satiates or intoxicates;"[22] nowhere is a distilled liquor mentioned. According to Salvatore Lucia in *A History of Wine As Therapy,*

> 'Strong drink' in the Bible apparently meant heavy wine altered by the addition of piquant, peppery, and highly aromatic substances, such as goat's milk, cheese, onion, and other alliaceous roots and bitter substances usually rich in tannin—all of which made the wine taste strong. It did not refer to spiritous liquor, since distillation was unknown to the ancients.[23]

Obviously God considered wine excellent for the human body, and designed it as a major means by which the nutritional value of grape juice could be preserved for months or years. Even the patriarchs Lot and Noah used wine, at times in excess (Gen. 9:21; 19:33). Timothy, a fervent and highly respected minister of God, was admonished to "drink no longer water, but use a little wine for thy stomach's sake and thine often infirmities" (I Tim. 5:23). The wisdom of Paul's advice is clearly spelled out by a recent article in the *Journal of the American Medical Association,* which revealed that the daily consumption of small to moderate amounts of alcohol—two ounces or less daily—is directly related to reduced deaths from coronary heart disease.[24] This relationship holds true for beer, wine, and hard drinks. It has been found that the protective type of cholesterol—high-density lipoprotein—increases in moderate (but never excessive) drinkers.[25]

Honey was also to be eaten in moderation, for as Solomon stated,

> If you find honey, eat no more than you need; you may surfeit yourself and vomit (Prov. 25:16).

In fact, John the Baptist nearly totally subsisted for some time on a diet composed of locusts and honey (Matt. 3:4), a diet wholesome and well suited to the spartan, outdoor type of life which he pursued.

In contrast to white table sugar, which is composed of nearly pure sucrose and no vitamins or minerals, honey is composed mainly of the sugars fructose and glucose (which are easier to digest than sucrose) and also small amounts of vitamin C, B complex, and the minerals potassium, calcium, magnesium, iron, copper, and manganese.[26] According to the *Journal of the American Medical Association,* honey is an excellent bacteria fighter.[27] It quotes a Chelsea, England, doctor as follows:

> I have been using pure natural honey for the past few months in the accident and emergency departments where I work, and have found that, applied every two or three days under a dry dressing, it promotes the healing of ulcers and burns better than any other local applications I've used before. . . . It can also readily be applied to any other surface wounds, including cuts and abrasions.[28]

A 17th century book entitled *History of the Bees* lists honey's many healing powers:

> Honey cleareth all the obstructions of the body, looseneth the belly, purgeth the foulness of the body and provoketh urine. It cutteth up and casteth out phlegmatic matter and thereby sharpens the stomach of them which by reason have little appetite. It purgeth those things which hurt the clearness of the eyes and nourisheth very much; it storeth up and preserveth natural heat and prolongeth old age.[29]

While not a great deal is revealed of Christ's personal eating habits (His emphasis on health was as much from the attitude as from the dietary viewpoint), He and the disciples apparently made it a practice to eat kernels of grain directly from fields (Matt. 12:1). This example and others indicate that Christ ate only foods naturally grown (there were no synthetic fertilizers, herbicides, and pesticides used at that time), and usually in their fresh state. If foods were not fresh they were preserved by drying (dried fruits or herbs) or fermentation (wine or cheese). Yogurt, piima, kefir, and similar fermented milk products common today in Middle Eastern countries may also have been used extensively (see Isaiah 7:15, where Christ was prophesied to eat "curds").

Cool storage of vegetables may also be implicated as a Godly practice, since little loss in food value occurs during such storage; they remain essentially fresh. Long-term food storage such as freezing or canning, two of the most common means of food preservation today, were not possible during Christ's day with no modern industrial system in existence. Freezing is an especially energy-dependent type of preservation, forcing one to depend upon the electrical or gas utilities controlled without the home; at the same time vitamin E in foods is greatly reduced. Canning likewise depends on the industrial society for jars and lids, and during heating a significant portion of the food value is destroyed. Invented in the early 1800s by a Frenchman named Nicoles Appert, the method was used primarily as a means of feeding the French armies.[30] France, incidentally, lost the war.

Our Pummeled, Adulterated Food Supply

Food processing techniques common to modern-day industrial America were largely unknown in Christ's day. These techniques include flour refining, sugar refining, substitution of synthetic or altered foods for natural foods, addition of preservatives, coloring agents, emulsifiers, conditioners, bleaching agents, heating and a host of others. The tremendous increase in many acute and chronic diseases during the past century parallels closely the high intake of highly processed foods and chemical additives, including pesticides and herbicides used to grow food crops. A comprehensive work by D. P. Burkitt and H. C. Trowell, entitled *Refined Carbohydrate Foods and Disease,* details the relationship of refined, high carbohydrate, low fiber diets and ulcers, dental caries, heart disease, gallstones, hiatus hernia, varicose veins, hemorrhoids, thromboses, colitis, diverticular disease, and appendicitis.[31]

Dr. T. L. Cleave, noted former director of Medical Research of the English Institute of Naval Medicine, has called conditions arising from the taking of refined carbohydrates such as sugar and white flour "the saccharine diseases;"[32] these conditions include the same diseases mentioned above. Recently, Crohn's disease, virtually unknown before the 1930s but today epidemic across the Western world, attacks one out of every 3,000 Americans.[33] Produced by a constriction around the last section of the small intestine, its etiology is closely tied to high sugar, low fiber diets. Figure 40 illustrates the close ties between the modern incidence of several diseases and the consumption of refined carbohydrate foods.

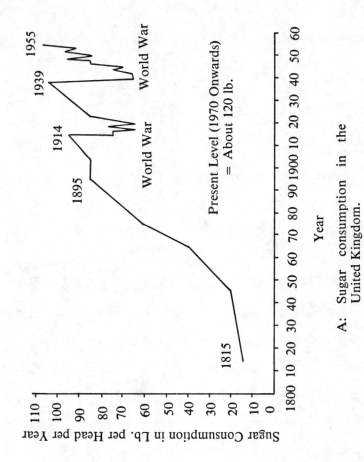

A: Sugar consumption in the United Kingdom.

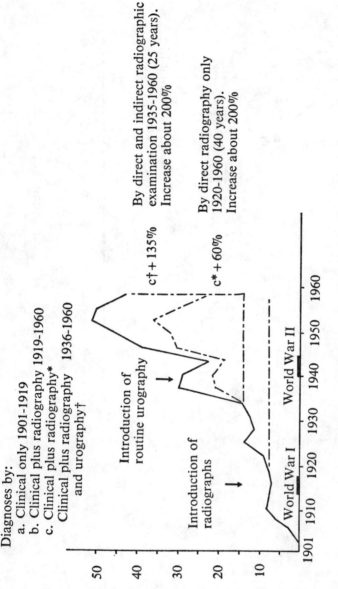

Diagnoses by:
a. Clinical only 1901-1919
b. Clinical plus radiography 1919-1960
c. Clinical plus radiography*
   Clinical plus radiography 1936-1960
   and urography†

Introduction of
routine urography

Introduction of
radiographs

c† + 135%

By direct and indirect radiographic
examination 1935-1960 (25 years).
Increase about 200%

c* + 60%

By direct radiography only
1920-1960 (40 years).
Increase about 200%

World War I   World War II

1901 1910 1920 1930 1940 1950 1960

50 40 30 20 10

B: Urinary stones detected in the
     upper urinary tract, Ullevaal
     Hospital, Norway.

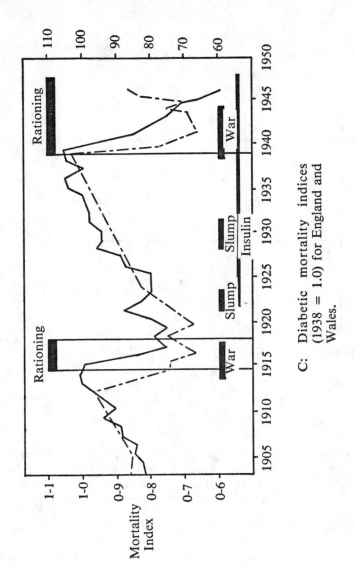

C: Diabetic mortality indices (1938 = 1.0) for England and Wales.

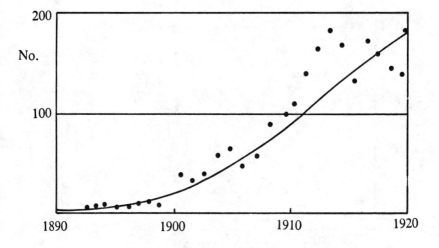

D: Appendicitis cases admitted to
the Radcliffe Infirmary, Oxford, England.

Figure 40. As sugar consumption (A) has risen dramatically since 1840, so
have a number of serious modern diseases, including urinary stones (B),
diabetes (C), and appendicitis (D).[34] Note how the incidence of diseases fell
as sugar consumption decreased during both world wars.

The classical work by Dr. Weston Price, *Nutrition and Physical Degeneration,* lucidly outlines the debilitative effects which the modern, refined, highly-sugared Western diet has upon health, especially when contrasted with the effects of "primitive" native diets.[35] He has shown how the incursion of the Western diet into isolated native populations, previously subsisting on natural foods, has brought with it mental, physical, and moral deterioration so often noted once the natives begin to partake of the low fiber, sweet, refined diets. Among his more fascinating discoveries is that a combination of cod liver oil and high vitamin butter oil added to the diet of certain families was extremely effective in eliminating tooth decay. The home diets of these families were responsible for the decay, being very low in body building materials and high in sweets and refined starches. When the diet supplements began, a new layer of calcium began to be deposited beneath the tooth cavities, and they ceased to increase in size, leading Dr. Price to the conclusion that dental caries must be thought of in terms of nutrition, not in terms of oral hygiene . . . even as important as that process is.[36] He stated, "In many of these cases, the open cavities were left without fillings; and, in all such cases, the exposed dentine took on a hard, glossy finish."[37] Along with improvements in dental health for these children came dramatic advances in athletic and academic performance.

Dr. Paul A. Fine, a consultant to major food companies, has defined the "American mainstream diet" which consists of "sandwich cookies, peanut butter, vegetable shortening, TV dinners, cake mix, macaroni and cheese, soft drinks, pizzas, gelatin, hamburgers, canned noodles, pork and beans, ketchup, and instant coffee. . . ."[38] Dependence on processed fare "has permanently dulled the nation's taste buds," bringing on what culinary critics John and Karen Hess have termed, "the death of the American palate. Good food in America is little more than a memory, and a hope. Americans have been mouthwashed by generations of bad food and brainwashed by generations of bad advice about food."[39]

Added to the list of refined and "foodless" foods most Westerners eat today are the scores of chemical additives intended to preserve shelf life and increase sales for conglomerate corporations . . . whose primary concern is profit maximization, not health optimization. The average American consumed about seven pounds of such additives in 1975![40] That amount increases year by year. Many of these, such as synthetic coal-tar dyes (Butter Yellow dye and Red dye No. 1), a synthetic flavoring (safrole), a weed killer (Aminotriazole), a pesticide (Aramite), artificial sweeteners (cyclamates), and a hormone (stilbesterol) have been shown to cause cancer. No assurance of safety at any level of usage can be implied for these chemicals. Time after time a government agency will declare a chemical "safe," only to apologize a few years later that it had made a mistake: the substance was found to cause cancer.

The ultimate hypocrisy regarding food consumption is the big chemical farmer who refuses to eat his own product. The farmer is considered simply a producer who must cut his costs and raise his efficiency by every possible device, even if he thereby destroys the health of the soil and the beauty of the landscape . . . and even if his end effect is the depopulation of the land and the overcrowding of cities. As Schumacher puts it in *Small Is Beautiful,*

> There are large-scale farmers, horticulturists, food manufactures, and fruit growers today who would never think of consuming any of their own products. 'Luckily,' they say, 'we have enough money to be able to afford to buy products which have been organically grown, without the use of poisons.' When they are asked why they themselves do not adhere to organic methods and avoid the use of poisonous substances, they reply that they could not afford to do so. What man-as-producer can afford is one thing; what man-as-consumer can afford is quite another thing. But since the two are the same man, the question of what man—or society—can really afford gives rise to endless confusion.[43]

Food chemicals may alter the biochemical structure of the food, cause derangements in the body's internal organs (enlargement of the detoxifying organs such as the liver, kidneys, or spleen), injure or deteriorate cells, interfere with the normal functioning of vitamins and enzymes, or cause chromosomal aberrations.[41] Catalase, an important enzyme found in most living cells, plays a vital role as a buffer against toxic substances, infection, viruses, radiation, and cancer. Normally there is a balance in cells between catalase and hydrogen peroxide, but when a food additive destroys catalase the peroxide level rises, giving rise to cellular abnormalities that may result in cancer. According to Dr. R. A. Holman,

> It is obvious . . . that if this fundamental biological mechanism is interfered with long enough by physical and chemical agents present in our environment, whether in food, drink, drugs, or in the air we breathe, then we shall see in the races so exposed a progressive increase in the incidence of cancer. By contrast, in those primitive communities where such agents are not used or encouraged, the incidence will remain at a very low level. In my opinion most of the chemicals added to food and drink for preservation or coloring could and should be abolished.[12]

If Christ were today directing that additions be added to the dietary laws of Leviticus 11, would He add, "You shall not eat refined foods, such as sugar and white flour, nor those containing harmful, synthetic additives"? The elimination of these items from one's diet is surely implied by God's Word. The examples and directions of using only untainted whole grains and wholesome, life-giving foods yet reverberate from Scripture, all pointing toward maintaining the body as the temple of the Holy Spirit (I Cor. 6:19-20). The human body has amazing built-in recuperative and restorative powers. It can exist in health within a reasonably wide limit of dietary choices. It can also flounder along at reduced efficiency, struggling to maintain life and energy while burdened under an assault of toxic foods. Science has abundantly shown to the discerning mind the evils of the modern Western diet. He can rely upon God's Word for direction today more than ever before.

Nutrition-robbing food preparation methods were very limited in Christ's day as well, and will not exist whatsoever during the Kingdom. Wheat and barley grains were ground whole and breads were baked in brick or stone ovens. Most vegetables and fruits were eaten fresh and untainted.

The Way You Fertilize Does Make a Difference

A point of major controversy has emerged during recent decades with the dramatic rise in the use of synthetic fertilizers. Food quality is at stake. On the one hand, proponents of modern agri-business and technology claim there is no reduction in food quality as yields are maximized through the application of acid-treated, highly soluble nitrogen, phosphorus, and potassium fertilizers. "Fertilize according to soil test and all is well," proclaim modern soil scientists. On the other hand, proponents of natural farming methods proclaim that organic or crushed rock fertilizer sources produce the highest quality, by intuition and common sense if not yet by scientific fact.

Although most plant quality studies have shied away from direct approaches to this controversy, an interesting study by Dr. Werner Schuphan at Geisenheim, West Germany, has shed considerable light on the subject.[44] In a 12-year experiment using a fen and a sandy soil, with additions each year of stable manure, "biodynamic compost," stable manure + N P K (nitrogen, phosphorus, potassium), and N P K the differences in composition of the various vegetable crops proved to be substantial:

Changes in desirable constituents when stable manure or "biodynamic compost" were used, vs. N P K (N P K = 100%):

Potatoes and spinach

Dry matter	$23%$
Protein	+ 18%
Ascorbic acid	+ 28%
Total sugars	+ 19%
Methionine	+ 23%

Spinach only

Potassium	+ 18%
Calcium	+ 10%
Phosphorus	+ 13%
Iron	+ 77%
Magnesium	± 0%

Changes in undesirable constituents when stable manure or "biodynamic compost" were used, vs. N P K (NPK = 100%):

Spinach only (1962, 1969, 1972)

Nitrates	- 93%
Free amino acids	- 42%
Sodium	- 12%

The fertilizer treatments clearly affect plant composition different-ly. The stable manured and "biodynamic compost" treated plants most nearly approach nature's system and clearly produce superior plants, higher in desirable constituents and considerably lower in undesirable components, such as nitrates and free amino acids. Also, despite yields 24% lower than N P K treatments, the two organic treatments yielded 23% more dry matter, meaning the real yield under both was virtually identical; the N P K treatment resulted in an increased water content (enlarged cells), a typical result from high nitrogen additions.

It must be remembered that most farmers using conventional N P K fertilizer formulations are also applying herbicides and pesti-cides to their grain, vegetable, or fruit crops. These synthetic chemicals usually penetrate the plant tissues and are consequently ingested by the consumer whether he is aware of their presence or not. Several of these chemicals were in common use over millions of acres for years before their carcinogenicity was uncovered. For instance 2, 4-D (2, 4-dichlorophenoxyacetic acid) has been used to kill broad-leafed weeds such as Canada thistle and mustard in grain fields, and brush in forested areas. The related compound 2, 4, 5-T also was used for years for similar broad-leafed weed control, but its use as an ingre-dient in "Agent Orange," a jungle defolient used during the Vietnam War, proved to be its undoing. Reports of miscarriages, deformities, and increased cancer and disease rates among the Vietnamese populace affected by the spray prompted the U.S. government to ban its use in 1971.[45] Its close relative, 2, 4-D, however, continues in general use by farmers, foresters, road crews, and railroads despite strong evidence that it too is a dangerous cancer causing agent.

Phenoxy herbicides, including 2, 4-D, promote uncontrolled ex-pansion and division of cells. This form of action prompted Pro-fessor J. Van Overbeck to state that the phenoxy herbicides "kill like cancer."[46] They cause normal growth to cease within a few hours following application. Bending of the plant top occurs in a few minutes, and in a few days tumors, secondary roots, and fasciated structures develop.[47] These changes are accompanied by the cessation of division of meristematic cells, plugging of the phloem, inhibition of photosynthesis, reduced ability of roots to absorb water, disrup-tions of the nucleus, and several other plant disturbances.[48]

Although the lethal dosage of 2, 4-D is quite low (a bit more than a teaspoon of the pure chemical is needed to kill an adult), its mutagenic capacity has been underscored by several researchers.[49] Especially dangerous are certain components of these phenoxy herbicides, such as TCDD (tetra-dioxin; one drop can kill 1200 people), one of the components from which 2, 4, 5-T is synthesized. On July 10, 1977, an industrial accident at the Sevesco, Italy, plant released a deadly cloud of TCDD over a local valley, prompting a regional health office in Italy to call it "our own little Hiroshima."[50] Documented human sufferings brought on by 2, 4-D contamination include birth deformities (spina bifida, cleft palate, club foot, hydrocephalus, etc.), cancer, miscarriages, still births, Downs Syndrome (Mongolism), and a host of "less serious" ailments (muscle spasms, muscle pains, numbness, paralysis, vomiting, diarrhea, etc.).[51]

The phenoxy herbicides is only one group of agricultural chemicals used today. Some have been banned from field use altogether, and probably all are carcinogenic. What of the other chemicals in use: the carbamates, acetamides, ureas, triazines, chlorinated hydrocarbons,* organophosphates, and others being synthesized year by year? Is there a better way, the way of nature, which never required a manmade synthetic compound . . . never desired one? Only through man's disruptions of the ecosphere and his concurrent chemical technology has the "need" for them arisen. A return to Edenic conditions will eliminate their need while the entire creation comes into total harmony with the laws designed for plants to grow and animals to live in peace.

The tremendous extent to which plant components may vary has been elucidated by numerous studies. In general, grains vary less in composition than leaf, stem, and root crops. Changes caused by differences in fertilization and crop variety produced the variations in certain components listed in the table below: [52]

---

* D D T has already been banned from most uses.

Crop	Crude protein	Minerals								
		Ash	Ca	P	Cu	K	Mg	Fe	Mn	Na
		5%		mg/kg		%			mg/kg	%
Corn grain (yellow dent)	High	14.1	5.0	0.11	0.50	9.0	0.73	0.90	0.010	54.0	0.06
	Low	8.3	0.9	0.00	0.03	0.9	0.32	0.08	0.002	0.7	0.00
Wheat grain (hard spring)	High	21.8	3.5	0.07	0.68	16.7	—	—	0.008	80.6	0.22
	Low	9.6	1.1	0.03	0.41	9.9	—	—	0.004	33.9	0.00
		Solids %				mg/100g				
Tomatoes (whole)	High	7.5	16.0	41	0.16		492	25	0.56	0.30	5.40
	Low	5.6	3.7	13	0.01		126	7	0.09	0.05	0.84
Sweet corn	High	32.1	9.7	231	0.15		579	90	1.30	0.58	0.45
	Low	21.6	2.0	73	0.03		101	27	0.22	0.06	0.00
Lettuce (iceberg)	High	5.0	24	31	0.09		202	15	0.49	0.41	10.00
	Low	3.9	16	16	0.01		73	7	0.21	0.09	0.58
Cabbage	High	8.8	60	27	0.03		280	23	0.57	0.54	25.0
	Low	7.7	22	12	0.01		140	6	0.16	0.12	2.0
Onions	High	10.4	95	41	0.11		211	17	0.32	0.70	14.00
	Low	8.7	12	17	0.01		114	6	0.09	0.03	0.74
Carrots	High	15.4	65	46	0.26		490	44	1.20	0.83	132
	Low	11.7	29	17	0.02		157	13	0.18	0.06	1

The forces of the environment causing magnitudes of change ranging from nearly zero up to 10-fold or more include a host of soil and climatic factors.* The manipulation of soil fertility, the point of prime concern here, may change the concentration of a plant component in several ways: (1) the "dilution effect"—as yield is increased by ap-

---

* The factors affecting plant composition include the following: soil chemical status (native nutrient levels, applied fertilizers), soil physical status (aeration and compaction, structure, texture, tillage methods and timing), soil microbiological status (organic matter level and type, herbicide and pesticide level and type), season of growth, solar radiation (day length, total radiation and intensity, radiation quality), temperature (air, soil), precipitation (soil moisture level, storm damage, amount and distribution), humidity, wind velocity, altitude, crop maturity, soil and air pollution, storage methods, and plant injury or disease.[53]

plying one soil nutrient, the concentration of one or more plant nutrients may decrease through (a) water dilution (especially from added cell-distending nitrogen) or (b) carbohydrate dilution (for dry seeds, a higher yield usually produces more starch at the expense of everything else); (2) the sum of calcium, magnesium, potassium, and sodium per unit of plant dry matter will tend to be constant, meaning that as one is increased the others are decreased (the same holds true for the anions); (3) an increase or decrease of a nutrient in plant tissues may "interact" and cause variations in the concentration of other plant components.[54]

The complexity of changes in the nutritional quality prompted by genetic and environmental variables is difficult to appreciate. Added to the factors already mentioned affecting composition—and thus nutritional quality—of a crop is the fact that nutrient *balance* is as important as the absolute quantity of nutrients in the diets of animals and men. In general, it may be safely stated that as yield is increased through the effects of fertilizers, climate, and variety, the nutritional value of that increased yield may not be maintained for several plant components.[55]

Can God be trusted, within a millennial environment of optimum climate, soil fertility, and crop genetic types, to cause the growth of food having the very highest nutritional quality possible? As surely as He lives, so will this utopian vision become reality. The puzzle is far too complex for man to search out within his fragmented approach to knowing things. He must look beyond his finite conception of facts to the infinite Designer of natural laws which are designed to produce optimum food quality and health—and learn to harmonize with this system.

Coupled closely with modern soil fertility practices and the use of herbicides and pesticides is the growing of hybrid or genetically altered crops. The admonition of Genesis 1:29 is to eat herbs and fruits bearing seed, which eliminates parasitic plants such as fungi and algae from the diet. One must highly question, however, the practice of crossing two homogeneous parent lines to produce a high yielding hybrid crop. While the second generation of this cross will still produce the same kind, the plants are usually stunted and of great variability. Hybrids have also oftentimes proven to be nutritionally inferior to open-pollinated varieties. As already shown, open-pollinated plant types tend to produce vigorous, nutritious plants naturally adapted to a specific environment. Seedless watermelons are produced through unnatural parental combinations. The seedless navel orange is a mutant that has been vegetatively propagated ever since its discovery, but without seeds it contradicts the Biblical admonition that to be edible it should have seeds; nature would select it out. Seedless variations of normally seeded crops are misfits in every sense of the word. Their nutritional value must be highly questioned.

In the Kingdom the natural process of selection will occur in the various habitats throughout the earth to yield the superbly nutritious crops people desire. Perhaps many of the crops to be grown are not yet even known, for since creation man has progressively selected grain, fruit, vegetable, nut and berry crops primarily for high yields; they have not often been the most nutritious available. Coupled with optimum soil fertility and climate the abundance of delicious, vitality-giving crops literally covering the landscape can hardly be imagined!

In passing, it should be mentioned that Leviticus 19:19 does *not* forbid planting hybrids, which were unknown in the days of the Israelites. This Scripture forbids the planting of two or more "kinds" [Hebrew *kilayim*[56]] of seed in a single field, such as oats and wheat. Companion planting of crops, such as a legume with a grain crop, is probably not forbidden here; rather, similar crops having similar phenologies are most likely implied. The usual reduction in nutritional quality of a hybrid vs. an open-pollinated crop must not be forgotten, however, as well as the viewpoint Almighty God has toward the manipulation and disruption of natural systems.

Foods Eaten Near Where They Are Grown

Because community life in the millennium will be centered in the home, nearly all foods will be consumed at or near their point of origin. The wisdom of this arrangement becomes more apparent than might first meet the eye: tomatoes, grapefruit, cantaloupe, and broccoli will no longer need to be trucked hundreds and thousands of miles, burning precious fuel, to feed the burgeoning population of metropolitan centers. A saving of energy, however, constitutes only part of this unique picture; even more important is the positive nutritional effect that locally grown animals and plants have upon a person. But does this make sense? Is there any proof for such a statement?

Unfortunately, no research has decisively shown an association of improved health and the eating of locally grown produce. However, if God's system of community organization is to exist as presented here, then it follows that locally grown crops *must* produce maximum health and energy for the people. Apparently the combined climate, soils, and plant and animal species for a specific locality are uniquely combined to suit the people living there in the best possible way. This relationship may be illustrated in a general way by relating a study of the late Dr. William Albrecht, a well-known soil scientist from Missouri, with the effects of climate on human metabolism. In 1947 he showed how the carbohydrate content of plants tends to be higher in the more humid southern regions of the country, while protein and mineral fractions of plants tend to be higher in the irrigated arid and semi-arid regions.[57] One year later the renowned soil chemist Firman E. Bear carried the thrust of Albrecht's investigation one step further by studying changes in the composition of the same varieties of cabbage, lettuce, snapbeans, spinach, and tomatoes from Georgia to New York along the Eastern seaboard, and from Ohio to Colorado through the prairie states.[58] Bear's findings are summarized in Figure 41. In general, the mineral and protein content of crops increase moving both north and west. With grain as well, protein and mineral content increase toward the drier, cooler climates of the northern Plains, while low protein (high starch) grains are typical of the South and East.*

---

* The tremendous effect of weather conditions on grain protein has probably never been revealed more conclusively than during a USDA study from 1905 to 1908. Using the same variety in Kansas and California, "in Kansas, the percentage of protein varied from 16.2 in 1905 to 22.2 in 1907, due to the excessive drought in 1907, falling to 14.7 in 1908, which was a comparatively wet year. The drought of 1907 caused the crop to shrivel, the weight per bushel decreasing from 58.8 pounds in 1906 to 51.3 in 1907. Moreover, the same change took place in every sample of wheat grown in Kansas, whether from Kansas, from California, or from Texas seed. . . . Kansas wheat contained as much as 22.8 percent of protein while the California wheat contained only 11.7 percent."[60]

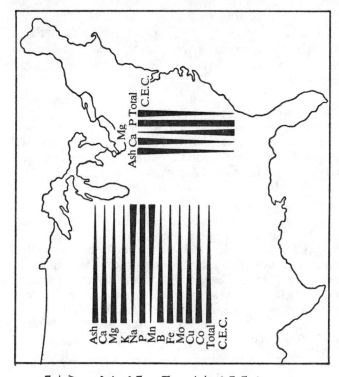

(1) P values tended to remain relatively constant, but wide variations were found in the same variety of vegetable.

(2) Greatest variations in K, Na, B, and Fe values were found in spinach.

(3) Greatest variations in Ca, Mg, and Cu values were found in tomatoes.

(4) Snapbeans from Ohio westward were relatively very high in Mo.

(5) Colorado vegetables, in comparison with those from the other states, were relatively high in Co, Mo, Fe, Ca, K, Mg, Cu, and B, in the order indicated; about average in P; and relatively low in Mn and Na.

Figure 41. Growing identical varieties of several vegetables across the country revealed that the protein and mineral contents of the crops tended to increase as drier and cooler climates were encountered.

Corresponding to the drier, cooler climates of the higher latitudes—those which encourage higher protein and mineral levels of crops, and which assist in body building and the maintenance of high energy levels—is the typical active, stimulating individual of these climates. The association is no accident. According to Bruce Palmer in *Body Weather,*

> As mean air temperatures cool, permitting easy loss of body heat, all animal growth tends to be rapid, with the young maturing quickly and body weight, height, and muscle mass combining in robust, round forms. Fertility is typically early and easy. Infants are born in large numbers; stillbirth and infant mortality rates are low. . . . Overall, temperate zone animals tend to live shorter lives than their tropical counterparts. Again, this is as true of men as it is of mice.
>
> Anthropologists, explorers, medical scientists, and zoologists have repeatedly observed that animal life is more active in cool climates than in the tropics. Humans born in temperate zones are demonstrably bigger—that is, both taller and heavier—than tropic zone humans. When humans are able to lose excess body heat, they can generate more heat to replace the loss. Available energy produced can be tapped in the form of work or vigorous play. The individual feels good, vital, and energetic. He tends to behave like it, full of noise and good humor and exhibiting an activity level he could not sustain in the hot, moist climate of the tropics.[61]

The relationship is indeed valid. Of course, the inheritance of tribes and individuals accounts for some observed differences in activity. Tropical and subtropical climates support populations unable to match the energy of mind and body of temperate regions. Bananas, pineapples, papaya, passion fruit, sugar cane, cassava, and other starchy or sweet fruits and vegetables support this less vigorous activity; they eminently suit the reduced metabolic rate of a warm, humid, constant climate. Northern and temperate climates with their reduced humidity, cooler temperatures, and much more stormy weather patterns demand an energetic body, one best fed on high protein grains, vegetables, and fruits. A high concentration of calcium, magnesium, phosphorus, and many minor elements in foods further bolster stamina and vitality.

Besides these general trends in climate as related to available food and human needs, perhaps each locality is "fine tuned" in its available food and its unique composition for that particular soil and climate, all in the interest of nurturing maximum health for human beings. This may well be true for the pristine, natural condition of the land, a condition long since lost in most of North America. The wisdom of transporting foods grown in tropic areas for consumption in temperate areas, or vice-versa, may thus be seriously challenged.

The American Indians out of necessity consumed foods within their areas of wandering (for the nomadic Plains tribes) or at their dwellings (for the mountain tribes). Figure 42 illustrates six generalized groupings of the Indians based upon the foods they ate, foods readily available and easily killed, cultivated, or gathered. It is of considerable interest to note that the physical condition and longevity of most Indians, when wholly subsisting on a native diet, was remarkably superb. Centenarians were not uncommon. Contacts with the white man's diet and horse initiated his precipitous downfall, resulting in the common misconception among many of today's Anglo-Saxons that the Indians were always a degenerate race of people. Of course, they have not wholly retrogressed today, though few of them maintain the vitality their forbears did. Perhaps white men are in a similar condition.

It is interesting that the so-called "macrobiotic diet" complements the ideas already given. This diet has been termed "an individual interpretation of what might be the harmonious diet for any one given climatic and geographical area. Therefore, the diet and food varies infinitely according to location and season."[63] One of the seven suggestions given regarding diet is the following:

Choose foods which grow and thrive naturally in your local area and eat them in season. Avoid foods which are imported from exotic places* and foods which do not and cannot grow in your climatic region. These foods are not suited for you.[64]

* The woman in Proverbs 31:14 who "fetches food-stuffs from afar" does not necessarily violate this principle. Foods procured "from afar" in Palestine would likely still be grown within the Mediterranean climatic region.

Figure 42. The food areas of the American Indians paralleled what was native and readily available to them.[62]

Fasting for Health

Fasting was a major part of Christ's program of living, one that will become a crucial part of the lives of people during the Kingdom. The 40-days of fasting observed by Christ (Matt. 4:2), Moses (Ex. 24:18; 34:28), and Elijah (I Kings 19:8) were not typical of the shorter fasts of other historic characters such as David, who fasted for seven days when Bathsheba's child was ill (II Sam. 12:16-18), Ahab (I Kings 21:29), and the whole nation of Israel (I Sam. 31:13). Usually fasting is associated with times of great decisions and *spiritual need,* such as bereavement, physical affliction, or humiliation.

The physical benefits of fasting have also been expounded by numerous individuals such as Paul Bragg, who claims restored health, vigor, and mental perception with wise fasting.[65] The body naturally fasts when disease strikes. Perhaps with perfect health for all people during the millennium, derived in part from foods having optimum nutritional value, fasting will become a practice perfectly dictated by the appetite, just as selection of food, the amount eaten, and when it is eaten ought to ideally be guided by an appetite in tune with nature.

The Laws of Diet

The overall laws of Godly diet may be simply summarized: (1) eat foods fresh, (2) eat unprocessed foods, (3) eat unpolluted foods, (4) eat with moderation only when hungry, and chew well, (5) eat a balanced diet, guided by a properly trained appetite, (6) select those foods which are included within God's dietary limits, and (7) eat with enjoyment!* Perhaps the millennial setting will also include a sitting

---

* Dr. T. L. Cleave has reduced the rules of diet to just two: (1) do not eat any foods unless you definitely want it—don't give in to the desire to eat routinely or when overtired or worried, because someone has gone to the trouble of preparing a meal, or because the social or business occasion demands your eating (the decision is always made most accurately before coming to the table); (2) avoid eating white flour and white or brown sugar—avoid white bread, pastry, cakes, biscuits, confectionery, jams, ices, chocolates, sweets, and sweet drinks, but rather use true wholemeal bread and wholemeal flour, and raw or dried fruit.[66]

or reclining posture while eating, as was customary with Jesus, the apostles, and other Middle Easterners.[67] How joyous and simple it will be to walk across a lush green meadow to pick delicious and juicy apples or peaches from heavily fruited trees, or to harvest plentiful cabbages, turnips, carrots, and berries among the trees and grass. The millennium holds this and much more in store for a land peopled with humble, thankful folks to whom He freely gives.

Flavor and Taste—Guides to Proper Eating

The human senses, especially those of taste and smell, have been designed to detect and savor those foods which one ought to eat. We tend to relish sweet foods, which in reality is a God-implanted craving since fruits and vegetables high in sugar also tend to be high in life-essential minerals and vitamins. Scientists are keenly aware of the fact that animals have instinctive abilities to balance their diets when provided an array of palatable foods. Could it be that people also possess a similar mechanism to assist in the choice of proper foods; e.g., the proverbial pregnant woman craving pickles or watermelon at midnight?

According to one source, "The level of water soluble phosphate in the soil is directly proportional to the sugar content of the crop. The higher the sugar content, the higher the mineral content."[68]

This profound ability of the human palate to discriminate between nutritious and unwholesome food on the basis of taste is a wonderful adjunct to healthful living . . . in the absence of a food processing industry, that is. Food makers know very well the sales enhancement of adding sugars (sucrose or glucose) to their products, be they canned peas or corn, corn flakes, or salad dressing.* The natural proclivity of

---

* For example, the sugar (sucrose) contents of several breakfast cereals are extremely high, even though natural grains contain very little sucrose:[69]

Kelloggs Apple Jacks	52.4%
Post Fruity Pebbles	48.51%
Quaker King Vitaman	42.40%
Post Super Sugar Crisps	42.16%
Quaker Cap'n Crunch	39.09%

the palate to savor sweetness—and concurrently gain the needed health-giving minerals and vitamins—thus becomes perverted. The tongue cannot distinguish between the built-in sweetness of canned corn and added sweetness from the canning factory. Added sugar deceives the senses into believing the food is good, when in reality it has most likely been grown through fertilization practices designed to maximize yield, meaning the soil has been loaded with nitrogen which has produced a high yielding, watery product, with minerals and vitamins diluted accordingly. Sweetness in a natural system implies nutritional value; the consumer is deceived into believing the nutritional value is present when it is not. The terms "empty calories" and "foodless foods" take on increased significance. The sense of taste discrimination becomes the victim of modern profiteering industries that place dollars before health (see I Tim. 6:10), even though health is a priceless possession.

Sweetness is only one of the taste senses man possesses. He also has taste buds which detect bitter, sour, and salty flavors. Since childhood, however, sweetness of the diet becomes the overriding force dictating what and how much he eats. In a book entitled *Taste and Development, the Genesis of Sweet Preference,* it is revealed that newborn infants consumed more and more solution as the sweetness increased, especially when sucrose and fructose were added.[70] As the child grows he becomes accustomed to the sucrose-laden diet presented to him—candy bars, chewing gum, sweet rolls, sugared cereals, and soft drinks—a diet guaranteed to bequeath to him a host of ills already described.

Kellogs Frosted Flakes	39.07%
General Mills Trix	37.27%
Kellogs Cracklin Bran	27.50%
Nabisco 100% Bran	19.77%
C. W. Post	18.20%
Quaker 100% Natural	17.09%
Post Raisin Bran	12.97%
Kelloggs Rice Krispies	8.62%
Wheaties	8.60%
Cheerios	3.07%

The biomedical hazards of the increased use of sugars is indicated by one interesting line of animal research which showed that if rats are allowed one hour per day to eat, they can properly regulate body weight. However, if a sucrose solution is available concurrently with the food, rapid weight loss and even death occur in about three weeks.[71] Animals drink the sucrose solution and fail to eat enough food in the hour to sustain life, emphasizing the continuity between overindulgence and addiction.

Human beings act much like rats and mice in selecting their diets, unless they use intellectual power to overcome degenerative human tendencies. Michele Bremer at the University of Massachusetts in 1975 conducted a feeding experiment with 600 mice, comparing a reasonably typical, standard American diet with a natural foods diet. A control group was fed a commercial animal formula. Miss Bremer's results are highly interesting:

> Results showed that the animals consuming the standard American diet (the 'supermarket group') had a high incidence of obesity and significantly more body fat than the other two groups. (No obesity was noted in the other two groups). In addition, the supermarket group seemed to have considerably less resistance to a staphylococcal infection which affected all three groups to some extent. The general physical condition of the supermarket group seemed inferior to both the natural foods group and the control group, which enjoyed the best health of all three groups.

> When given free choice, animals of all three diets displayed an overwhelming preference for the supermarket diet, even though their health deteriorated when they consumed it for a period of three weeks.[72]

Apparently the sensory mechanisms of animals are so fine-tuned that a difference of only 0.1% sugar can be detected between different lots of the same crop.[73] The cow, sheep, or horse will always eat the sweeter lot. Pasture management techniques aimed at complementing natural laws that encourage the production of high sugar, high mineral vegetation result in a reduced need for feeding grains to cattle in order to promote rapid weight gains, since the animals will obtain more of the gain-enhancing carbohydrates from the grass.[74]

Additional benefits besides enhanced health accrue from an increased sugar content of the crop. Keeping times of vegetables and fruits are oftentimes increased, such as experienced by Dr. Carey Reams, who kept three watermelons in his office for three years while he watched them gradually dehydrate to hard lumps, not a one of them spoiling.[75] High sugar levels of foods are well known to aid in food preservation. A higher sugar content of plant tissues also tends to reduce vulnerability to frost damage due to a reduction of the freezing point of water containing more dissolved ions. Insects are apparently less apt to attack plants possessing higher sugar contents, a point substantiated by observations that plants having increased protein levels (and thus less of everything else, including sugars) through added synthetic nitrogen or herbicides, are more susceptible to insect and microbiological attack.[76] The composition of plants as created and grown within the bounds of natural laws established from creation—and raised within an environment replete with a full complement of predator insects, microorganisms, amiable weather conditions, and no pollutants—lead to no devastation from insects and plant diseases. A harmony must exist between various plant components and the insects and microbes whose task it is to eliminate the weak and sickly.*

---

* Faulkner proposed a similar theory to explain why plants grown in fertile, native soils are disease and insect resistant. The decomposition of mineral and organic matter releases plant foods that in tilled soils may be lost through leaching or erosion. The only certain way to prevent this loss is to have roots of growing plants always present when decomposition is occurring in the soil, as in undisturbed natural soils of forests and grasslands. " . . . the more decaying material there is in the soil, the richer the solution these roots pick up will be; the richer the soil solution carried in by the roots, the richer in minerals the plant sap will be . . . variations in the richness of the plant sap may affect the attractiveness of the plant for its customary parasites. . . . Possibly cucumber beetles, for example, could be starved for lack of palatable juices, even when their host plant is enjoying the richest possible food from the decay in progress in the soil. . . . Further, it appears that the environment that is best for the disease and the insect is poorest for the host plant; and the conditions that favor the host plant's development are intolerable for insects and diseases."[77]

Perhaps few people have stopped to consider the nutritional consequences of the oftentimes inferior flavor of today's large-sized produce. Native apples, pears, grapefruit, plums, cherries, strawberries,
and most other fruits were noticeably smaller before plant breeders
commenced to select for size. These larger fruits are often pulpy and
bland, lacking the pungent, crisp, flavorful fleshness of the native
varieties. In a discussion on the subject of size and flavor, Kurup
made the statement, " . . . there is no better index of the quality of a
fruit or vegetable than its flavour."[78] He added, " . . . it appears as
if the fruit quality as indicated by its flavour and fruit size are nearly
inversely related."[79]

No farm boy who has stopped at a favorite wild plum tree and
eaten of the small but incredibly tasty fruit in early summer will dare
argue that larger store-bought plums are better. Neither will the large
breeds of strawberries surpass the delectable, tart sweetness of small
wild berries. It seems as if the craving for bigger and bigger size in
most everything—buildings, cities, corporations, farm tractors, or
GNP—has been generalized into the minds of plant breeders and
agronomists that "bigger means better," whether one is dealing with
fruit or vegetable size or crop yields.

God's way again proves to be far superior to man's. His quest for
the development of quality in mankind entails the enhancement of
humility (becoming "low" or "small") at the expense of pride
(becoming "big" or "puffed up"). He is a champion of the poor and
oppressed, the downtrodden, the orphan, and the widow (Prov.
14:21; Isa. 5:15)—those under economic hardship who find humility
easier to come by. In like manner, the smaller, more humble
creations of nature oftentimes possess the highest quality, be they apples, plums, blueberries, or cattle. A Jersey cow may produce half
or less what a larger Holstein can, but her milk is richer and more
satisfying. Bigger is usually not better; rather, the smaller things of
nature are oftentimes packed with much nutritional power to "lift
up" the body.

"So shall the last be first and the first last" (Matt. 20:16).
"He sets the lowly on a height, and helps the forlorn to victory" (Job
5:11).
"Whoever humbles himself like this child, he is the greatest in the
Realm of heaven" (Matt. 18:4).

Sunlight, Fresh Air, and Clean Earth

Diet alone is not enough to preserve a body in health, today or during the future. However, it will briefly be shown below that the agrarian way of living which has been envisioned to exist during the millennium will of its own accord facilitate obedience to all seven laws of radiant health.

Within a society where outdoor life will be the rule, no lack of sunlight or fresh air will occur. The air will be pollution free and mountain fresh! Prescott, Arizona, reputed to be the "Climate Capital of Arizona," claims the following in a Chamber of Commerce bulletin:

> Prescott takes pride in the enviable reputation she enjoys in the relief of asthma, especially in children. . . . Here in the light mountain air, surrounded by the pine clad forests and the mountains, they have found rest, peace, and happiness. They can breathe in Prescott . . . . 93 percent have found 100 percent relief.[80]

Sunlight is likewise essential for proper functioning of the body; several effects upon the body and organs involved are indicated in Figure 43. In addition, the Takata reaction, a sudden rise in the blood albumin level, is a reaction tied in women to the monthly menstrual cycle, and in men to solar flare activity which alters the magnetic field of the earth.[82]

John Ott, noted father of time lapse photography and author of *Health and Light,* suffered from arthritis in his hips and elbow during the peak of his illustrious career. He tried tinkering with diet, vitamin therapy, hot baths, and injections of glandular extracts, only to find little relief. When he accidently broke his sunglasses, and worked outside in full sunlight, however, his symptoms abruptly improved. First his elbow no longer bothered him, and then his hip condition eased, so much so in fact that he could discard his cane.[83] Other improvements began to mark his life: periodic colds and sore throats decreased markedly in number and severity, and his eyesight improved so much that his oculist, thinking a mistake had been made, recalled him for a second examination.

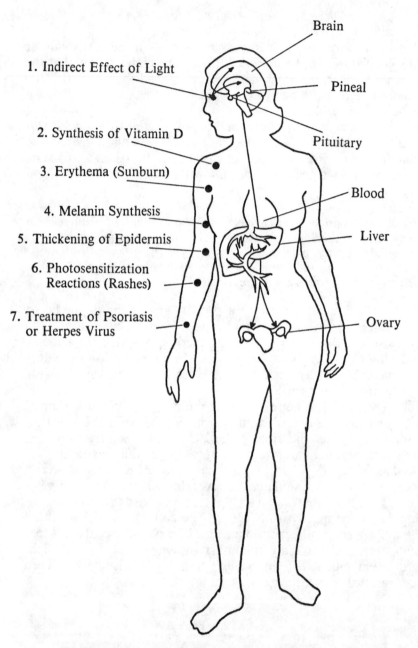

Figure 43. Some direct and indirect effects of light on the human body

Lots of indirect, unfiltered sunlight helped work a remarkable recovery for John Ott. It will also assist in the maintenance of exuberant health in a world of supreme climate and agrarian, outdoor living during the millennium. The positioning of the water canopy above the atmosphere will doubtlessly improve light quality as the earth is restored to the Edenic condition. Humidity will increase and erase the cold, dry winters and parched desert conditions extant over large areas of the earth, for a mist will water the surface of the earth. The healing properties of adding steam to the rooms of those having respiratory ailments during winter of cold continental climates are known by many.

A totally clean environment—air, land, lakes, streams, and oceans—will mean additional health benefits. Few of the modern generation have experienced the joy of kneeling beside a crystal-clear stream or lake and drinking deeply during a hot summer day, without worrying that a deathly disease might lurk in the waters. Perhaps just a few have imagined bathing in a lake or stream without having to later wash off the accumulated grime. In the Kingdom *every* stream and lake will be pristine and pure, untainted, and lifegiving (see Rev. 22:1), teeming with fish, never muddied through erosion-conducive tillage practices. Well water will no longer be threatened with leaching nitrates.

Physical Conditioning, Rest, and
Freedom from Accidents

Since animal and human power will be primary energy sources, physical conditioning will be part and parcel with daily living, entwined within the very fabric of agrarian existence. A great many Americans are plagued today by sedentary lives which contribute to physical and mental illness, when pent-up physical energy is not able to be dissipated in the form of useful work. Pressures build and bodies ache while sitting endless hours.

God's way is to "do whatever your hand finds to do with your might" (Eccl. 9:10). Likewise, " . . . a diligent man is a rare treasure," and "Go to the ant, you sluggard . . . " (Prov. 6:6). Solomon stated in Proverbs 21:25-26, "A lazy man's ease in his undoing . . . while the good man works on unceasing." At the same time balance and moderation in all things are advocated as a fruit of the Spirit (Gal. 5:23), not "workaholism" which is so prevalent today but which also inhibits the attainment of full, vibrant living.

Many Americans have taken up jogging, tennis, basketball, handball, or cycling as a means to overcome the pitfalls of the sedentary life. Yet, as enjoyable as these and other sports might be, they overlook the one most common form of physical activity that will occur in the Kingdom: *walking*. The Hunzakut people of Kashmir provide perhaps the best current example of physical stamina imbued through daily walking that will be enjoyed during the coming age.

> The Hunzakut people are the best proof that walking is beneficial. They walk for miles every day, since they have no vehicles. Their fields are usually quite far from their homes and as a rule located on hillsides. Then men also travel from village to village, 10 to 15 miles each way, and some of them walk to Gilgit, 68 miles from Baltit, their capital. This is done in one stretch, and if they return home in the daytime, they go about their work as though they have just come from taking a nap.[84]

Current findings by medical authorities concur with the fact, known for centuries by the Hunzas, that walking is extremely beneficial:

> . . . after all these years of research, several groups of scientists and doctors are telling us that an excellent way to protect against heart disease is something as simple as . . . *walking. Not* jogging. Running, either. It isn't that those forms of mega-walking aren't good for you; they just aren't necessary. They're overkill.
>
> Until very recently, it was widely thought walking was a nice thing to do if you didn't expect too much from it. . . . Now we know different. . . . 'Metabolically speaking,' Dr. Steja [a California endocrinologist] told us, 'walking is as good as jogging. To favorably alter cholesterol, to lower sugar, insulin, and triglycerides, and to lose weight, walking will do it. I expect it would lower blood pressure as well.'[85]

"Bodily exercise profits for a little time" (I Tim. 4:8), meaning that the routine of exercise must be repeated daily or every few days to maintain physical conditioning. Will not guiding an ox across a field, walking to a neighbor's house or to a nearby town, or playing vigorous games fulfill this requirement?

With fulfilling work comes rewarding rest: "Sweet is the worker's sleep, whether he has much to eat or little . . . " (Eccl. 5:12). God's entire message accentuates life and the living, not the third of one's life taken up by sleep . . . as important as that third is. Solomon admonished the Israelites to "Love not sleep, lest you fall into poverty: waken, and you will have ample food" (Prov. 20:13).

Another law of health, the prevention of accidents, will find its perfect fulfillment during the Kingdom when peace, harmony, and all the fruits of God's Spirit will reign supreme. No longer will contentions smolder and erupt between men, or dangerous factory work be tolerated. Machines will be designed to complement people's work but never replace it, leaving people in charge of machines, not vice-versa as is so often the case today. Automobile transportation, which snuffs out about 50,000 lives each year, will be replaced by foot or animal travel. War and its cruel warping pain and death for soldiers and civilians will no longer be known (Micah 4:3).

Animals will take on a new nature and no longer be dangerous to people; they will become mild and friendly, to people and to each other: " . . . the infant shall play at the hole of an asp, with the baby's feet at the nest of a viper. None shall injure, none shall kill . . . " (Isa. 11:8-9). No longer will a bull be prone to gore a person, causing injury or death (Ex. 21:28). Speaking of Israel in the latter days, Hosea painted this picture of peace and safety to enfold the entire earth:

> On that day I will make a league for them, with the wild beasts and birds and creeping things of earth; and I will wipe out of their land bow, sword, and all munitions, to let them lie down in security (Hosea 2:18).

Attitudes: Guideposts to Health

A world bereft of fear is, to many, an impossibility, a giant fairy tale. The fear of death and of where one's food, clothing, and other necessities will come from is a constant, dismal cloud hanging over the heads of billions of people across the world. Yet, amid the travail in the world Jesus Christ said, "Seek God's riches and his goodness, and

all that [food, clothing, etc.] will be yours over and above" (Matt.
6:33). Clearly, Christ pictured death as an enemy, for through the
apostle Paul He stated that "Death is the last foe to put down" (I
Cor. 15:26), a death certain to overtake all people ever since Adam
and Eve first sinned in the Garden of Eden. John also stated
" . . . perfect love casts off fear," for perfect love embodies the un-
dying hope of eternal life . . . and living the Godly life which casts
aside fear in the present. Only a resurrection to immortality can now
save mankind from the bonds of corruption to which his flesh is tied
(I Cor. 15:50-57).

The way of sin and death (Rom. 3:23) which all men have followed
(Rom. 6:23) to one degree or another is the source of all evil which
men perpetrate on themselves and others. Proceeding from this way
of sin come the "deeds of the flesh," including "sexual vice, impuri-
ty, sensuality, idolatry, magic, quarrels, dissention, jealousy, temper,
rivalry, factions, party-spirit, envy, murder, drinking bouts, revelry,
and the like" (Gal. 5:19-21). It is this way of the flesh that S. I.
McMillen in *None of These Diseases* outlines as being the root cause
of many of our diseases. Emotions such as fear, sorrow, envy, resent-
ment, and hatred are responsible for from 60 to nearly 100% of our
illnesses, depending on the authority one quotes. This highly
respected physician remarks,

> Emotional stress can cause high blood pressure, toxic goiter, migraine
> headaches, arthritis, apoplexy [stroke], heart trouble, gastrointestinal
> ulcers, and other serious diseases too numerous to mention. As physi-
> cians we can prescribe medicine for the symptoms of these diseases,
> but we cannot do much for the underlying cause—emotional
> turmoil. . . .[86]

The case of a refined, highly educated patient fraught with severe
emotional problems points up a typical problem case. The patient did
not respond to psychiatric counseling, and her psychosomatic symptoms persisted. The doctor projected that at least a year would be
needed before the patient's mental life could be set in order and the
psychic slivers removed. Yet, a few days following this diagnosis the
woman walked into the doctor's office and informed him that her
troubles were over:

... the things she had assured me a few days previously she 'could never do' had all been done, that everything I had asked her to do as a part of her 'cure' had been set in operation—she had completely overhauled her social, family, and personal life, had made numerous 'confessions,' and had accomplished a score of almost impossible mental and 'moral' stunts.[87]

When asked how she made such a dramatic change in less than one week, she smilingly replied, "Dr. Lena taught me to pray."[88] She had experienced immediate healing and the promise of Jesus expressed in John 14:27: "Peace I leave with you, my peace I give unto you: not as the world giveth, give I unto you. Let not your heart be troubled, neither let it be afraid."

The sage advice of Dr. John Schindler in his book *How to Live 365 Days a Year* on how to overcome the fear-ridden anxieties and downward pulls of the fleshly nature—which Paul states "is all I can manage" despite his desire to do good (Rom. 7:21)—is summed up in six simple points[89] . . . points that closely parallel God's own way of love expressed throughout the Bible:

1. Give more than your share of love to others.
2. Do not add worry to a bad situation; run up emotionally healthy flags on your masthead.
3. Use creative expression; nothing is holding you back.
4. Give recognition to other people; some of it will come back.
5. Go out and get new experiences; be planning something all the time.
6. If you have lost self-esteem, recall that you are just as good as the next person.

When God's Kingdom is established and fills all the earth, problems will still exist. However, unlike in this present age, God's *knowledge* and *wisdom* of how to cope with these problems will also exist. Conditions which could potentially lead to debilitating diseases stemming from anger, fear, sorrow, and other emotions will not strike people down. Instead, true to the words of Solomon that "grief is better than gaiety, for sadness does the soul good" (Eccl. 7:3), they will build them up. A poet once said, "Sorrows are our best educators. A man can see farther through a tear than through a telescope."[90] Building character from sorrow and grief is an ongoing process that will not end as long as man is physical, even though the

Kingdom will reign in all of its majesty. Only when a new heaven and new earth become realities, when the Father's dwelling place is with men, will God "wipe every tear from their eyes, and death shall be no more—no more wailing, no more crying, no more pain . . . " (Rev. 21:4).

The Wisdom of God-plane Genetic Counseling

Why did God require that no person marry a close relative? In Leviticus 18 the Eternal spoke to Moses saying that a man was not to marry his mother, sister, daughter, aunt, daughter-in-law, a woman and her daughter or granddaughter, a sister-in-law, or a neighbor's wife. Aside from the prohibitions relating to chastity within marriage, most of these unions would mate two closely related individuals. Any children born to such close relatives would run a greatly increased risk of death through the expression of a lethal gene.*

The Eternal knew very well the degenerative effects such incestuous practices were having among the Canaanites and the Egyptians. These illicit relationships, probably common before the Flood (Gen. 6:2), also began shortly after the Flood when Nimrod married his mother Semiramis and fathered Horus, a renowned Egyptian ruler.[91] Inbreeding among the kingly Egyptian lines is well known, along with the gross distortions of bodily form so evident from drawings on the walls of ancient Egyptian tombs.

In order for lethal genes to be deadly they must become homozygous within a diploid individual (i.e., at the specified site along the double-stranded, or diploid, chromosome, both of the strands must contain the lethal gene). Since humans are diploid, each parent must contribute the lethal gene. If one parent happens to carry a particular lethal gene, the chances of a close relative carrying the gene are greatly increased compared to a non-relative. If close relatives carrying the same lethal gene marry and bear a child, the chances of the child dying due to the gene's expression are then one in four.

---

* A lethal gene is a gene on a chromosome that, when expressed, results in the death of the organism. Death usually occurs before or at birth, but may occur later as well.[92]

To illustrate the greatly increased probability of expressing a lethal gene from the marriage of close relatives, suppose that first cousins marry. The lethal gene is for a skeletal abnormality that causes death during birth as defective bones are crushed and injure vital organs. This gene occurs in one out of every 5,000 persons. Unrelated mates would end up having a child dying from this deformity only one time in 20,000. The first cousins, however, have *one chance in 16* if both have the same grandparents![93]

God's rule of forbidding Israelites from marrying Canaanites or certain other foreign people was primarily to discourage the worship of false gods, gods which the wife would continue to worship in her new household and eventually lead the entire nation into idolatry (Ex. 34:16). The foremost example of the powerful effect wives may have on enticing a man's heart from the true God is found in I Kings 11:1-6:

> Now Solomon was a lover of women . . . . He married many foreign women—Moabites, Ammonites, Edomites, Phoenicians, and Hittites—belonging to nations against whom the Eternal had warned the men of Israel, 'You must not mix with them, nor let them mix with you, for they will be sure to seduce you to follow their gods. . . .' His wives seduced him to follow foreign gods.

Allowance was made for the marriage of a soldier to a beautiful captive woman. The restrictions on such a marriage were quite stringent, however, and she was free to leave her new mate under certain conditions.

The preservation of racial purity is a major object within God's directives, beginning with Noah (and before)* and extending down

---

* Genesis 6:2 implies rampant intermarriage among different peoples and races when it says, " . . . they took them wives [women] of all which they chose." God's disapproval of this practice, along with the wickedness of men (v. 5), prompted Him to announce the Flood that would destroy all men from the earth (v. 7). It is interesting to note that in Genesis 6:8-9 Noah found favor in God's sight because he was *without blemish* (Hebrew tamin[94]) as to breed or pedigree. All flesh was corrupted in pedigree except Noah's family: " . . . for all flesh had corrupted his way [of purity of lineage] upon the earth" (Gen. 6:12).

through the line of Abraham, Isaac, Jacob, and Jacob's 12 sons. The tribes of Jacob were encouraged to maintain their genetic integrity due to geographical positioning of the tribes in the Promised Land; at the very least, Israelites were expected to marry Israelites (Ex. 34:16; Deut. 7:3-4; I Chron. 23:22; Ezra 9:1-2, 12; Neh. 10:30; 13:26-27; Mal. 2:11). Under the New Covenant the admonition of Paul for spiritual Israelites to marry spiritual Israelites perfectly parallels Old Covenant teaching (I Cor. 7:39).

Reasons beyond the strictly spiritual implications of forbidding extra-tribal marriage may have much to do with God's desire to retain specific abilities within the various races and clans of people. Nations have been described as "families grown big," each noted for one or more peculiar traits inherited from the original parents: Germans are known for their mechanical ingenuity and militaristic spirit, the Japanese for their innovative skills, the Italians for their volatile spirit, the Norwegians for their straight-laced morality, and the Russians for an impassive, bearlike character.

Within a nation such as Israel, comprised of several clans, the separation of heritable traits within the clans would serve very well to enhance overall national strength as these abilities complemented one another. A maintenance of integrity for these skills down through the generations was probably originally intended by God, since Jacob's death-bed prophecy to his twelve sons in Genesis 49 includes general traits possessed by their progeny. The Levites were gifted in talents that qualified them to minister to the religious duties of the nation. They tended to be good musicians, scholars, and teachers. The Jews tended toward excellence in business and finance, and many have to this very day been at the forefront of the business and banking fields. The sons of Joseph, Ephraim and Manasseh, were to be extremely prolific, excellent at overspreading the fairer portions of the earth and defending themselves against their enemies. The other tribes likewise possessed identifying traits.

The great Master Geneticist, who created all nations from a common origin, "fixing their alloted periods and the boundaries of their abodes" (Acts 17:26), can be utterly trusted as the perfect guide to whom all people and nations may come for direction. Current trends in society encouraging interracial marriage can only be a product of

Satan, the adversary of God's ordered plan, whose own diabolical plot is bent on destroying the joy and fulfillment that all may experience through coming into full harmony with the Creator.

What Is the Nature of Disease and Healing?

Health is defined as "the condition of being sound in body, mind, or soul, especially freedom from disease or pain."[95] *Disease,* on the other hand, means "an impairment of the normal state of the living animal or plant body that affects the performance of the vital functions; a particular instance or kind of such impairment."[96] Since health is a foremost desire of every normal human being, and disease means the partial or complete absence of it, then the definition of what disease is—its nature—becomes incredibly important; for based on the definition of its nature comes its treatment.

Modern medical science treats the symptoms of disease through the sale of services or prescription drugs. Little attention is generally paid to the causes of these maladies, for little incentive exists to encourage their disappearance. Without ill people patronizing clinics and hospitals a large number of doctors, nurses, administrators, and allied industrial personnel manufacturing drugs and medical equipment would find themselves looking elsewhere for work. Long years of medical training and internships have oftentimes brought lucrative incomes . . . not that most people in the medical field are not dedicated, overworked, resourceful, and well-intended participants in the medical business. The problem is that they are just human, subject to the same sheep-like tendencies of all other humans. In the case of medical practitioners, the tendency to become like other medical practitioners carries with it a great deal of job security and professional status, ultra-strong pulls which will not serve to jolt a person out of his present frame of reference except through some powerful outside force.

Moreover, as F. I. Scott states in *American Laboratory,*

Neither do I mean to impugn business. It can be, though it is not always, an admirable extension of the social contract. Someone who becomes skilled in certain activities barters that skill or exchanges it for coins of the realm to obtain goods and services from others skilled in appropriate activities. The seller may tout those goods and services and certainly implies the warrantability of them. However, there is no appeal to ideological rightness or superiority such as suggested by the term *professional* which, though entirely secular in meaning now, retains the aura of dedication to higher (religious) principles than the aggrandizement of one's personal assets. It is the fuzzy melding of *business* and *profession* and the legalization of its monopoly [the American Medical Association] that rigidifies the medical business and nullifies its good intentions.[97]

The ideal of society possessing a class of physicians totally bent upon eliminating their jobs is, in the present era, an untenable ideal. Yet, one scientist has advocated this very thing! Speaking of science as a whole, but medical science specifically, he stated,

> The idea of working diligently to abolish one's job is an intriguing one and should be examined closely by most of us . . . after centuries of sheer guesswork and the crudest sort of empiricism, medicine began to recognize that almost all of the complicated treatments then available for disease did not work and that most of them did more harm than good, but then began evolving into an art and now toward a science. All of this progress, however, has not discernibly lowered our ignorance. Though still confused, it seems to me, we are confused on a higher level about more important things.[98]

Satan is the author of confusion (I Cor. 14:33) and the father of lies (John 8:44), the god of this present world system (II Cor. 4:4). He is the one responsible for the present dilemma of sickness in the world, for as a law breaker he has led the entire world down that same pathway: breaking physical laws that lead to physical illnesses and eventually death. Medical science, the established, multi-billion dollar health-related industry in this age, by its very nature which treats symptoms through drugs, radiation, and surgery, is Satan's science. It is the antithesis of God's system of healing which relies upon faith in God, not on mere men (doctors).

Rather than further impugn the symptom-oriented medical system of today, one ought to instead take the approach of Jesus Christ and get at the root *cause* of disease . . . and cast it out. Thomas Edison was on the right track when he suggested that some day physicians would not administer drugs and medicines but would teach patients how to live so as to avoid illness.⁹⁹ It is obvious that physicians themselves are not personally to be condemned, for Luke, one of Christ's chosen apostles, was termed "the beloved physician" (Col. 4:14). *How* they practice is of utmost importance. A man such as Luke, having God's Spirit, would understand that only God has the power to heal through the restorative powers placed within the body at creation. The proverb, "Physician, heal yourself" (Luke 4:23), was stated by Christ in direct opposition to the notion that a doctor is able of his own power to bring health to a broken body.

God heals. He is called the *rapha,* or "healer": " . . . for I am the Lord that healeth thee" (Ex. 15:26). He stated that

> If you will listen carefully to the voice of the Eternal, your God, and do what is right in his eyes and pay heed to his commands and follow all his rules, then the Eternal promises never to afflict upon you any of the diseases he inflicted on the Egyptians (Ex. 15:26).

John restated this desire of good health when he said, "Beloved, I pray you may prosper in every way and keep well" (III John 2).

It is quite apparent that good health is contingent upon keeping certain laws of health, many of which have already been discussed. Christ's ministry of healing on earth entailed the forgiving of physical sins through miraculous healing, demonstrating the infinite forgiving and healing nature of the Spirit which He was the embodiment of. He also, through the pages of His Word, has revealed those laws of health which prevent disease.

What, then, is the nature of disease itself? Does modern medicine have the answer? The answers to these questions are as revealing as they are encouraging, for they give people the hope that they *can* change the course of events in their own lives toward improving upon the past. One *can* wipe away the causes of illness by obeying the health laws God has given. After all, "garbage in" yields "garbage out" for both mind and body.

First of all, it must be understood that the body is a marvelously homeostatic entity that functions at any instant with the greatest possible effectiveness considering its current resources and history. It "rolls with the punches" to a remarkable degree. However, like a finger that is smashed with the hammer day after day for years, eventually the breaking of health laws will cause a permanent debilitation of one or more organs, leading to symptoms we term disease. The self-perception and overall mental balance of an individual significantly affects the response of the body through the multitude of ties between the mind and the body.

Perhaps the most forward-looking (and probably correct) view of the nature of disease has been expounded by F. I. Scott, editor of *American Laboratory*. Its chief theorem is that disease symptoms manifest themselves when the body falls behind in its continual task of eliminating wastes; it becomes overburdened with toxins, which leads to an "elimination crisis." The attractiveness of this theorem, underscoring its credibility, is that it possesses a spiritual counterpart. God's physical creation is based upon a spiritual model. The mind is constantly imbibing thoughts, perceptions, and nuances from the physical and spiritual world. It must consciously or unconsciously sort out the silver and gold from the chaff, and purge the chaff, using the "organs of disposal" at its command through the indwelling Spirit of God.*

A remarkable amount of evidence supports the following perception of health. First, germs do not cause diseases. They are nature's way of dealing with damaged tissues. The initial damage is caused by toxins resulting from incompletely or improperly metabolized foods, usually of long-standing, or from physical or chemical insults to the system. The essential tasks of therapy are to identify and remove the external sources from which the toxins eventually arise, to support the body's natural eliminative channels in removing the toxins and germ excreta, and to supply the nutritional elements necessary to support the metabolic and eliminative processes of the body.

Disease becomes manifest when the eliminative capacity of the digestive organs, the liver, and the kidneys are overwhelmed and the burden of toxic elimination falls on the endocrine glands. The specific

---

* It may not be too absurd to liken the organs of elimination in the body to the Spiritual weapons in God's arsenal that help ward off the "fiery darts of the wicked one" (Eph. 6:16). Thus, the liver, kidneys, digestive tract, endocrine glands, mucous membranes, and sweat glands may have their counterparts in truth, righteousness, the gospel of peace, faith, salvation, and God's Word (Eph. 6:14-17).

symptoms of a disease more accurately reflect the biochemically unique balance in an individual's glandular structure than they do the external sources or 'causes' of the disease. Thus the same toxin might be created in different individuals but from different external causes and manifest as the same or as different 'diseases' based on symptomatic diagnosis. Appropriate therapy then might differ not only for individuals with different diseases but for individuals with the same disease. Contagion arises because there is sufficient 'food,' i.e., damaged tissue, and insufficient eliminative capacity in other individuals to enable the ubiquitous germs to feed and multiply. The case for vaccination as preventive is extremely weak in the light of this and a broader examination of evidence adduced in its support. In fact, a rather substantial case can be made against that evidence and the rationale of the practice.

Disease is the manifestation of an elimination crisis and represents the body's continuing attempt to signal the existence of a problem and to discharge toxic material. Most 'treatment' of disease seeks to interfere with the manifestation and thus interferes with the healing process. Drugs and medicine exert that interference either by whipping or sedating the endocrine glands controlling the elimination channels [the pituitary signals the thyroid and adrenals to direct elimination through the paths they control. The thyroid controls elimination through the skins—outside (the hide), inside (mucous membranes), and middle (serous membranes). The adrenals control elimination through the bowels or kidneys or through hyperoxidation (fever). The determination of appropriate therapy involves careful assessment of hereditary and environmental influences on the strengths of these glands.] Since most elimination crises (diseases) are self-limited, it is difficult to separate the apparent effectiveness of medicines from the natural completion of the crises and the accelerated completion induced by whipping the glands. . . .

The coincidence of the decrease in infectious disease and the increase in chronic disease with the development of ever more powerful glandular whips and sedatives suggests that an extremely high price is being paid for the fast relief of symptoms. Because the external food-related causes are seldom eliminated, the toxins continue to develop, tissue damage increases, and elimination channels are blocked, leading to different manifestations of the crises, hence different 'diseases.' Repeated sedation or whipping of the glands attempting to effect elimination of the toxic material further burdens them, in time weakening their capacity to respond. Chronic disease is substantially worse than infectious disease because it indicates that the glands have insufficient strength to invoke an elimination crisis. Most drug research seeks the development of more powerful whips to induce the benefits of an elimination crisis without either its discomforting symptoms or complete glandular exhaustion."[100]

Knowing the cause for disease means one may remove the cause. Obedience to all seven laws of health indeed will provide the radiant health every person desires, unless, of course, God directly allows Satan to afflict the body (see Job 2:1-10). The tremendous resilience of the body to overcome illness when treated with respect is a mighty tribute to the Almighty Healer who designed the human body as the temple of God (I Cor. 6:19): " . . . then glorify God with your body" (v. 20).

Unheard of Longevity

We marvel at the few isolated celebrated tribes across the earth whose age at death oftentimes exceeds 100 years, far older than the average "threescore and ten" years allotted to man (Ps. 90:10). The villagers of Vilcabamba, a small, isolated community in the rugged Andean mountains of southern Ecuador, possessed nine centenarians out of a total population of 819 in 1971; the U.S. averages only three centenarians per 100,000 population![101]

According to Grace Halsell, who lived with the villagers for three years, the Vilcabambans live uncluttered, peaceful lives among lush tropical foliage at the 4,500 foot level. The temperature is a fairly steady 68 °F, with a climate similar to Taos and Santa Fe, New Mexico.[102] The people live in simple huts made of mud and sticks, having thatched roofs. There are no industries or automobiles to belch noxious fumes into the air, and since few people can afford to own donkeys most travel is by foot. One man aged 110 (in 1971) walked 10 miles to attend Sunday church services, wearing sandals or going barefoot.[103] These people are constantly out-of-doors and on their feet, prompting many of the elders to remark that their two best doctors are their right and left feet! The younger people are developing a taste for candies and ice cream, and many doubt that any will live as long as the older generation.

Another group of particularly long-lived people are the Hunzas. Like the Vilcabambans they are born into a life filled with activity until the day of death. Retirement is unknown in the high Himalayan mountains of northern Pakistan where these healthy people live, nestled in a valley only 100 miles long and in areas hardly a mile wide. As one older citizen wisely stated, "The idleness of retirement is a much greater enemy to life than work. One must never retire 'from' something. One must retire 'to' something. Our people continue to work on by choice."[104] They consider life to be divided into three periods: the *young years,* filled with pleasure, excitement, and a yearning for knowledge; the *middle years,* with their development of poise and appreciation; and the *rich years*—by far the best period—having mellowness, understanding, the ability to judge and tolerate, with the qualities of the first two periods as well.[105]

In Hunza, people often live to over 100 years of age in perfect mental and physical health, the men sometimes fathering children at age 90. Sickness is rare, and cancer, heart disease, heart attacks, high or low blood pressure, and childhood diseases are virtually unknown. Divorce is rare, and juvenile delinquency is nonexistent. As Renee Taylor stated in *Hunza Health Secrets,* "There are no jails, police, or army, and there is no need for them, as there hasn't been a crime reported for the last 150 years."[106]

The brilliant English surgeon Dr. Robert McCarrison wrote of these unusually healthy and long-lived people in 1921:

> My own experience provides an example of a race unsurpassed in perfection of physique and in freedom from disease in general. I refer to the people of the State of Hunza, situated in the extreme northernmost point of India. . . . Amongst these people the span of life is extraordinarily long, and such service as I was able to render them during the seven years I spent in their midst was confined chiefly to the treatment of accidental lesions, the removal of senile cataract, plastic operations for granular lips, or the treatment of maladies wholly unconnected with food supply.

> During the period of my association with these people, I never saw a case of asthenic dyspepsia, of gastric or duodenal ulcer, or appendicitis, of mucous colitis, or cancer. . . . Among these people the 'abdomen oversensitive' to nerve impressions, to fatigue, anxiety or cold was unknown. The consciousness of the existence of this part of their

anatomy was, as a rule, related solely to the feeling of hunger. Indeed, their buoyant abdominal health has, since my return to the West, provided abundant contrast with the dyspeptic and colonic lamentations of our highly civilized communities.[107]

McCarrison did not end his studies with simple observation, but proceeded to compare the diets of the well-fed, healthy Hunzas to the diets of other Indians who were moderately and poorly fed. Using albino rats, he chose foods normally eaten by each group: wholewheat chapattis smeared with fresh butter, sprouted pulse, fresh raw carrots, raw cabbage, and unboiled milk for the Hunzas, and more starchy grains, cooked vegetables, condiments, and other foods representative of the other Indians. He found that the health status of the rats directly paralleled the health of the people using these same diets! The faulty south Indian diet produced eye ailments, ulcers, boils, bad teeth, crooked spines, hair loss, anemia, skin disorders, heart and kidney problems, glandular weaknesses, and several stomach and intestinal disorders.[108] The Hunza diet produced healthy rats remarkably free of disease.

In addition, he placed diseased rats on the Hunzakut diet; they all recovered. Follow-up experiments included feeding rats the diet of the poorer English classes: white bread, margarine, sweetened tea, tinned meats, and jams and jellies. On their diet the rats not only developed all types of diseases but became nervous wrecks![109]

Another essential component of the Hunza's dietary routine is an enforced annual late spring fast . . . when food runs out before the new harvest has been gathered.

> Frequently . . . there is very little left of any edibles, and the people simply have to wait for the new crop of fruit, berries, grains and vegetables. They turn thin and scrawny, but they do not forget how to smile. They go on with their work with a friendly attitude and faith that soon they will have plenty of food. . . . This physical *rebirth*, as it were, might well be a major factor in the physical superiority of the Hunzakuts. And it is more than likely that their seasonal fasts tend to keep them humble, friendly, helpful and devotional.[110]

A third well-known area of the world where people often live to be over 100 years old is the Caucasus Mountain region of the southern Soviet Union, between the Black and Caspian Seas. Cases of people as old as 160 have been recorded! As with the people of mountainous regions of Ecuador and Hunza, the Caucasians live vigorous outdoor lives filled with abundant fresh air, natural foods, herbal remedies, and strong family ties. Walking is an especially prominent form of exercise from childhood until death.

According to Dr. Sula Benet, an anthropologist who has studied these people for several years, a major source of the healthfulness of this mountain life may be its rhythmic regularity:

> Order in daily routines and in the entire arc of life from cradle to grave contributes to the security of the individual and the group. Continuity and regulation in diet, work, sex life, and leisure appear to lessen the strain on the body by avoiding sudden discontinuities and changes.[111]

Old people remain involved in their family, their lineage, and their community, both emotionally and physically. They feel a meaningful contribution to their community and gain physical activity through the work they perform. According to Sula Benet,

> It is my feeling that the high incidence of longevity in the Caucasus is a result of the complete immersion of the individual in an atmosphere of inner, consistent values, creating a biological and spiritual rhythm. There is no lost energy spent attempting to introduce elements alien to the established patterns of life into the culture, resulting in a conflict-free, uncompetitive society.[112]

Are not the traits responsible for superb longevity common to all these groups going to be present during the Kingdom? Vigorous activity, an excellent diet, fresh air and water, definite purpose in life, serene mental attitudes, continuity in life, and respect for the elderly will serve to build durable individuals who will live long, useful, fulfilling lives.

A rule of thumb deduced from animal longevity studies states that the time from birth to reproductive age, multiplied by from seven to 10, will equal the total expected lifespan of the creature. If a person reaches sexual maturity at age 15 he should live to be from 105 to 150 years old! Yet, during pre-Flood days lifespans were considerably longer than these present ancient ages may seem (see Figure 44). As Genesis 5 reveals, Adam lived 930 years, Seth lived 912 years, Jared

962 years, and Methuselah 969 years, old ages indeed! According to C. F. Keil, "Every attack upon the historical character of its [Gen. 5] numerial statements has entirely failed, and no tenable argument can be adduced against their correctness."[114] In short, these ages are authentic.

How could people have lived so long in the past? Will they not live as long—possibly even longer—in the future once conditions are restored to Edenic perfection? Is it impossible that some men, though doomed to ultimately die in the flesh because of its physical nature, will survive the entire millennium as flesh and blood human beings?

At the time of the Flood something extremely important happened to the earth to cause a reduction in the life expectancy of man. One is tempted to explore the impact of the removal of the water canopy upon the transmission of additional age-enhancing radiation to the earth's surface. As already mentioned, certain forms of radiation are able to cause breakages in the hereditary material and perhaps contribute heavily to aging, i.e., the reduced ability of body cells to rejuvenate themselves. The increase in radiation after the Flood would have been very sharp, the life expectancy decreasing especially rapidly the first few post-Flood centuries until the present 70 year equilibrium age was reached.

Dr. Richard Severs, Associate Professor of Environmental Sciences at the University of Texas Health Science Center in Houston, speculates there may be a relationship between planetary charge, air ions, magnetic field, atmospheric potential, and the average productive lifetime of humans. He cites a number of studies and anomalies about these factors and, referring specifically to the Biblical accounts of pre-Flood longevity, suggests that cyclical and other changes in them may be linked to wide differences between present and past life spans.[115]

F. I. Scott in *American Laboratory* has added the possibility that food, nutrition, and lifestyle may severely affect longevity. He feels that the connections between soil depletion, food crops, and the health of animals and humans are strong enough to account for the decreases in life expectancy experienced over past millennia.[116] Indeed, recent studies with laboratory rats have shown that "restriction of caloric intake sufficient to retard growth of rats resulted in significant increases in life span."[117] Are overfed but undernourished Westerners killing themselves prematurely by allowing themselves to become stuffed with empty calories—fed *ad libitum* like shorter-lived animals—while sitting behind a desk most of the day?

Referring to extreme reduction in longevity following the Flood, William R. Vis says the following:

> . . . something extremely significant happened to the earth and to man at the time of the flood. It would seem that whatever it was, it probably removed the dominant factor for the long life of the patriarchs. The spiritual message of the Bible is clear: the length of life decreased because of the entrance of sin into the human family. However, the scientific explanation is not evident. Could some antediluvian climatic or other condition have been extremely favorable for long life in man? Perhaps future scientific research will cast some light on this.[118]

A prominent researcher on aging once said, "If the cause of aging can be found, there is no good medical reason to believe that it will not be possible to find some practical way of slowing the process down or even bringing it to a standstill."[119] The Creator of mankind, of course, knows every secret there is to know about slowing down the aging process. In fact, He is the author of long life and the Savior from death's clutches (Rom. 8:2), whereas the god of this world has as his aim the reduction of human lifespans and the hastening of death.

Jesus Christ, the victor over Satan and the future ruler over all the earth, has proclaimed a promise of long life that should bring tears of joy to the hearts of all people looking forward to the time when all nature will enfold mankind within her living principles:

> No sound of tears, no voice of crying, shall ever be heard in her; no babe shall die there any more in infancy, nor any old man who has not lived out his years of life; he who dies youngest lives a hundred years; anyone dying under a hundred years must be accursed by God. . . . My people shall live long, as lives a tree, long shall my chosen folk enjoy their earnings; they shall not work in vain, nor rear their children to die suddenly, for they are a race whom the Eternal blesses, and with them shall their children live (Isa. 65:19-20, 22-23).

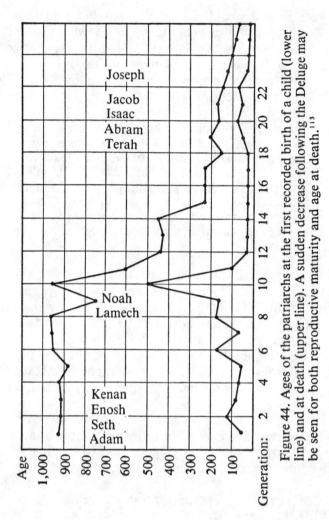

Figure 44. Ages of the patriarchs at the first recorded birth of a child (lower line) and at death (upper line). A sudden decrease following the Deluge may be seen for both reproductive maturity and age at death.[113]

Chapter Thirteen

What Can We Do Today?

A
ll of mankind—all of creation—is immersed in a sick society, a world under the jurisdiction and distortive wiles of the cunning, deceitful adversary of Jesus Christ. Isaiah wrote in about 757 B.C. the following scathing indictment against Judah and Jerusalem, a charge which could just as easily be laid against modern America and the West:

> Ah sinful nation, folk whose guilt is heavy, ah race of wrongdoers, sons degenerate—they have abandoned the Eternal, and spurned the Majesty of Israel! Why will you earn fresh strokes, for holding on in your revolt? Your whole head is sick, your whole heart is diseased; from the sole of the foot to the head, no part is sound; nothing but bruises and gashes, and raw, bleeding wounds, unsqueezed, unbandaged, unsoftened with oil (Isa. 1:4-6).

Treat the Land as God's Creation, Not as a Machine

This moral sickness—this lawlessness—is generalized to potently affect man's views and treatment of the land. We speak of "land sickness," of the erosion and scars of unprotected soils, of the unexplained disappearance of animal and plant species despite efforts to protect them, and the explosive increase of others despite valiant efforts to control them. Only wilderness areas hold the picture of what we might term perfect health. Man may terrace a corn field here or plant a tree line there, but finds his local alleviation of environmental pain is not a cure; just as in the human body, symptoms may lie in one organ and the cause in another. The body must be viewed as an organic whole and treated in ways that are health productive, not health destructive.

251

There is no reason why man could not, given the proper respect for natural laws and all life within nature, live in harmony with the world around him as an integral part of it, a creative force unwilling to tyrannize the environment for exploitative gain, viewing with kindness his role as "tender and keeper" of the biosphere . . . not the bespoiler and exterminator of his native earth.

The command expressed in Proverbs 12:10 to care affectionately for one's beast is but typical of the respectful attitudes one ought to hold toward all of creation. As H. Fielding Hall once reported concerning the people of Burma,

> To him (the Burmese) men are men, and animals are animals, and men are far the higher. But he does not deduce from this that man's superiority gives him permission to illtreat or kill animals. It is just the reverse. It is because man is so much higher than the animal that he can and must observe towards animals the very greatest care, feel for them the very greatest compassion, be good to them in every way he can. The Burmese's motto should be *noblesse oblige*. He knows the meaning, if he knows not the words.[1]

Can modern man logically think so humbly of himself, a mere being composed of chemicals with a market value of a few dollars, that he thinks even more humbly of the creatures who serve him—and relegates to them the role of machines? As he thinks and feels toward animals so he tends to act toward his fellow man. Yet, the modern profit motive demands that animals and nature be viewed as mere dollar signs, figments of commodity market manipulators, or pawns on the pages of banker's ledgers.

Perhaps the ultimate insult to dignity and respect toward land, beast, and plant—and thus toward man himself—has been expressed in the Mansholt Plan for European Agriculture. Herein lies a flagrant attempt of urban dwellers, ignorant of basic life-precepts of the farm, to apply industrial principles to agriculture. Promoted by Dr. Sicco L. Mansholt, former Vice President of the European Economic Community (EEC), the plan proposes to

> . . . achieve, as quickly and humanely possible, the amalgamation of many small family farms into large agricultural units operated as if

they were factories, and the maximum rate of reduction in the community's agricultural population. Aid is to be given 'which would enable the older as well as the younger farmers to leave agriculture.'[2]

Mansholt believes that farmers are "a group that has still not grasped the rapid changes in society." His views of *why* farmers should leave the land are as devious as his plans to amalgamate farm units:

> . . . factory workers, men on building sites and those in administrative jobs—have a five-day week and two weeks' annual holiday already. Soon they may have a four-day week and four weeks' holiday per year. And the farmer: he is condemned to making a seven-day week because the five-day cow has not yet been invented, and he gets no holiday at all.[3]

Dr. Mansholt never questioned whether or not farmers *enjoyed* life on the farm, despite its long hours and lack of holidays, and preferred it to city life and factory or office work. Neither did he face the reality that agriculture and industry *are* fundamentally different. The difference is a metaphysical one which does not fit into the materially-oriented equation of economists . . . much less be even entertained by them. Agriculture deals with living substances produced by living organisms based upon the soil; modern industry deals with man-devised processes that function reliably only when updated to non-living substances.

The utter incompatability of industry and agriculture has been lucidly outlined by E. F. Schumacher in *Small is Beautiful:*

> The ideal of industry is the elimination of living substances. Man-made materials are preferable to natural materials, because we can make them to measure and apply perfect quality control. Man-made machines work more reliably and more predictably than do such living substances as men. The ideal of industry is to eliminate the living factor, even including the human factor, and to turn the productive process over to machines. As North Whitehead defined life as "an offensive directed against the repetitious mechanism of the universe," so we may define modern industry as 'an offensive against the unpredictability, unpunctuality, general waywardness and cussedness of living nature, including man.'[4]

Agriculture is basic to all life. Industry is secondary, and ideally is complementary in serving the functions of agriculture. Agriculture can continue without industry, but not industry without agriculture. To solely place monetary concerns ahead of the priceless long-term values of protecting the productive capacity of the life-producing biosphere is the crudest slap in the face to "mother nature." As Schumacher put it,

> No serious exception can be taken to these statements if we adopt—as the experts have adopted—the metaphysical position of the crudest materialism, for which money costs and money incomes are the ultimate criteria and determinants of human action, and the living world has no significance beyond that of a quarry for exploitation.[5]

Considerations Beyond Contemporary Economics

What about *health,* our most valuable physical asset which we are commanded to guard (I Cor. 6:19-20)? What about *beauty,* which affects our total outlook on life and spurs us on to aspire toward the joy and perfection of altruistic goals? Can we maximize profits in agriculture, industry, and land development using today's twisted ethics and hope to develop priceless beauty in the biosphere which leads to the wholesome character required of God's true people? The apostle Paul intimated the following:

> Finally, brothers, keep in mind whatever is true, whatever is worthy, whatever is just, whatever is pure, whatever is attractive, whatever is high-toned, all excellence, all merit. . . . So shall the God of peace be with you (Philip. 4:8-9).

What about *permanence* in the face of a God who is "always the same, yesterday, today, and forever" (Heb. 13:8)? When Christ returns to establish His Kingdom will He not discern every thought and intent of every human being, and hold lawyers, politicians, farmers, industrialists, and garbage collectors responsible for everything they have done?

With our personal stake in the future so high we should come to actively learn and obey the laws of nature. They follow quite simply the law of love—God's very character—as summarized in the Ten Commandments. By first gaining the fear of God, and then the knowledge of His ways through diligent searching, the respect and obedience to the precepts which guide the entire creation will become a part of the individual (see Prov. 1:7; 2:1-8).

The basic concept of life cycling forms a cornerstone to understanding the operations of nature. No plant or animal can establish the permanent right to possess the materials of which it is composed. Stated another way, Paul B. Sears in *Deserts on the March* said,

> The face of the earth is a graveyard, and so it has always been. To earth each living thing restores when it dies that which has been borrowed to give form and substance to its brief day in the sun. From earth, in due course, each new living being receives back again a loan of that which sustains life. What is lent by earth has been used by countless generations of plants and animals now dead and will be required by countless others in the future. . . .

We can avoid the attitudes of arrogant and cultivated ignorance proclaimed by scientists and technologists who aid in accelerating the destruction of today's ecosphere. It is clear that powerful links exist between soils, pesticides, herbicides, fertilizers, crop varieties and the health of humans and animals. One treatment of the environment cannot be segregated from another. Yet, since there is no economic gain for government, industry, the lay public, or even scientists themselves in the conservation of topsoil and forests compared with, say, the development and production of petroleum-based fertilizers or herbicides, it is relatively easy for people to avoid acting on the evidence connecting soil and health.[7]

Learn to Live With the Land

Despite the failings of our present system which "passes the buck" down the chain of command so that supposedly no one is ultimately responsible for errors, we must realize that we, possessing knowledge, *are* responsible for making changes based on that truth: "Therefore to him that knoweth to do good, and doeth it not, to him it is sin" (James 4:17). Understanding the evils of soil erosion we should strive to eliminate it, and aim at rebuilding soil fertility instead of depleting it further. We should plant only the best, flattest land to crops and maintain the proper number of stock on the more erosive, sloping fields to prevent overgrazing. Forests containing native species should be planted on many sloping lands previously forested. Native fruit and nut trees interspersed frequently across the landscape could provide untold harvests of plenty year after year.*

Land need not be tilled excessively, if at all; rather, one should strive to emulate the prairie or forest environment native to the specific site. Edward Faulkner, author of *Plowman's Folly,* built soils to highly productive levels using a disk harrow to incorporate crop residues into the upper few inches of soil, similar to what occurs within a natural system.[8] Masanobu Fukuoka in southern Japan does not till at all, scattering rice seeds on the soil surface in the spring, and barley seeds in the fall, both crops achieving yields equivalent to surrounding fields raised under conventional or traditional methods.[9] The chisel plow, field cultivator, and similar implements serve well to leave crop residues on the soil surface, a primary goal of most tillage methods, reducing erosion and runoff and allowing decomposition to proceed near the soil surface. Some systems of cultivation require more labor than others, and with labor being at such a premium for today's Western farmer a disk could function well to serve tillage needs.

One may question why conventional tillage is discouraged despite our living yet within the 6,000 year era allotted to man to till the soil and prune fruit trees. However, it will be recalled that the type of tillage practiced by the ancient Israelites was very minimal, the making of an indentation into which seeds were dropped. Also, the present system is immersed in Satan's realm who is the current "god of this world" (Luke 4:6), the system God's people are admonished to come out of (Rev. 18:4) and "be ye separate" (II Cor. 6:17). The people intent upon living God's way will be striving to emulate God's character as revealed in His natural laws, and come into harmony

---

* Fruit trees nowadays often bear only every other year. The tree exhausts itself of minerals and energy while producing an abundant crop one year, but without optimum soil fertility the tree is unable to rejuvenate its reserves for the following year's production. Providing adequate soil minerals each year can assure abundant crops year by year.

with them, living utopian lives even today.

The pervasiveness of economic powers that tend to control our every action needs to be tempered with an element of faith in God. Without this gift of faith we could not spiritually survive within the present system, much less challenge entrenched dogmas of agriculture that may prove to be ultimately erroneous. All evil, or contravention of the Divine order of natural and spiritual law, will eventually meet its just recompense; order will become reestablished as the artificial foundational principles and their misguided superstructure collapse. To step out on faith and come into harmony with the natural scheme of nature is an ideal well worth exploring despite economic and social pressures discouraging such changes.

After all, the Amish in America and the natives of many third world countries produce excellent yields using animal power and what conventional farmers might call "antiquated" methods. Their very existence alongside modern agri-business technology—and their prosperity that laughs in the face of rural economic planners—proves that the ox and plow may indeed plod relentlessly through ages while "flash in the pan" technologies come and go with alarming rapidity.

The call is not necessarily to a wholesale conversion to animal power. However, the idea is well worth exploring and would very likely help many small farmers cope with exorbitant fuel prices and fuel shortages, as well as eliminate the purchase of expensive machinery and farm chemicals. If five to 40 acres of productive land can be purchased it is not difficult to become self-sufficient—provided the skills needed for such living are achieved. Hand labor may be adequate to support such a living (a very reward-ing one) if time permits, though an individual working many hours off the land to meet land payments may find small power implements a necessity . . . at least to begin with.

The feasibility of a nationwide system of small land holders—the idea envisioned by Washington and Jefferson—is dramatized by the systems of agriculture in Japan and China in the early 1900s. F. H. King in *Farmers of Forty Centuries* pictured how their system has supported farming in one place for over 2,000 years, the only place on earth this has occurred without the soil being ruined. The three main islands of Japan in 1907 had a population of 46,977,000, main-tained by 20,000 square miles of cultivated fields. This leaves 2,349 people per square mile, or more than three people per acre. Besides, Japan fed a very large animal population on these same acres: 69 horses and 56 cattle, nearly all employed as draft animals, plus 13 swine, sheep, and goats.[10]

In Shantung Province of China, conditions are similar to those in Japan. A farmer with a family of 12 kept one donkey, one cow, and two pigs on 2.5 acres of cultivated land, a population density of 3,072 people, 256 donkeys, 256 cattle, and 512 pigs per square mile. The average of seven Chinese holdings visited by King gave a maintenance capacity of 1,783 people, 212 cattle or donkeys, and 399 pigs—nearly 2,000 consumers and 400 rough food transformers per square mile of farmed land.[11] In comparison with these remarkable figures, corresponding statistics for the U. S. in 1900 per square mile were: population, 61; and horses and mules, 30.[12] Climate, of course, is more favorable for intensive year-round cultivation in much of the Far East than in the U. S. However, the ability of a land to support high population densities if the law of return is obeyed cannot be underrated.

Gardeners One and All

Most people are not farmers, but nearly everyone can garden. The millennium will unveil a world full of gardeners, for "The time is coming . . . when I bring back the exiles of my people Israel, to . . . plant vineyards and drink their wine, to lay out gardens and to eat their fruit" (Amos 9:13-14). The benefits of raising one's own food supply, or a significant portion of it, are numerous and may be outlined as follows:

(1) Top quality of the crops can be assured provided that one follows a natural system of culture: adding organic fertilizer sources, choosing open-pollinated varieties high in nutritional value, using little tillage, and avoiding toxic chemicals. A substantial reduction in diseases and increased vitality in living may be expected by eating this produce.

(2) Health-giving exercise is an essential component of most garden operations: fertilization, seedbed preparation, planting, weed removal, and harvesting.

(3) One is required to be outdoors where fresh air and sunshine yield additional health benefits.

(4) Economic returns from vegetable production are substantial, ranging from well over $1,000 fo a well tended large plot (even more if excess production is sold) to several hundred dollars for smaller gardens.* If fruit trees or berries are available even more savings may be realized.

(5) By involving the entire family in gardening operations closer family ties can be encouraged.

(6) A multitude of lessons regarding God's natural world—reproduction, the miracle of growth, fragrances and textures of leaves and flowers, the cycles of the biosphere, and many more—can be learned and enlarged upon year by year.

(7) A more independent existence can be achieved, relieving one's dependence upon other food suppliers and the petroleum based agri-business complex they depend upon.

The examples of many gardening patriarchs may be valuable to us. Adam and Eve tended the Garden of Eden (Gen. 2:15), Noah was a husbandman of the land and planted a vineyard (Gen. 9:20), and Ahab was a vegetable gardener (I Kings 21:2). Virtually all of the patriarchs were in some way tied closely to the land due to the very nature of agrarian existence in post-Flood, pre-modern times. We could do well to emulate their examples.

Keep the Land Sabbath

There is no way to avoid the conclusion that the Land Sabbath should be kept. This seventh year land rest, outlined in Exodus 23 and Leviticus 25, is couched between commands to keep the weekly

---

* In recent years an average 30-by-30 foot urban garden plot in Milwaukee County, Wisconsin, produced $252 worth of vegetables. According to the Oklahoma Extension Service, with the right information and a lot of hard work a typical 20-by-20 garden can produce enough to save $400 in food costs annually.[13] Saving seeds from open-pollinated crops for next year's planting can save even more money.

Sabbath, the annual Holy Days, avoid perversions of justice, refuse bribes, keep the Jubilee Year, and not blaspheme God's name.

A major problem arises in knowing which year to observe this land rest, since unless one is able to pinpoint which year Israel was commanded to keep it one will be out of phase with the Divine plan. Israel was to keep the land rest as a nation, an act requiring considerable faith in God to provide sustenance during those years that tillage and pruning were not performed—though it is doubtful more than three Land Sabbaths were ever kept. In the same sense one should keep the Jubilee Year and return land to the rightful owners every 50 years.

Yet, was the land ever *given* to families in America as permanent homesteads, never to be sold? No, so can the laws governing the Jubilee be applied in this day of perverted law, when the forgiveness of debts which is commanded during this 50-year celebration would rightfully apply to all? Our banking system does not allow forgiveness of debt. The system of land sale, taxation, and slim profit margins in many cases tie a deeply indebted farmer so firmly to the dictates of his lender that he cannot rest his land the seventh year even if he desired to. The entire system has become so far removed from the God-ordained order of things that unless one possesses only a small parcel of land which is debt free can he hope to simulate the conditions surrounding the Land Sabbath and Jubilee Years.

This present system of Satan's inspiration survives only as long as enough of the God-ordained precepts are adhered to which maintain its viability. Eventually the corrupted economic system that holds sway over the earth will break down and be forced to allow the land to keep its sabbaths. Leviticus 26:43 says, "The land must be left by them to enjoy its sabbaths, while it lies desolate, deprived of them; they must submit to be punished for their sin, for they did spurn my regulations and they abhorred my rules." Those people intent upon striving toward the utopian life in this age, becoming perfect as God is perfect (Matt. 5:48), should indeed treat the land as God intended it to be treated.

In reference to man's weekly rest, in commemoration of the creation week, Jesus said, "The sabbath was made for man, not man for the sabbath" (Mark 2:27). Analogously, referring to the seventh year land rest, may it not be inferred that "the Land Sabbath was made for the land, not the land for the land rest''? The purpose of the Land Sabbath is primarily for the rest and rejuvenation of the soil and all it produces. That being the case, since we cannot be absolutely assured which year is the Land Sabbath—and since the land owners around us do not adhere to the Biblical commands regarding this land rest—should not a person still be intent on keeping God's will and strive to do the best he can? Perhaps he is convicted that the year 1980-81 is *the* Land Sabbath year (and maybe it is). Will not God Almighty note his attitude and willingness to obey His orders and bless the man accordingly?

What about the farmer—a captive debtor struggling to pay for his land—who intends to keep the Land Sabbath? Not knowing the precise year to rest his land could he legitimately rest a seventh of that land each year until all of it had been rested during a seven year cycle? On the other hand, could he arbitrarily choose a year to observe the land rest for his entire farm, say, the seventh year from his personal conversion and entrance into God's Church? Surely God is able to discern the thoughts and intents of the heart, and within our society so disinclined to obey God's ways He is able to judge perfectly the total array of factors impinging upon a decision one has made. Moreover, God is a magnanimous forgiver of our shortcomings should we err, though ever encouraging us to step out on faith and latch on to the Divine directives which lead toward the joyful results all people desire: peace of mind, wisdom, judgment, patience, and ultimately the establishment of the Kingdom of God upon the earth when He will apply perfectly the God-plane laws which we struggle to apply today . . . however imperfectly.

The overall principles of the Land Sabbath boil down to these two: (1) rest on the seventh year for the land, and the plant and animal kingdoms and people living upon it, and (2) faith and obedience toward God for provision of one's imperative personal need for food. The Land Sabbath also provides time for planning the next six years of land husbandry.

New Age Nutrition

A major change everyone can make in his life is to reject the refined Western diet. Nature provides a fine array of foods, ideally raised under natural methods using native varieties, which will guarantee improved health to the consumer if he at the same time forsakes processed foods. A minimum of processing and preparation will assure that life-giving vitamins and minerals are not removed. Careful avoidance of any foods containing white sugar (sucrose) and bleached flour will virtually eliminate the host of disorders termed the "saccharine disease," ranging from tooth decay to appendicitis. Elimination of chemical additives from the diet will further reduce the chances of contracting diseases such as cancer.

By raising food in one's own garden and orchard, the abundance of chemical sprays which find their way into the food supply can be avoided, while quality of the crop will usually be enhanced compared to the same crop raised under conventional large-scale operations. The replacement of the typical supermarket fare with home grown and carefully purchased additional items—especially those grown in the local area—will go a long way toward improving one's health by raising energy levels and reducing the incidence of disease.

Nutrition, of course, is not the single, simple answer to radiant health. Exercise, fresh air, sunshine, rest, and a wholesome frame of mind are vitally important as well, though proper nutrition forms, along with one's "diet of the mind," the chief cornerstone upon which abundant living is built. It must also be understood that true abundant living cannot be obtained in any ultimate sense until this temporal dead-end, physical existence is translated into the hope of a new life and body within the spirit realm. Only with the joy and "peace of mind that passes all understanding" (Philip. 4:7) that accompanies the spirit-led life can one truly realize the full potential of human life.

Some Parting Comments

Until the Kingdom of God arrives, the people intent upon living "perfect as God is perfect" will find difficulties in changing their present routine to the more perfect way. Not only are entrenched habits difficult to uproot, but swimming upstream against the trends of society requires additional effort. The added effort, however, is well worth it. God's laws are living, active laws that *work*! The closer we come to living in harmony with them the more we are blessed.

Agriculture has strayed far from the ordained way. While agronomists, soil scientists, plant breeders, plant pathologists, other supporting scientists, and farmers may think they are "progressing" toward a better way—fewer farmers, larger farms, more and bigger machinery, dependence on petrochemicals and toxic pesticides and herbicides, and monoculture—in due time this whole superstructure based on a false, temporary foundation will collapse. Natural laws that are broken must in time kick back. We observe some of these kickbacks already as floods and siltation of streams, reduced soil organic matter and a resulting loss of soil fertility and soil water storage capacity, expanding deserts, and increasing weather upsets.

We can only guess what might be the coming events. We understand, for instance, that crop yields may drop by a third if highly soluble chemical fertilizers were suddenly not added. This scenario is really not rational, however, for if energy supplies were so disrupted that insufficient volumes of fertilizers could be manufactured or transported to farmers, then there would surely not be enough fuel to operate the tractors which plant, cultivate, and harvest the crop. It is an all or nothing situation. There is no middle ground.

So will come the devastation of our current agricultural system. Having raped our soils of the vast organic reservoirs of fertility over past decades, especially since the last world war, there will be no further "chemical fix" available to coax out additional bushels of corn or wheat when the fertilizer and agri-chemical supplies fail. It takes years to rebuild the soil to resemble its native fertility condition; in a crisis, time has no compassion on past mistakes. When the fuel supplies are cut off there will be few power sources to turn the wheels of agriculture. Fuel alcohol might help for a short time, but repairs for machines depend on factories which require petroleum energy, as do factory workers to fuel their automobiles. A buildup of animal power to provide farmers with a truly self-sufficient power source again takes time . . . years of time.

Will a war signal the destruction of our agricultural system? Will a foreign oil embargo cripple our productive capacity and so limit food production and deliveries to cities that the hellish chaos which erupts paralyzes the country's productive capacity? Such visions are not beautiful, but they are necessary consequences of the present course our society is embarked upon. We can either ride this doomed ship to destruction, or plead sanity and jump aboard the upstream steamer toward a better world.

Few things that are worthwhile do not require a great deal of effort to accomplish. The pains necessary to assure a place in the upcoming Kingdom of God are well worth the effort . . . for "present suffering, I hold, is a mere nothing compared to the glory that we are to have revealed" (Rom. 8:18). Once the wars and destruction are past (termed the "Great Tribulation," followed by the "Day of the Lord" in prophecy), agriculture—indeed the entire society—in the Kingdom will be a most splendid scene to behold, and to have a part in; a scene of lush, green pastures and woodlands, of amiable climate, of tame wildlife, of truly utopian living so utterly different from the present oppressive, competitive world of today.

Perhaps the words of Ralph Waldo Emerson, written about a beautiful day he experienced, best typify the glorious oneness with God and nature that will enthrall and warm the hearts of all dwellers on the earth in the coming age, the age which Paul spoke of when he said, "What no eye has ever seen, what no ear has ever heard, what never entered the mind of man, God has prepared for those that love him" (I Cor. 2:9):

> These enchantments are medicinal, they sober and heal us. These are plain pleasures, kindly and native to us. We come to our own, and make friends with matter, which the ambitious chatter of the schools would persuade us to despise. We never can part with it; the mind loves its old home: as water to our thirst, so is the rock, the ground, to our eyes and hands and feet. It is firm water; it is cold flame; what health, what affinity! . . . There are all degrees of natural influence, from these quarantine powers of nature, up to her dearest and gravest ministrations to the imagination and the soil. There is the bucket of cold water from the spring, the wood-fire to which the chilled traveller rushes to safety—and there is the sublime moral of autumn and of noon. We nestle in nature, and draw our living as parasites from her roots and grains, and we receive glances from the heavenly bodies, which call us to solitude and foretell the remotest future. . . .

> I am taught the poorness of our invention, the ugliness of towns and palaces. Art and luxury have early learned that they must work as enchantment and sequel to this original beauty. I am over-instructed for

my return. Henceforth I shall be hard to please. I cannot go back to toys. I am grown expensive and sophisticated. I can no longer live without elegance, but a countryman shall be my master of revels. He who knows the most, he who knows what sweets and virtues are in the ground, the waters, the plants, the heavens, and how to come at these enchantments,—is the rich and royal man. Only as far as the masters of the world have called in nature to their aid, can they reach the height of magnificence. . . .

Nature is always consistent, though she feigns to contravene her own laws. She keeps her laws, and seems to transcend them. She arms and equips an animal to find its place and living in the early. . . .[14]

APPENDIX I

The Incredible Legacy We Threw Away

When the white Anglo-Saxon race first set foot on the territory now known as the United States there was such untold, untainted wealth that mere words cannot express the vision. The virgin scenes lived among only the first inhabitants that visited an area—the mountain men such as Jim Bridger and Kit Carson, Norwegian explorers, Spanish conquistadors, or Jamestown settlers—for in a few short years the seemingly inexhaustible wildlife, forests, and prairies were utterly raped of their virgin wealth, never more to reappear.

The purpose of this discussion, which will be mostly quotes of the original observers, is to paint a picture of the America that God created, in harmony with natural laws, disturbed only slightly by the American Indians. The Indians regarded their homeland as the center of the universe, held in collective ownership within the entire tribe.[1] There was affection for the land, and no idea of private ownership. According to Stewart Udall, former U.S. Secretary of the Interior,

> The idea that land could be bought and sold was an alien concept to the Indians of America. They clung possessively to certain chattels, but lands were nearly always held in common. An individual might have the use of a farm plot, but at his death it reverted back to the community.
>
> Englishmen, especially, coveted the land. It was something to be owned outright. Had not the English King given the charter deeds? The sixteenth-century Spaniard, by contrast, was not primarily interested in seizing land: the soldier wanted personal plunder; the priest came with his seeds and livestock to save Indian souls.

To the joint-stock companies of Virginia, intent on commercial profits, and to the colonizing Pilgrims, exclusive possession was the be-all
and end-all of ownership. But the Indian's 'title,' based on the idea
that he belonged to the land and was its son, was a charter to use—to
use in common with his clan or fellow tribesmen, and not to *use up*.
Neither white nor Indian fully grasped the concept of the other. The
Indian wanted to live not just in the world, but with it; the white man,
who thought in terms of estates and baronies, wanted land he alone
could cultivate and use.[2]

In order to gain a foothold on the continent the first colonists practiced neighborliness and upright conduct with regard to the Indians,
for the colonists were badly outnumbered. The powerful chiefs in the
area of Massachusetts generously helped the early settlements to survive. However, when the ranks of the colonists swelled and stockades
were built, "the Indians were pressed remorselessly when their
friendship became of less value than their land."[3]
As Udall continued,

In Virginia, the Indians watched with consternation aı.d alarm as the
white men planted tobacco, used up the soil, and every few years
moved on to clear new fields. The planters took the Indians' land, first
by cajolery and trade, then by force. So swiftly did events move that,
within forty years of the founding of Jamestown, the mighty
Powhatans were landless and in beggary at the edge of their former
homes. Elsewhere the details were different, but white expansion
followed the same general pattern.[4]

Barriers of misunderstanding arose between the Indians and white
men which neither could break down. Tecumseh, the warrior chief,
stated the philosophy of nearly all the tribes when approached by
white land buyers: "Sell the country? . . . Why not sell the air, the
clouds, the great sea?"[5] The Indians could not envision land as a
commodity which could be bought and sold; rather, they said it
belonged to their ancestors whose bones were buried in it, to the present generation which used it, and to the children who would inherit
it.[6] As an Iroquois corn planter told George Washington in 1790,
"The land we live on, our fathers received from God, and they
transmitted it to us, for our children, and we cannot part with
it. . . . Where is the land on which our children and their children
after them are to lie down?"[7]

Despite their land policies which were harmonious with natural laws, and which have been restated by many prominent Anglo-Saxon agriculturalists, including Sir Albert Howard,* Edward Faulkner,[9] Friend Sykes,[10] and Wendell Berry,[11] the Indians were not to ultimately inherit the land. In general, they were respecters of natural laws but not of high moral principles, inspiring D. H. Lawrence to write, "In the dust where we have buried the silent races and their abominations we have buried so much of the delicate magic of life."[12] The totem poles, demonic dances, pagan rituals, war paint, and savagery of many tribes are reminiscent of the "groves [carved trees] and images" (Isa. 27:9), idolatrous worship, sacrificing children on altars, and other abominations which the pagan tribes of Canaan practiced. Herman L. Hoeh, in his *Compendium of World History,* cites that the American Indians,

> . . . led by Odin or Voltan across the Atlantic to the New World were not exclusively the sons of Tiras from Thrace; some tribes were called Chivam, reports Ordonez the early Spanish writer. It is the very Hebrew spelling used for the English word Hivites [see Josh. 3:10; 9:1; etc], some of whom once lived in Mr. Seir, the land of caves, near Babylonia! So the Mexican Indians were a mixed people.[11]

The American Indians are of basically the same racial stock as the Mexican Indians, with a skin color ranging from nearly white to copper brown and to nearly black in some tribes.[14] Just as the ancient Israelites pursued and displaced the ancient Canaanites, so the modern Israelites inhabiting America[15] have overpowered and displaced the native nations (Canaanite at least in part) which held the land when they arrived.

---

* Howard, in *An Agricultural Testament,*[8] summarized the main characteristics of nature's farming methods: "mother earth never attempts to farm without livestock; she always raises mixed crops; great pains are taken to preserve the soil and to prevent erosion; the mixed vegetable and animal wastes are converted into humus; there is no waste; the processes of growth and the processes of decay balance one another; ample provision is made to maintain large reserves of fertility; the greatest care is taken to store the rainfall; both plants and animals are left to protect themselves against disease."

The white man's disregard for our nations' teeming wildlife, forests, and prairies—viewing them usually as commodities to exploit—is related by Robert McClung in his excellent discourse on extinct and vanishing American wildlife, *Lost Wild America*. A "scorched earth" policy reminiscent of Sherman's Civil War march to the sea in Georgia—except on a slower, more insidious, and considerably more massive scale—was practiced. "Cut, burn, plant, destroy, move on!" became the battle cry for the white conquistadors. No thought was given to preservation of the abundant natural resources surrounding them; the settlers were too busy making clearings, burning stumps, reaping their first meager harvests, or fighting the Indians.[16]

> The ages-old virgin forests had to go before any farming could be started, so the settlers cut down the towering trees and let in the sunlight. They burned the fallen monarchs and used the trunks of smaller trees to build their log-cabin homes. . . . The pioneers engaged in unrelenting warfare against wolves, panthers, wildcats, and all other 'varmints.' . . . Massachusetts Bay Colony offered a one-penny bounty on wolves as early as 1630 . . . . more than two million pounds of deerskins (nearly half a million deer) passed through the single port of Savannah, Georgia, in the brief span between 1764 and 1773.

> To many pioneers, game existed just to be killed, whether needed or not. Game drives were sometimes organized in pioneering communities with the object of killing as much wildlife as possible in the surrounding countryside. One such drive was organized in central Pennsylvania in 1760 by Black Jack Schwartz, known as the Wild Hunter. As related by Colonel H. W. Shoemaker, a compiler of early Pennsylvania lore, the hunters in this one drive massacred '41 panthers, 109 wolves, 112 foxes, 114 mountain cats, 17 black bears, 1 white bear, 2 elk, 98 deer, 111 buffaloes, 3 fishers, 1 otter, 12 gluttons (wolverines), 3 beavers, and upwards of 500 smaller animals.' The choicest of the hides were taken together with buffalo tongues, and then the heap of carcasses, 'as tall as the tallest trees,' was heaped with rich pine and fired. This created such a stench that the settlers were compelled to vacate their cabins in the vicinity of the fort, three miles away.[17]

Daniel Boone, in a rare burst of talkativeness when he met John James Audubon in the early 1800s, spoke of the early years when he had first visited Kentucky, when the lower parts of the region were "still in the hands of nature:"

> But, ah! Sir, what a difference thirty years make in a country. Why, at the time when I was caught by Indians, you would not have walked out in any direction for more than a mile without shooting a buck or a bear. There were thousands of Buffaloes on the hills of Kentucky; the land looked as if it never would become poor; and to hunt in those days was a pleasure indeed. But when I was left to myself on the banks of the Green River, I dare say for the last time in my life, a few signs only of deer were to be seen, and, as to a deer itself, I saw none.[18]

Enough said! Let the following paragraphs reveal the tremendous natural wealth the United States held in store when the inheritors of this land came to possess it.

An Overview of the Entire Nation

> The American continent was in a state of climax at the time of the first Indian intrusions. . . . Superlatives alone could describe the bewildering abundance of flora and fauna that enlivened its landscapes: the towering redwoods, the giant saguaro cacti, the teeming herds of buffalo, the beaver, and the grass were, of their kind, unsurpassed.[19]

This land was, and is, a geological and geographical masterpiece, with its ideal latitude and rich resources, a two billion acre "promised land" for active, imaginative men.

To the north the primitive, red-skinned hunter found vast stretches of arctic tundra with herds of musk oxen and caribou, and an abundance of ptarmigan and trout. In the south, dry desert country was cut by deep canyons of sculptured rock. Between these were glistening snow-capped mountains and vast grasslands where bison ranged, with pronghorns, elk, quail, and waterfowl in countless millions.

> The endless eastern forests harbored deer and elk and many kinds of furbearers. Rivers teemed with fish; lakes and marshes sent up clouds

Figure 45. The North American wild turkey.

of waterfowl. . . . Tribes of the Northland shaped their way of life to the comings and goings of vast herds of caribou. Along the Pacific Coast they became fishermen, hunting the abundant salmon, the whales, and other gifts of the sea. The nomadic tribes of the Great Plains followed the bison. . . .[20]

The virgin forests of North America were among the masterpieces of the natural world: east of the Great Plains nearly every acre was covered by trees; to the west softwood stands flourished on the slopes and in the valleys of the Rocky Mountains; and rising above the Pacific shore line, in the most productive timber zone in the world, redwood and fir stands provided a crescendo of arboreal splendor.[21]

Among the animals which once ranged over much of the nation was the wild turkey. The Pilgrims found a "great store of wild Turkies" in Massachusetts Bay Colony, which helped sustain them during the first difficult years, for a hunter was almost sure to bag a bird or two whenever he hunted.[22] A New England traveler in 1674 commented, "I have also seen three-score broods of young turkies on the side of a marsh, sunning themselves in a morning betimes."[23] Within thirty years of this statement the wild turkey was rarely seen in New England, though it still was commonly seen elsewhere in the country.

"The high forests ring with the noise, like the crowing of the domestic cocks, of these social sentinels," remarked naturalist William Bartram in the 1770s, describing a trip in Florida.[24] At that time wild turkeys ranged over most of the continent, from New England, Michigan, and Colorado in the north to Florida, southern Mexico, and Arizona in the south. Many of these early birds (cocks) weighed up to 40 or 50 pounds.[25] They would eat acorns, chestnuts, and beechnuts along with tubers, bulbs, grubs, and weed seeds as they wandered many miles in search of food. Benjamin Franklin expressed regret that the turkey was not chosen as the bird for our national emblem when he stated, "For in truth, the turkey is in comparison [to the bald eagle] a much more respectable bird . . . a bird of courage."[26] Even the prairies of the Plains contained turkeys in the wooded creek and river valleys. Laura Wilder in *Little House on the Prairie* remarked how "pa" had found a place where a flock of wild turkeys roosted; "Our Thanksgiving and Christmas turkeys. . . . Great, big, fat fellow," he had said.[27]

Today, the wild turkey has been restocked in many protected areas across the nation they formerly inhabited. Never in this age will their flocks gain the vitality they once possessed in years past, for most of their habitats are gone.

Another bird which frequented the entire area east of the Rocky Mountains was the passenger pigeon. Now extinct, this bird once existed in numbers so tremendous as to defy the imagination! According to Alexander Wilson, a Scottish-born ornithologist who came to America in 1794, the food consumption and number of a single flock he observed was enormous:

The vast quantity of mast which these multitudes consume, is a serious loss to the bears, squirrels and other dependents on the fruits of the forest. I have taken from the crop of a single Wild Pigeon, a good handful of the kernals of beech nuts, intermixed with acorns and chestnuts. To form a rough estimate of the daily consumption of one of these immense flocks, let us first attempt to calculate the numbers of that above mentioned, as seen in passing between Frankfurt and the Indiana territory. If we suppose this column to have been one mile in breadth (and I believe it to have been much more), and that it moved at the rate of one mile in a minute; four hours, the time it continued passing, would make its whole length two hundred and forty miles. Again supposing that each square yard of this moving body comprehended three Pigeons, the square yards in the whole space, multiplied by three, would give two thousand two hundred and thirty millions, two hundred and seventy-two thousand pigeons [about 2.23 billion birds]! An almost inconceivable multitude, and yet probably far below the actual amount. Computing each of these to consume half a pint of mast daily, the whole quantity at this rate, would equal seventeen millions four hundred and twenty-four thousand bushels per day! Heaven has wisely and graciously given to these birds rapidity of flight, and a disposition to range over vast uncultivated tracts of the earth; otherwise they must have perished in the districts where they resided, or devoured up the whole productions of agriculture, as well as those of the forests.[28]

These pigeons migrated far and wide in search of food in tremendous flocks, seldom following regular seasonal migrations as do many other bird species. Many lingered in the Hudson Bay area even into December.[29] After depleting the local stock of beech nuts, a

Figure 46. 'The passenger pigeon.

chief food in areas of Ohio, Kentucky, and Indiana, another area of nuts may be discovered some 60 to 80 miles away, to which the flock would regularly fly each day, and then return that evening to the home roosting place. After frequenting a roosting area for some time the ground became covered with several inches of dung, destroying all vegetation, and large limbs would litter the ground beneath the trees; the birds would cluster tightly together on the trees over thousands of acres, "killing [them] as completely as if girdled with an axe. The marks of this desolation remain for many years on the spot; and numerous places could be pointed out where for several years after, scarce a single vegetable made its appearance."[30] Up to 100 nests might occupy nearly every single tree within an area several miles wide and 40 miles long.[31] According to Wilson, " . . . the noise in the woods was so great as to terrify their [the pigeon hunter's] horses, and . . . it was difficult for one person to hear another speak without bawling in his ear."[32] The ground was strewn with broken tree limbs, eggs, and squab—that had fallen from nests above—on which herds of hogs fattened. Wilson also added,

> It was dangerous to walk under these flying and fluttering millions, from the frequent fall of large branches, broken down by the weight of the multitudes above, and which in their descent often destroyed numbers of the birds themselves; while the clothes of those engaged in traversing the woods were completely covered with the excrements of the Pigeons.[33]

Within 100 years the passenger pigeon, in its heyday comprising perhaps one-third of the total bird population in America, passed into oblivion. The last bird of the species, an old female named Martha, died September 1, 1913, in the Cincinnati Zoo.

Many animals, birds, insects, fish, trees, and other creatures which ranged across much of the country now have become extinct or restricted to very limited ranges in national or state parks or wilderness areas. These include the elk, wood duck, timber wolf, and mountain lion. Each species has its story, but from here on the creatures, trees, and setting as the early settlers found them will be discussed for different areas of the country.

The East Coast and New England

Settlers of the New American colonies found thick, tall stands of wild-rye and brown-straw grasses all along the Atlantic seaboard.[34] Even before Columbus set sail for the North American continent it had been touched by many a white man. Edward Graham in *The Land and Wildlife* relates the following tale of the Norsemen:

> Greenland had been discovered in 986 by Eric the Red, and in 1003 Eric's son, Leif the Lucky, set foot upon the North American continent somewhere in New England. He built houses there, and the sagas tell us of the things the Norsemen saw. They saw rolling country, well timbered close to the beach which had white sand, in low spots 'wheat,' grapevines, and grapes, and brooks full of fish.[35]

Wildlife and fruit were in abundance everywhere. The first Thanksgiving, in 1621, featured a gourmet's delight, with such foods as

> . . . deer, duck, sea food, fish, corn, and other native foods. . . . Turkey stuffed with oysters, chestnuts, or hazelnuts, white or sweet potatoes, lima beans, cranberry sauce, pumpkin pie, corn chowder or corn bread, salad with sweet peppers, tomatoes, Concord grapes, peanuts, pecans, and other nuts—all these are indigenous to the New World and an inseparable part of the cultural heritage of America.[36]

The fact that so many early colonists suffered such privation in a primeval environment of abundance may be explained by their English and Dutch background. They were, in the eyes of many historians, "too civilized" to take adequate advantage of the provender of the woods, seashore, and streams that surrounded them; few had ever killed an animal or caught a fish. Only with time, experience, and help from the Indians did the pilgrims eventually learn to live off the land and become the expert woodsmen that writers have come to describe their descendant as being.

In 1602, five years before Jamestown was founded, an obscure English cleric named John Brereton journeyed to America with Bartholomew Gosnold and wrote a pamphlet about the voyage. After first landing along the southern coast of Maine they headed south to the Cape Cod, Massachusetts area, the region which he described in part below:

> . . . in five or six hours absence, we had pestered our ship so with Cod fish, that we thru numbers of them overboard again: and surely, I am persuaded that in the months of March, April, and May, there is upon this coast better fishing, and in as great plenty, as in Newfoundland: for the sculles of mackerel, herrings, Cod, and other fish, that we daily saw as we went and came from the shore, were wonderful; and besides, the places where we took these Cods (and might in a few days have laden our ship) were but in seven fathoms water, and within less than a league of shore; where, in Newfoundland they fish in forty or fifty fathoms water, and far off.
>
> The chiefest trees of this Island, are Beeches and Cedars; the outward parts are overgrown with low bushy trees, three or four feet in height, which bear some kind of fruits, as appeared by their blossoms; Strawberries, red and white, as sweet and much bigger than ours in England, Raspberries, Gooseberries, Hurtleberries, and such; an incredible store of Vines, as well in the woody part of the Island, where they run upon every tree, as on the outward parts, that we could not go for treading upon them; also, many springs of excellent sweet water, and a great standing lake of fresh water, near the sea side, an English mile in compass, which is maintained with the springs running exceeding pleasantly through the woody grounds which are very rocky. Here are also in this Island, great store of Deer, which we saw, and other beasts, as appeared by their tracks, as also diverse fowls, as Cranes, Hernshawes, Bitters, Geese; Mallards, Teals, and other fowls, in great plenty; also, great store of Peas, wnich grew in certain plots all the Island over.
>
> . . . on the outsides of this Island are many plain places of grass, abundance of Strawberries and other berries before mentioned: in mid May we did sow on this Island (as for trial) in sundry places, Wheat, Barley, Oats and Peas, which in fourteen days were sprung up nine inches and more: the soil is fat and lusty; the upper crust, of gray color, but a foot or less in depth, of the color of our hemp-lands in England; and being thus apt for these and the like grains; the sowing or setting (after the ground is cleansed) is no greater labor, than if you should set or sow in one of our best prepared gardens in England. This Island is full of high timbered Oaks, their leaves thrice as broad as ours; Cedars, staight and tall; Beech, Elm, Holly, Walnut trees in abundance, the fruit as big as ours, as appeared by those we found under the

trees, which had lain all the year ungathered; Hazelnut trees, Cherry trees, the leaf, bark and bigness not differing from ours in England, but the stalk bears the blossoms or fruit at the end thereof, like a cluster of Grapes, forty or fifty in a bunch: Sassafras trees plenty all the Island over, a tree of high price and profit; also diverse other fruit trees, some of them with strange barks, of an Orange color, in feeling soft and smooth like Velvet: in the thickest parts of the woods, you may see a furlong or more round about. On the Northwest side of this Island, near to the sea side, is a standing Lake of fresh water, almost three English miles in compass, in middle whereof stands a plot of woody ground, an acre in quantity or not above: This Lake is full of small Tortoises, and exceedingly frequented by all sorts of fowls before rehearsed, which breed, some low on the banks, and others in low trees about this Lake in great abundance, whose young ones of all sorts we took and eat at our pleasure: but all these fowls are much bigger than ours in England. Also, in every Island, and almost in every part of every Island, are great store of Ground nuts, forty together on a string, some of them as big as hens eggs; they grow not two inches under ground: the which nuts we found to be as good as Potatoes. Also diverse sorts of shell-fish, as Scallops, Mussels, Cockles, Lobsters, Crabs, Oysters, and Whelks, exceeding good and very great. But not to cloy you with particular rehearsal of such things as God and Nature both bestowed on these places, in comparison whereof, the most fertile part of all England is (of itself) but barren; we went in our light-oarsman from this Island to the main, right against this Island some two leagues off, where coming ashore, we stood a while like men ravished at the beauty and delicacy of this sweet soil; for besides diverse clear Lakes of fresh water (whereof we saw no end) Meadows very large and full of green grass; even the most woody places (I speak only of such as I saw) do grow so distinct and apart, one tree from another, upon green grassy ground, somewhat higher than the Plains, as if Nature would show herself above her power, artificial.[37]

Walt Whitman wrote with warm emotion about the fresh details of nature he experienced all across America. The following paragraph comes from "May-Month" in his *Speciman Days,* which describes a journey into the somewhat altered wilderness, but yet peaceful serenity, of rural Camden, New Jersey. His lush descriptions capture the poetic music inherent within the natural landscape.

As I write, I am seated under a big wild-cherry tree—the warm day temper'd by partial clouds and fresh breeze, neither too heavy nor light—and here I sit long and long, envelop'd in the deep musical drone of these bees, flitting, balancing, darting to and fro about me by hundreds—big fellows with light yellow jackets, great glistening swelling bodies, stumpy heads and gauzy wings—humming their perpetual rich mellow boom. (Is there not a hint in it for a musical composition, of which it should be the background? some bumblebee symphony?) How it all nourishes, lulls one, in the way most needed; the open air, the rye fields, the apple orchards. The last two days have been faultless in sun, breeze, temperature and everything; never two more perfect days, and I have enjoy'd them wonderfully. My health is somewhat better, and my spirit at peace.[38]

Known to few modern Americans is the fact that salmon runs, similar to those of the Pacific Northwest, were an annual phenomenon in most New England rivers during the early days of settlement. Mill dams and stream pollution soon eliminated these salmon entirely.[39] Equally remote to the knowledge of most Americans is the once numerous eastern bison. In colonial days these eastern bison ranged from western New York, Pennsylvania, and Virginia on south to Georgia.[40] The English navigator Sir Samuel Argall in 1612, while sailing up the Potomac River and marching inland, reported he saw "great store of Cattle as big as Kine, of which, the Indians that were my guides, killed a couple, which were found to be very good and wholesome meate. . . ."[41]

The eastern bison had little or no hump, its hind legs were about as long as the front legs, its color was very dark, and the horns flared upward like those of an Ayrshire, quite unlike the Plains bison.[42] As McClung has pointed out,

Traveling in bands that sometimes numbered several hundred animals, eastern bison made annual migrations north and south, often following well-worn trails from summer feeding grounds to sheltered wintering areas. These trails frequently led past salt springs where the bison gathered to drink and to lick the salty earth.

One of the earliest settlers of western Pennsylvania built his log cabin near just such a salt spring that the bison were accustomed to visiting. As related to the English traveler, Thomas Ashe, the bison 'sought for no manner of food, but only bathed and drank three or four times a day and rolled in the earth. . . . ' In the first and second years this old man, with some companions, killed from six to seven hundred of these noble creatures, merely for the sake of the skins, which were worth only two shillings each. . . .[43]

Also forever gone from the eastern seaboard are the Labrador duck and the heath hen. Never plentiful, the beautiful Labrador duck ranged as far south as Chesapeake Bay and was harvested for its meat and colorful black and white plumage. The last recorded specimen was shot on Long Island, New York, in 1875.[44] The heath hen was the eastern race of the greater prairie chicken, a plump, square-tailed game bird with long tufts of feathers on either side of its neck, and which acted very much like its western relative. As McClung so graphically related,

In Colonial days the heath hen ranged from New England to Virginia, and possibly to the Carolinas. Every springtime cocks assembled on communal 'booming grounds' during the breeding season and performed elaborate courtship rites before gatherings of hens. They 'boomed' by inflating orange-colored air sacs on either side of their necks, then expelling the air forcefully with a resultant hollow sound.

In early Colonial days heath hens were abundant throughout their range. Around Boston they were so plentiful that 'servants stipulated with their employers not to have Heath Hen brought to the table oftener than a few times a week.'[45]

The last survivor of the species, a lone old male, was last seen March 11, 1932, on Martha's Vineyard, an island off Cape Cod, Massachusetts.[46]

In Colonial days the elk ("wapiti," meaning "light rump" in Shawnee language) was a widespread species of big game not only in the western states, where it is yet found, but over the entire nation. A separate eastern race lived largely east of the Mississippi River. It was hunted so enthusiastically that by the time of the Civil War few remained; a few years later it became extinct.[47]

A description by William Bartram of the flora and fauna of areas in the southeastern United States tells of the incredible abundance in that portion of the country before man's intrusions into the environment upset and decimated this well-structured natural reservoir of wealth. While traveling along the St. Johns River and through the nearby area of Florida in the summer of 1774 he wrote the following:

How shall I express myself so as to convey an adequate idea of it to the reader, and at the same time avoid raising suspicions of my veracity? Should I say, that the river (in this place) from shore to shore, and perhaps near half a mile above and below me, appeared to be one solid bank of fish, of various kinds (large-mouthed bass, shadines, etc.), pushing through this narrow pass of St. Juan's into the little lake, on their return down the river, and that the alligators were in such incredible numbers, and so close from shore to shore, that it would have been easy to have walked across on their heads, had the animals been harmless? What expressions can sufficiently declare the shocking scene that for some minutes continued, whilst this mighty army of fish were forcing the pass? During this attempt, thousands, I may say hundreds of thousands, of them were caught and swallowed by the devouring alligators. I have seen an alligator take out of the water several great fish at a time, and just squeeze them betwixt his jaws, while the tails of the great trout flapped about his eyes and lips, ere he had swallowed them.[48]

The Great Plains

Whenever the Plains of pioneer days is mentioned the vision of massive buffalo herds come to one's mind . . . and for good reason. Though no one knows how many buffalo there were when the Louisiana Purchase was made, informed guesses range from 10 to 100 million![49] According to Udall,

The size of the buffalo herds was a source of awe to the plainsmen, and Colonel R. I. Dodge once wrote of a herd he saw in Arkansas in the early 70s: 'From the top of Pawnee Rocks I could see from six to ten miles in almost every direction. This whole vast space was covered with buffalo, looking at a distance like a compact mass.'[50]

In his book *The American Bison,* Martin Garretson records this creation legend of the Indians as told to an old scout:

The first day the Great Spirit planted by the side of the waters the Great Way Tree whose boughs extended into the Heavens, by way of

Figure 47. The Plains buffalo.

which all creatures were sent down upon the Earth, and lastly a Kiowa man and woman who walked about the creation, but in the evening they returned to the Great Way Tree, and there met the Buffalo, and the Great Spirit descended and said: 'Here are the Buffalo. They shall be your food and your raiment, but in the day you shall see them perish from off the face of the Earth, then know that the end of the Kiowa is near—and the Sun set.'[51]

The Kiowas, Commanches, Cheyennes, Sioux, and other Plains tribes, called "Buffalo Indians," depended utterly upon the buffalo for their existence as they followed the great herds. When the beasts vanished, the way of life of the Plains Indians vanished as well. According to McClung,

The Indians ate buffalo flesh raw or cooked; they dried it for winter use. They fashioned teepees and clothing from buffalo hides, and used the wooly robes as sleeping spreads and floor coverings. They made soup ladles of the horns, tools and weapons from the bones. Very little of the animal was wasted.[52]

Cortez and his conquistadors were probably the first Europeans to see the Plains bison. In 1521 they apparently visited the menageries of Montezuma where they reported "The Mexican Bull; a wonderful composition of divers Animals. It has crooked Shoulders, with a Bunch on its Back like a camel . . . its Neck covered with Hair like a Lion. It is cloven footed, its Head armed like that of a Bull, which it resembles in Fierceness, with no less strength and Agility."[53]

Bands of huge buffalo wolves trailed the herds, feeding upon the calves, older animals, or stragglers. Drought, winter blizzards, disease, and mass drownings when the animals crossed swollen streams took their toll, as did the Indians who sometimes surrounded a herd and stampeded it over a cliff; yet, the numbers never were depleted, and the herds flourished magnificently. Only white men with rifles and greed in their eyes could effect the devastation of this great sea of majestic beasts. By 1897 only 20 or so Plains buffalo remained in the United States, those all in Yellowstone Park.[54]

Writing about the western adventures of Captain Bonneville, Washington Irving described wildlife along the route of a journey:

In these rugged and elevated regions they began to see the black-tailed deer, a species larger than the ordinary kind, and chiefly found in rocky and mountainous countries. They had reached also a great buffalo range; Captain Bonneville ascended a high bluff, commanding an extensive view of the surrounding plains. As far as his eye could reach, the country seemed absolutely blackened by innumerable herds. No language, he says, could convey an adequate idea of the vast living mass thus presented to his eye. He remarked that the bulls and cows generally congregated in separate herds.[55]

Pronghorn antelope, deer, elk, and other animals were found in great abundance as well on the unmolested Plains of America before the Anglo-Saxons made their appearance. As John James Audubon exuberantly wrote in his journal after seeing some pronghorns on a trip up the Missouri River in 1843, "Hurra for the prairies and the swift antelope. They fleet by the hunter like flashes or meteors. . . . "[56] These antelope, the fastest mammals in America, which may travel on lightning-like legs up to 60 miles per hour, flourished until the white man invaded its territory.

Prairie birds in the early days of the U.S. presented a spectacle to man seldom appreciated by the present generation. Besides the limitless flocks of passenger pigeons (though these tended to frequent the eastern wooded areas to a greater extent), ducks, geese, and prairie chickens were everywhere abundant. Paul Errington, a native South Dakotan who grew up along the Big Sioux River, wrote extensively about the birds and animals of the wetlands he loved, and the necessity of bogs and marshlands in the broad ecological outlook. He wrote the following about the abundant ducks during the earlier years in South Dakota sloughs and lakes:

Some forty years ago, from a duck pass on the old farm, I saw flights of the now-scarce redheads during which I am sure that more redheads passed over or near me in two hours than I have seen all together in the past twenty years. Redhead flocks roaring sixty to eighty yards overhead, a half-dozen flocks abreast at times, and more and more of them coming in, all traveling in the same direction at the same speed and alighting, flock after flock, in the middle of a lake—a spectacle of magnificence that I doubt any man now living will see again on any north-central lake or perhaps anywhere in the world. I do not contend that my memories are without sadness.

Figure 48. The pronghorn antelope.

The central waters of lakes also had their panoramic views of ducks other than the by-gone wonders of the canvasbacks and redheads. The divers among these other ducks were mostly bluebills and ringnecks, and they gave the appearance of black and white dots on the surface. Flights of bluebills and ringnecks would come in at any hour of day, but usually toward evening, sometimes flock after flock dropping out of the sky, gliding, zigzagging, almost tumbling down to splash with outstretched feet. Or they would fly low over the water, bunched up or in spread-out formation. On a rainy or foggy day or evening, a lake might be covered with bluebills and ringnecks. In stormy weather, they might either seek the quieter waters in the shelter of points or in-lands or hills or wooded stretches of shore or ride the waves of the lake centers. Great rafts of mallards might likewise ride waves or huddle close to shore on stormy days or cover lake centers in calm weather.[57]

The abundance of ducks on the early prairies prompted Ole Rolvaag to include an episode about these birds in his classic *Giants in the Earth*. The Norwegian settlers of Spring Creek in eastern South Dakota had no apparent means of capturing any of the multitude of ducks that filled the sloughs near their sod houses. They eventually resorted to using fish nets at night:

One Sunday evening the boys had come home wild with excitement. They had made a long trip westward on the prairie to some big swamps which lay out there, with tall grass growing from them, and long stretches of open water in between. They told of thousands upon thousands of ducks, so tame that you could almost take them in your hand. Store-Hans vowed that never in his life had he seen anything like it. He described the ducks, how many and how tame they were, until the words stuck in his throat, and his whole body trembled; his brother raged even worse.

From then on the boys were always talking about the ducks. Was there no way to get them? . . . But they had no shotgun . . . So the ducks continued to live there, swimming leisurely about in countless numbers, and flying from one pond to the next whenever the boys came too close. . . .

But in the opinion of the boys, the duck hunt with the net was the crowning adventure. . . . For three nights they had stayed out in the swamps to the westward, toiling and fighting among the myriads of birds; in the morning they would come home after daylight, wet as crows, numb all over, and blue in the face with cold. But they always brought a catch! . . . As soon as the evening came they would be off again.[58]

The character of the prairie land on which the prairie chickens, wild turkeys, and Plains game roamed was, in its native state, a fabulous spectacle to behold.

Between the Mackenzie River of Canada and the highlands of northern Mexico, there is a vast inland sea of grasses, more than 3,000 miles long, bordered on the east and west by forests. . . .
From Ohio to eastern Oklahoma is the tall-grass prairie, where the native grasses once grew higher than the height of a tall man. Such tall grasses once mantled the whole central heartland of the continent, regardless of differences in soil and topography. These diverse lands had in common a flora of waving grasses dotted with colorful flowers. In this sea of grass during the millennia, deep roots had built a sod so dense that in turning it the homesteaders broke their plows. The characteristic native grasses of the prairie are big and little bluestem and Indian grass; nowadays most of the land they covered makes up the corn belt. To the west is a transition zone where grasses do not grow so high, nor as a continuous carpet. June grass, wheat grass, and little bluestem grow in clumps, the spaces between the clumps being filled with an abundance of wildflowers; this is the great winter wheat region. Farther still to the west, in the rain shadow of the Rockies, grow the short grasses of the high plains: grama, needle grass, buffalo grass; today this is an extensive grazing area.[59]

Prairie chickens of various species ranged across the Plains and prairie states in profuse numbers. Laura Ingals Wilder in *Little House on the Prairie* wrote of how she and her sister hunted for birds' nests in the tall grass of Kansas. Bird and animal life were extremely abundant during those early days, when "in the tall grass they lay still as mice and watched flocks of little prairie chickens running and pecking around their anxiously clucking, smooth brown mothers."[60] After carrying home a huge rabbit and two plump prairie hens one evening, Laura's father exclaimed, "This country's cram-jammed with game . . . I saw fifty deer if I saw one, and antelope, squirrels, rabbits, birds of all kinds. The creek's full of fish. . . . I tell you, Caroline, there's everything we want here. We

Figure 49. The greater prairie chicken.

can live like kings!''[61] The utter contentment experienced by a young girl in such a fragrant, wholesome, productive environment was voiced in these words that same evening: "That was a wonderful supper. They sat by the camp fire and ate the tender, savory, flavory meat till they could eat no more. When at last Laura set down her plate, she sighed with contentment. She didn't want anything more in the world."[62]

Today the prairie chicken lives only in isolated areas where the original prairie plants yet exist. One species, Attwater's greater prairie chicken, which at one time ranged from the coastal prairies of western Louisiana to Texas, is in imminent danger of extinction, while the eastern race has been extinct since 1932.[63]

In the drier portions of the Plains, near the Bighorn Mountains of Wyoming, Francis Parkman in 1849 wrote of "the abundance of strange insects and reptiles" he found along the Oregon Trail.[64] "Huge crickets, black and bottle green, and wingless grasshoppers of the most extravagant dimensions, were tumbling about our horses' feet, and lizards without number darting like lightning among the tufts of grass."[65] Tremendous numbers of prairie dogs abounded in the area. "Frequently the hard and dry plain was thickly covered, for miles together, with the little mounds which they make at the mouth of their burrows. . . ."[66] Even grizzly bears frequented the Plains areas, as Parkman noted their huge tracks on several occasions.

Streams of the Midwest and Plains abounded with fish. Even a small stream such as the Sioux River in eastern South Dakota yielded great quantities of fish to early pioneers.

Per Hansa had taken both boys with him on the great expedition east to the Sioux River; there they had made a tremendous catch with the help of a net. . . . Heaps of frozen fish now lay outside all along the wall.[67]

Along the Minnesota River pioneer women found fish so plentiful that they could flip them out of the water with a pitchfork.[68] The waters were pristine in those days, enabling trout to thrive in most streams.

The herb and fruit production on the American Plains were as prolific as the wildlife, especially along streams; in fact, the abundance of the animals and the vitality of native plant growth go hand in hand. Josiah Gregg, in a vivid discourse on life and commerce along the Santa Fe Trail, described prairie vegetation on the southwestern Plains:

> With regard to fruits, the Prairies are of course not very plentifully supplied. West of the border, however, for nearly two hundred miles, they are covered, in many places, with the wild strawberry; and the groves lining the streams frequently abound in grapes, plums, persimmons, mulberries, paccans, hackberries, and other 'sylvan luxuries.' The high prairies beyond, however, are very bare of fruits. . . . Upon the branches of the Canadian, North Fork, and Cimarron, there are, in places, considerable quantities of excellent plums, chokecherries, gooseberries, and currants—of the latter there are three kinds, black, red, and white. About the ravines and marshy grounds . . . there are different kinds of small onions, with which the traveler may season his fresh meats. On the plains, also, I have met with a species resembling garlic in flavor.
>
> But the flowers are among the most interesting products of the frontier prairies. These gay meadows wear their most fanciful piebald robes from the earliest spring till divested of them by the hoary frosts of autumn. When again winter has fled, but before the grassy green appears, or other vegetation has ventured to peep above the earth, they are bespeckled in many places with a species of erythronium, a pretty lilacous little flower, which springs from the ground already developed, between a pair of lanceolate leaves, and is soon after in full bloom. But the floriferous region extends only about two hundred miles beyond the border: the high plains are nearly as destitute of flowers as they are of fruits.[69]

Near the Platte River of Nebraska, Washington Irving related how Captain Bonneville and his expedition found game scanty, forcing him to live from the plants he could find, consisting of "wild roots and vegetables, such as the Indian potato, the wild onion, and the prairie tomato, and they met with quantities of 'red root,' from which the hunters make a very palatable beverage."[70] Most streams provided banks lush with fruits and herbs, such as that described by Parkman near Ft. Laramie: " . . . we came to a little brook traversing the barren prairie. All along its course grew copses of young wild-cherry trees, loaded with ripe fruit, and almost concealing the gliding thread of water with their dense growth."[71]

The Mississippi and Ohio River Valleys

The marvelous productivity of the Mississippi and Ohio Rivers and their expansive, fertile valleys in the early 1800s cannot be appreciated by words alone. The following picture painted by Timothy Flint, a missionary who spent much time traveling as well, describes a trip down these rivers from the viewpoint of a highly educated river traveler.

It was now the middle of November . . . . The wide, clean sand-bars stretching for miles together, and now and then a flock of wild geese, swans, or sand-hill cranes, and pelicans [sic], stalking along on them; the infinite varieties of form of the towering bluffs; the new tribes of shrubs and plants on the shores; the exuberant fertility of the soil, evidencing itself in the natural as well as cultivated vegetation, in the height and size of the corn, of itself alone a matter of astonishment to an inhabitant of the northern states, in the thrifty aspect of the young orchards, literally bending under their fruit, the surprising size and rankness of the weeds, and, in the enclosures where cultivation had been for a while suspended, the matted appearance of every kind of vegetation that ensued,—all these circumstances united to give a novelty and freshness to the scenery. The bottom forests everywhere display the huge sycamore, the king of the western forest. . . . in all the trees that have been stripped of their leaves, you see them crowned with verdant tufts of the viscous or mistletoe, with its beautiful white berries, and their trunks entwined with grapevines, some of them in size not much short of the human body. . . .

I observed the cotton [wood] trees [near the Missouri confluence with the Mississippi] to be immensely tall, rising like Corinthian columns, enwrapped with a luxuriant wreathing of ivy, and the *bigonia radicans,* with its splendid, trumpet-shaped flowers, displayed them glittering in the sun, quite on the summits of the trees. The prairie itself was a most glorious spectacle. Such a sea of verdure, in one direction extending beyond the reach of the eye, and presenting millions of flowers of every scent and hue, seemed an immense flower garden. . . .

Large flocks of cattle and horses are seen grazing together. It is often that a flock of wild deer is seen bounding over the plain. In the autumn, immense flocks of pelicans (possibly white pelicans), sand-bills, cranes (sand-hill cranes), geese, swans, ducks, and all kinds of aquatic fowls, are seen hovering over it. The soil is of the easiest culture and the most exuberant productiveness. The farms are laid out in parallelograms. At the foot of the Mamelles are clumps of hazel bushes, pawpaws, wild grapes, and prairie plums, in abundance. The grass is thick and tall. Corn and wheat grow in the greatest perfection. When I first saw this charming scene, 'Here,' said I to my companion who guided me, 'here shall be my farm, and here I will end my days!' In effect, take it all in all, I have not seen, before nor since, a landscape which united, in an equal degree, the grand, the beautiful, and fertile. It is not necessary in seeing it to be very young or romantic, in order to have dreams steal over the mind, of spending an Arcadian life in these remote plains, which just begin to be vexed with the plough, far removed from the haunts of wealth and fashion, in the midst of rustic plenty, and of this beautiful nature.[72]

An earlier expedition of La Salle in 1682 down the lower Mississippi inspired Henri de Tonti, La Salle's lieutenant, to describe a countryside very prolific in growth and beauty:

Their [the Indians'] country is beautiful, having abundance of peach, plum, and apple trees, and vines flourish there; buffaloes, deer, stags, bears, turkeys, are very numerous. They have even domestic fowls. . . .

. . . a league or two from the river [was] the most beautiful country in the world, prairies, woods of mulberry trees, vines, and fruits that we were not acquainted with. The savages gather the Indian corn twice in the year.

. . . there are a large number of buffaloes, bears, large wolves, stags and hinds in abundance, and some lead mines which yield two-thirds of ore to one of refuse.[73]

Adding to de Tonti's description of the middle reaches of the Mississippi River, Mark Twain (Samuel Clemens) wrote with great clarity about the river which was woven into the very fabric of his life. Having grown up on the Mississippi River in Missouri, he wrote *Life on the Mississippi* in 1883, during a time when the upper reaches of the Great River were yet fairly stabilized against the ravages of erosion and relatively free of pollution. His description of this now highly polluted river bear out this truth:

We noticed that above Dubuque the water of the Mississippi was olive-green—rich and beautiful and semitransparent, with the sun on it. Of course the water was nowhere as clear or of as fine a complexion as it is in some other seasons of the year; for now it was at flood stage, and therefore dimmed and blurred by the mud manufactured from caving banks.

The majestic bluffs that overlook the river, along through this region, charm one with the grace and variety of their forms, and the soft beauty of their adornment. The steep, verdant slope, whose base is at the water's edge, is topped by a lofty rampart of broken, turreted rocks, which are exquisitely rich and mellow in color—mainly dark browns and dull greens, but splashed with other tints. And then you have the shining river, winding here and there and yonder, its sweep interrupted at intervals by clusters of wooded islands threaded by silver channels; and you have glimpses of distant villages, asleep upon capes; and of stealthy rafts slipping along in the shade of the forest walls; and of white steamers vanishing around remote points. And it is all as tranquil and reposeful as dreamland, and has nothing this-worldly about it—nothing to hang a fret or a worry upon.[74]

The West and Southwest

Descriptions of the native West and Southwest are among the most vivid and captivating of any in the United States. Among the most colorful writers of the bygone era who knew so intimately the natural wonders of the mountains, valleys, and deserts, is the renowned naturalist John Muir. Born in Scotland, he came to the U.S. in 1849 at the age of eleven, and was reared in Wisconsin, finally set-tling in California. He is largely responsible for the creation of Yosemite National Park, and saving California's redwoods and mountain wilderness areas. First a fruit farmer, but then naturalist and conservationist, he also wrote descriptive books about the un-tainted world he loved so dearly and strove to protect, from which comes the following paragraphs:

When California was wild, it was one sweet bee garden throughout its entire length, north and south, and all the way across from the snowy Sierra to the ocean. Whenever a bee might fly within the bounds of this virgin wilderness—through the redwood forests, along the banks of the rivers, along the bluffs and headlands fronting the sea, over valley and plain, park and grove, and deep, leafy glen, or far up the piny slopes of the mountains—throughout every belt and section of climate up to the timber line, bee flowers bloomed in lavish abundance. Here they grew more or less apart in special sheets and patches of no great size, there in broad, flowing folds hundreds of miles in length—zones of polleny forest, zones of flowery chaparral, stream tangles of rubus and wild rose, sheets of golden compositae, beds of violets, beds of mint, beds of bryanthus and clover, and so on, certain species blooming somewhere all the year round. . . .

The Great Central Plain of California, during the months of March, April, and May, was one smooth, continuous bed of honey bloom, so marvelously rich that, in walking from one end of it to the other, a distance of more than four hundred miles, your foot would press about a hundred flowers at every step. Mints, gilias, nemophilas, castillias, and innumerable compositae were so crowded together that, had ninety-nine per cent of them been taken away, the plain would still have seemed to any but Californians extravagantly flowery. The radiant, honeyful corollas, touching and overlapping, and rising above one another, glowed in the living light like a sunset sky—one sheet of purple and gold, with the bright Sacramento pouring through the midst of it from the north, the San Joaquin from the south, and their many tributaries sweeping in at right angles from the mountains, dividing the plain into sections fringed with trees.

Along the rivers there is a strip of bottom-land, countersunk beneath the general level, and wider toward the foothills, where magnificent oaks, from three to eight feet in diameter, cast grateful masses of shade over the open, prairie-like levels. And close along the water's edge there was a fine jungle of tropical luxuriance, composed of wild-rose and bramble bushes and a great variety of climbing vines, wreathing and interlacing the branches and trunks of willows and alders, and swinging across from summit to summit in heavy festoons. Here the wild bees reveled in fresh bloom long after the flowers of the drier plain had withered and gone to seed. And in mid-summer, when the 'blackberries' were ripe, the Indians came from the mountains to feast—men, women, and babies in long, noisy trains, often joined by the farmers of the neighborhood, who gathered this wild fruit with commendable appreciation of its superior flavor, while their home orchards were full of ripe peaches, apricots, nectarines, and figs, and their vineyards were laden with grapes. But, though these luxuriant, shaggy river-beds were thus distinct from the smooth, treeless plain, they made no heavy dividing lines in general views. The whole appeared as one continuous sheet of bloom bounded only by the mountains.

When I first saw this central garden, the most extensive and regular of all the bee pastures of the State, it seemed all one sheet of plant gold, hazy and vanishing in the distance, as a new map along the foothills at my feet.

Sauntering in any direction, hundreds of these happy sunplants brushed against my feet at every step, and closed over them as if I were wading in liquid gold. The air was sweet with fragrance, the larks sang their blessed songs, rising on the wing as I advanced, then sinking out of sight in the polleny sod, while myriads of wild bees stirred the lower air with their monotonous hum—monotonous, yet forever fresh and sweet as everyday sunshine. Hares and spermophiles showed themselves in considerable numbers in shallow places, and small bands of antelopes were almost constantly in sight, gazing curiously from some slight elevation, and then bounding swiftly away with unrivaled grace of motion. Yet I could discover no crushed flowers to mark their track, nor, indeed, any destructive action of any wild foot or tooth whatever.[75]

The Indians of the old West highly valued wildlife of all sorts, and were perhaps the first people to set aside game refuges. This bit of history, passed on by Theodore Roosevelt in his book *Winning of the West,* captured the following story of abundance which the Creek Indians related to him:

The bears had been exceedingly abundant at one time, so much so as to become one of the main props of the Creek larder, furnishing flesh, fat, and especially oil for cooking and other purposes; and so valued were they that they hit upon the novel plan of preserving them, exactly as Europeans preserve deer and pheasants. Each town put aside a great tract of land which was known as 'the beloved bear ground,' where persimmons, haws, chestnuts, muscadines, and fox grapes abounded, and let the bears dwell there unmolested, except at certain seasons, when they were killed in large numbers.[76]

Casteñada, the recorder on Coronado's expedition into the U.S. Southwest 200 years before the colonists settled on the Atlantic coast, described the virgin condition of that relatively dry territory:

This country [the Zuñi area of west-central New Mexico] is a valley between rocky mountains. They cultivate corn, which does not grow very high. . . . There are large numbers of bears in this province, and lions, wild-cats, deer, and other.[77]

Many modern geologists of the Western states have considered the muddy, roiling waters of rivers like the Colorado, Pecos, or Rio Grande to be typical of years past, before man's intervention into the natural order of things. However, according to Aldo Leopold, author of the famous *A Sand County Almanac,* "In many cases we literally do not know how good a performance to expect of healthy land unless we have a wild area for comparison with sick ones."[78] Lepold continued by contrasting early reports of streams in the Southwest with similar undisturbed rivers in Mexico:

Thus most of the early travelers in the Southwest describe the mountain rivers as originally clear, but a doubt remains, for they may, by accident, have seen them at favorable seasons. Erosion engineers had no base datum until it was discovered that exactly similar rivers in the Sierra Madre of Chihuahua, never grazed or used for fear of Indians, show at their worst a milky hue, not too cloudy for a trout fly. Moss grows to the water's edge on their banks. Most of the corresponding rivers in Arizona and New Mexico are ribbons of boulders, mossless, soil-less, and all but tree-less.[79]

The logical extrapolation of this information is that the rivers and streams of arid regions, often subject today to cloudbursts and massive rapid erosion from cloudburst, were not so seriously affected when virgin order was maintained within the untampered wilderness. Likewise, streams nation-wide were in a state of purity and balance with natural laws, the water drinkable nearly everywhere and teeming with fish.

The observations of Captain Bonneville's expedition in the mountains near Fort Laramie, Wyoming, in 1830 revealed "flocks of the ahsahto or bighorn, an animal which frequents these cliffs in great numbers."[80] These mountain sheep apparently extended far to the east as well, inhabiting cliffs along the North Platte River near Scottsbluff.

Some of the grandest accounts of the Southwest during pre-Colonial days have been left us by Don Juan de Oñate, a Spanish explorer and governor of New Mexico from 1595 to 1608.[81] In 1601 he led an expedition to the northeast and penetrated as far as modern Kansas and recorded with great clarity the character of the untainted wilderness of the Southwest. Some portions of that record are presented below.

Having traveled five days we all came to a river in an opening, with peaceful waters, covered with shady groves of trees, some bearing fruits, and with very good fish. . . .

. . . we found it [the Canadian River] to be so verdant, pleasant, and so covered with vines and other fruits on all sides that we clearly saw that it was one of the best rivers which we had seen in all the Indes. . . . [The Apache Indians] brought to us some small black and yellow fruit of the size of small tomatoes, which is plentiful on all that river. It was as healthful as it was pleasant to taste, for although eaten freely it injured no one.

At times it became necessary for us to depart from the main river in order to find a road for the carts; and although we feared the lack of watering places for the cattle, there are so many in this country that throughout the journey at distances of three or four leagues there was always sufficient water for the cattle and for the men; and in many places there were springs of very good water and groves of trees. . . .

Each day the land through which we were travelling became better, and the luxury of an abundance of fish from the river greatly alleviated the hardships of the journey. And the fruits gave no less pleasure, particularly the plums, of a hundred thousand different kinds, as mellow and good as those which grow in the choicest orchards of our land. They are so good that although eaten by thousands they never injured anybody. The trees were small, but their fruit was more plentiful than their leaves, and they were so abundant that in more than one hundred and fifty leagues, hardly a day passed without seeing groves of them, and also of grapevines such that although they hid the view in many places they produced sweet and delicious grapes.

. . . God was pleased that we should begin to see those most monstrous cattle called cibola [buffalo]. . . . On the following day . . . we now saw great droves of bulls and cows, and from there on the multitude which we saw was so great that it might be considered a falsehood by one who had not seen them, for . . . nearly every day and wherever we went as many cattle came out as are to be found in the largest ranches of New Spain; and they were so tame that nearly always, unless they were chased or frightened, they remained quiet and did not flee. The flesh of these cattle is very good, and very much better than that of our cows. In general they are very fat, especially the cows, and almost all have a great deal of tallow. By experience we noted that they do not become angry like our cattle, and are never dangerous . . . the wool is . . . so fine and soft that it could be spun and woven like that of the Castilian sheep. . . . This river is thickly covered on all sides with these cattle and with another not less wonderful, consisting of deer which are as large as large horses. They travel in droves of two or three hundred and their deformity causes one to wonder whether they are deer or some other animal [possibly wapiti].

. . . the fields there were covered with flowers of a thousand different kinds, so thick that they choked the pasture. The cattle of this territory must eat these flowers far better than ours are wont to do, because wherever they were there were multitudes of cattle.

. . . [we] reached a small river, carrying little water but so grown with timber that its banks resembled thickly wooded mountains. Here we found many walnut trees loaded with nuts which were nearly as good as those of our country, the trees being taller and having more abundant foliage, and the land being so grown with pasture that it could scarcely be seen. Having slept one night in this pleasant spot, we went on next day three leagues from this point to where flowed a river carrying more water than the last one, and with many fish and larger groves, both of walnuts and of oak, and other valuable timbers. The land was better than that which we had hitherto seen, so good indeed that all said that they never had seen any better in their lives. The cattle were innumerable, and of all kinds of game there was a great abundance—Castilian partridges, turkeys, deer, and hares. . . .

Here [at the Arkansas River] we found a small fruit the size of the wild pear or yellow sapodilla, of very good flavor. The river contained an abundance of very good fish . . . its waters were fresh and pleasant to taste. Here the land was fertile and much better than that which we had passed. The pastures were so good that in many places the grass was high enough to conceal a horse. . . .

. . . it became necessary to go to the banks of a large river called the Rio de San Francisco, whose banks in these parts were most beautiful to look upon and were covered with mulberry trees and other trees bearing fruit of very fine flavor. Many people constantly came and went to see us, bringing ears of maize. . . .[83]

In Summary . . .

When the pioneers arrived in America to carve out a new life in a new land they found it well ordered after natural laws, abounding in animals, fish, birds, fruit, herbs, and grass. Each environment was equally blessed with whatever flora and fauna was adapted to the multitude of niches it provided. From north to south, and from east to west the land was all set for man to enter and settle, to "tend and keep" species of livestock and vegetation they lived upon, just as the Creator had planned things. America's pioneers were not ordained to exploit—take selfish advantage of and reorder after their own whims—the resources which had been given to them.

The Indians for centuries coexisted peacefully with the beasts and trees, the ducks and berries, the fish and roots found nearly everywhere across the continent. They did not deplete the great buffalo and elk herds, nor did they use more than they required to live, while the white man seemed bent on destroying whatever good he might find in this beautiful new land having seemingly inexhaustible resources (the Myth of Superabundance). Rather than multiply the native fruit trees, berries, grapes, and roots, and carefully harvest from the buffalo, pronghorn, deer, elk, mountain goat, moose, and caribou populations, he killed for sport until there were hardly any more to kill. He decimated the passenger pigeon and prairie chicken until none or few remained, and first overfished and then polluted the lakes and rivers so future generations could not enjoy the plenty which the land would have provided to countless millions of people had these resources been tended properly.

It is entirely feasible that a population well in excess of 200 million people could have been well fed and clothed by the well-tended animals and plant kingdoms in America, which would have eliminated the need for massive cultivation of the prairies and woodlands to produce corn, wheat, barley, rye, potatoes, flax, cotton, and soybeans. Nature well tended by men could do all that . . . and better, using plants uniquely adapted to each environment as man found them in place, rather than using introduced plants of questionable nutritional value.

Man's technique has been to cut, burn, destroy, and then rebuild upon the ruins according to his own unproven whims. Why does he

Figure 50. "The Still Hunt"; the shooting of buffalo from secluded positions as the herd calmly grazes.

not view the admonitions of the Great Master Ecologist, who says,

> If you happen to come upon a bird's nest on a tree or on the ground, with young ones or eggs and the mother-bird sitting on the young ones or on the eggs, you must not take away the mother-bird along with her brood; what you must do is let the mother-bird go, as you take the brood for yourself, that all may go well with you and that you may have a long life (Deut. 22:6-7).

"That all may go well with you." Things are not going too well today as our own cattle—not nearly as well adapted to the Plains as the buffalo, elk, pronghorn, or deer—have been pushed to the outer margins of our lands, if not the outer portions of our minds. The overall principle here is to maintain the wild breeding stock—the adult bird, animal, or fish—so they may proliferate to provide game for following generations, and never become depleted. The need of a harvest is not questioned, but rather the method of harvest in order to maintain perpetual viability of the breeding population.

Aldo Leopold, the gifted writer, noted naturalist, and militant conservationist who in his boyhood days roamed the outdoors of his native Iowa, once wrote,

> The most important characteristic of an organism is that capacity for internal self-renewal known as health.

> There are two organisms whose processes of self-renewal have been subjected to human interference and control. One of these is man himself (medicine and public health). The other is land (agriculture and conservation).

> The effort to control the health of land has not been very successful. It is now generally understood that when soil loses fertility, or washes away faster than it forms, and when water systems exhibit abnormal floods and shortages, the land is sick.

> Other derangements are known as facts, but are not yet thought of as symptoms of land sickness. The disappearance of plants and animal species without visible cause, despite efforts to protect them, and the irruption of pests despite efforts to control them, must, in the absence of simpler explanations, be regarded as symptoms of sickness in the land organism. Both are occurring too frequently to be dismissed as normal evolutionary events.

The status of thought on these ailments of the land is reflected in the fact that our treatments for them are still prevailingly local. Thus when a soil loses fertility we pour on fertilizer, or at best alter its tame flora and fauna, without considering the fact that its wild flora and fauna, which built the soil to begin with, may likewise be important to its maintenance. It was recently discovered, for example, that good tobacco crops depend, for some unknown reason, on the preconditioning of the soil by wild ragweed. It does not occur to us that such unexpected chains of dependency may have wide prevalence in nature.

When prairie dogs, ground squirrels, or mice increase to pest levels we poison them, but we do not look beyond the animal to find the cause of the irruption. We assume that animal troubles must have animal causes. The latest scientific evidence points to derangements of the *plant* community as the real seat of rodent irruptions, but few explorations of this clue are being made.

Many forest plantations are producing one-log or two-log trees on soil which originally grew three-log and four-log trees. Why? Thinking foresters know that the cause probably lies not in the trees, but in the micro-flora of the soil, and that it may take more years to restore the soil flora than it took to destroy it.

Many conservation treatments are obviously superficial. Flood-control dams have no relation to the cause of floods. Check dams and terraces do not touch the cause of erosion. Refuges and hatcheries to maintain the supply of game and fish do not explain why the supply fails to maintain itself.

In general, the trend of the evidence indicates that in land, just as in the human body, the symptoms may lie in one organ and the cause in another. The practices we now call conservation are, to a large extent, local alleviations of biotic pain. They are necessary, but they must not be confused with cures. . . .[84]

The "cures" Aldo Leopold refers to here would involve an environmental transformation unparalleled in the annals of human history—a reversion to the natural environment as man first found it on the North American continent, in a state of unsurpassed beauty and climax. Of course, only a powerful hand from above can bring about such a dramatic change to the land, a hand that reeducates the mind of everyone from the greed, lust, and disregard for the preservation of order and plenty to the laws of harmony, generosity,

joy, and patience found within a land structured around permanence.

George Perkins Marsh, a native of Vermont with a deep love of the
land and its need to be conserved—and a leader in America's conservation movement—wrote his classic *Man and Nature* in 1864 in
which he stated the following words:

> . . . [my object is] to point out the dangers of imprudence and the
> necessity of caution, in all operations which, on a large scale, interfere
> with the spontaneous arrangements of the organic and inorganic
> world. . . .
>
> The ravages committed by man subvert the relations and destroy the
> balance which nature has established . . . ; and she avenges herself
> upon the intruder by letting loose her destructive energies. . . . When
> the forest is gone, the great reservoir of moisture stored up in its
> vegetable mould is evaporated. . . . The well-wooded and humid hills
> are turned to ridges of dry rock, . . . and . . . the whole earth, unless
> rescued by human art from the physical degradation to which it tends,
> becomes an assemblage of bald mountains, of barren, turfless hills,
> and of swampy and malarious plains. There are parts of Asia Minor,
> of Northern Africa, of Greece, and even of Alpine Europe, where the
> operation of causes set in action by man has brought the face of the
> earth to a desolation almost as complete as that of the moon. . . . The
> earth is fast becoming an unfit home for its noblest inhabitant,
> and another era of equal human crime and human improvidence . . .
> would reduce it to such a condition of impoverished productiveness,
> of shattered surface, of climatic excess, as to threaten the depravation,
> barbarism, and perhaps even extinction of the species.[85]

Several generations have passed since 1864 and men still live on the
earth. Yet, they live in a world far removed from the natural beauty
and serenity of the environment in America generations ago. It is a
"shattered surface" in many ways and would suddenly cease to produce much of its stores of the field should fertilizers, pesticides, and
herbicides fail to be applied. Dams are needed to control floods from
rainwater and snowmelt unable to be absorbed by denuded, low-
porosity soils. Several species of wildlife barely cling to survival, and
many, such as the whooping crane and sea otter, are kept alive only
through massive conservation efforts.

We have thrown away an incredible legacy . . . the legacy of our natural fields, forests, and flocks. It is too late to turn back, and what's more, most people are not convinced they ought to. Only direct intervention by the Creator of all life can restore the world to its potential verdure, even beyond our present conceptions of prolific abundance envisioned through scant remnants of the original un-stained flowered prairies, pine-covered mountains, and fruited streambanks in parks and wilderness areas. It is too late to turn back.

APPENDIX II

"Mother Earth": Much More Than a Pleasant Platitude

Down through the ages the common, perhaps overused phrase "mother earth" has come to mean many things to many people. These two words normally imply our inextricable and inseverable ties to the soil from which all flesh and grass are fabricated, the pathway of synthesis of organic molecules in plants from soil nutrients, and their incorporation within the bodily organs of man. The earth—with its multitude of life-feeding cycles involving water, solar energy, heat, nutrient elements, weather systems, and so forth—is thus the umbilicus of life to all living things, from which every life form obtains its nourishment.

The God-plane nature of this life-earth, or more specifically the man-earth relationship is first expressed in Genesis 1:26, 28:

> Then said God, 'Let us make man in our own likeness, to resemble us, with mastery over the fish in the sea, the birds of the air, the animals, every wild beast of the earth, and every reptile that crawls on the earth . . . . ' God said to them, 'Be fruitful, multiply, fill the earth and subdue it, mastering the fish in the sea, the birds of the air, and every living creature that crawls on earth.

Man is pictured here as a husbandman to the natural world, which he cares for and tends . . . and for every husband there must be a wife. That wife can be nothing else but the natural world itself!

The husband-wife relationship as revealed by Scripture may be paralleled with man's relationship to the earth. Ephesians 5:21-25, 27-30, succinctly describes this marital relationship as it ought to be practiced:

> Be subject to one another, from reverence for Christ. Wives, be subject to your husbands as to the Lord, for the husband is the head of the wife as Christ (though he is the savior of the Body) is the head of the church; as the church is subject to Christ, so wives are to be subject to their husbands in every respect. Husbands, love your wives, as Christ loved the church and gave himself up for her . . . [the church] standing before him in all her glory, with never a spot or wrinkle or any such flaw, but consecrated and unblemished. So ought husbands to love their wives—to love them as their own bodies (he who loves his wife loves himself). For no one ever hates his flesh; no, he nourishes and cherished it (just as Christ does the church, for we are members of his Body).

As God loves and cares for His wife, the church, so God placed the relationship of man and nature on a par with the relationship of God to His creation . . . for man was made in God's image, an image which in its sinless perfection was "very good" (Gen. 1:31). A summary of these relationships is given in the table below.

Party to the relationship*		Biblical reference	Responsibilities and nature of the relationship within the marriage
Husband	Wife		
Christ	Church	Eph. 5:21-20 I Cor. 11:3	(1) The husband is the head of the wife.
Man	Woman	Eph. 5:21-30 I Cor. 11:3	(2) The husband is the savior of the body, though the body could not survive with a head alone; all parts of the body are interdependent and work in

* The overall relationship of God to man is (1) God the Father, (2) God the Son (Christ, the Word), (3) the human husband, and (4) the human wife (I Cor. 11:3). Value judgements are not implied here among humans.

| Mankind | Nature (the land and everything in it) | Gen. 1:26-28 | harmony (see I Cor. 12).** |

(3) The wife is subject to the husband in every respect.

(4) The husband must love the wife, and ultimately sacrifice himself for her if need be to present her spotless and flawless through his saving actions.

(5) The husband must nourish and cherish the wife.

(6) The woman was made for the man to be a helper (Gen. 2:18; I Cor. 11:9).

(7) The wife is a "special possession" for the husband (I Peter 2:9).

(8) The wife must be spotless and unblemished before the husband (as was the creation before Christ in Gen. 1:31, and according to Eph. 5:27 and II Pet. 3:14).

** In I Cor. 12 it is also revealed that the church is made up of many members, each having a specific and essential function. Similarly, nature, patterned after the church-brethren and husband-wife relationships, is comprised of a multitude of plant and animal species—from single-celled microorganisms to gigantic whales and elephants—which all function harmoniously and point toward a marvelously integrated plan of nature where each environmental niche is dynamically situated with a unique set of organisms, perfectly in balance with the climate at that particular point on the earth. Thus, in nature one should find plants and/or animals fulfilling roles, in type, of (1) apostles, (2) prophets, (3) teachers, (4) workers of miracles, (5) healers, (6) helpers, (7) administrators, and (8) speakers of tongues (I Cor. 12:28). We are familiar with healers (certain herbs) and perhaps the prominent but relatively uncommon apostles (giant sequoia trees), but we may be hard-pressed to classify the others due to our ignorance.

Another family relationship which enters the picture here is the father-son-child association. God the Father is the head of Christ, who in turn heads the man who heads the wife. The church is composed of the faithful elect who are the sons of God (Rom. 8:29, 33). The church is also pictured as the mother of the brethren (Gal. 4:26, 31). From this fact follows the truth that members of Christ's body, the church (Eph. 1:23)—on a par with keepers of the natural world—are cared for by the collective fellowship of the membership, who in turn contribute their part to the entire body, each through special talents given according to God's spiritual gifts (I Cor. 12); likewise, each member of the human race is to care for the natural world, his mother, once he grows up and comes to a state of maturity where he understands his responsibility to the parent that nourished him from the womb (I Tim. 5:8).

Since man's relationship to "mother earth" emanates from, and parallels, his relationship with God, one cannot truly understand and practice in daily life the God-plane relationship of man and the land until he understands and practices in daily life the God-plane relationship of the husband and the wife. Also essential in the proper care of nature is a working knowledge of Christ's relationship to the church, who is "the Savior of the body" (Eph. 5:23).

If one possesses love for God and family, that Spirit working through him will automatically lead him to the proper care in tending the land and its life, for "the Spirit fathoms everything, even the depths of God" (I Cor. 2:10). The land will then yield its produce. Treat a wife with love and respect and she will shower you with productive, wholesome, energetic, profitable increase in her labors. Encourage and entrust in her your heartfelt secrets and desires and she will yield bountifully. Mistreat, malign, curse, beat, and abuse your wife and watch her shrivel in her efforts, withdraw into her cocoon of repressed emotions, and grow pale and weak, more and more helpless and anemic; eventually she will rebel and utterly refuse to do your bidding, to produce the fruits needed to properly maintain your household. Watch unhappiness increase and misery stalk your every step. The fruit of this repressed existence will become rotten and inferior. By and by she will divorce you, leaving you with no fruit (snatching your own children from you) and sapping from you the wealth accumulated from generations of growth and effort, extracting from your illicit ravings and beatings their just recompense. You will be left penniless as nature procures her sure payment: " . . . an eye for an eye, a tooth for a tooth . . . . " (Deut. 19:21).

Now, substitute the earth and its animal and plant world in place of the wife, and mankind as a whole in place of the husband. Is not the treatment so many people now give nature like the beating of a wife, and the abandonment of one's children?

In like manner, picture the earth and nature as our mother. Who in his right mind would dream of beating and pummeling his own mother, the one who raised him from childhood? Yet civilization in general has disregarded its debt to our great giving, vibrant, lively mother earth who in many respects bounces back mightily in the face of repeated and continued abuse . . . yet in other respects is so very fragile, and cries out in agony when tortured through the abrogations of natural laws perpetrated by modern man.

"Mother earth" and her perfect set of natural laws, installed at the recreation of the earth (Gen. 1), is indeed much more than a pleasant platitude. It is an idea rooted in antiquity which carries with it a great deal of deep meaning, paralleling the husband—wife and mother —son associations found in Scripture. Nature has lately rebelled quite vehemently to our abuses leveled against her—polluted air, sewage-filled streams, diminished or extinct numbers and species of wildlife and plants, ugly cities and roads, and massive monocultured fields—and must surely be ready to completely divorce the human race as men continue to make a folly of the good earth. Mother earth has patiently endured the beatings for generations in the great, resilient love which characterizes the Creator of the whole dynamic scheme. Yet man and his lust for taking more than he needs, and mercilessly beating the prairies, forests, deserts, mountains, sea-coasts, and rivers for the sake of profit maximization, must surely soon reap the just recompense for his acts. His wife will divorce him, his mother will desert him, and, as Moses wrote, "Then the land will get its sabbaths of rest, as long as it lies desolate, as long as you are in your enemies' land . . . . " (Lev. 26:34).

FOOTNOTES AND COMMENTS

Chapter One

1. Toffler, A. 1970. *Future Shock.* Bantam Books, Inc., New York.
2. Toffler, A. 1975. *The Eco-Spasm Report.* Bantam Books, Inc., New York.
3. Toffler, A. 1975. The "Future-Shock" Man Sees More Drastic Changes Ahead. *U.S. News and World Report,* May 5, p. 53.
4. Heilbroner, R. L. 1974. *An Inquiry Into Human Prospect.* W.W. Norton, New York.
5. Ehrlich, P. R. 1968. *The Population Bomb.* Ballantine Books, New York.
6. Ehrlich, P. R. 1974. *The End of Affluence.* Ballantine Books, New York. p. 34.
7. Commoner, B. 1976. *The Poverty of Power.* Bantam Books, Inc., New York.
8. *Ibid.,* p. 1.
9. Berry, W. 1977. *The Unsettling of America: Culture and Agriculture.* Sierra Club Books, San Francisco.
10. Eckholm, E. P. 1976. *Losing Ground—Environmental Stress and World Food Prospects.* W. W. Norton and Company, Inc., New York.
11. Meadows, D. H., D. L. Meadows, J. Randers, and W. W. Behrens III. 1972. *The Limits of Growth: A Report for the Club of Rome's Project on the Predicament of Mankind.* Universe Books, New York.
12. Wattenberg, B. J. 1976. *The Statistical History of the United States.* Basic Books, Inc., New York. p. 8.

13. Emerson, R. W. 1876. Nature. *Essays: Second Series. In Our Natural World* (Hal Borland, ed.). Doubleday and Company, Inc., Garden City, New York. 1965. p. 802.
14. Wattenberg. *Op. cit.* Bacheller, M. A. (ed.). 1979. *The Hammond Almanac, Inc.,* Maplewood, New Jersey. p. 244.
15. Zeldin, M., and S. Jackson. 1978. *National Wildlife's 1978 Environmental Quality Index.* National Wildlife Federation, Washington, D. C. p. 16. The judgements on resource trends represent the collective thinking of the editors and the National Wildlife Federation staff, based on extensive consultation with government experts, private specialists, and academic researchers.
16. Wattenberg. *Op. cit.* p. 716. Delury, G. E. (ed.). 1979. *The World Almanac and Book of Facts.* Newspaper Enterprise Association, Inc., New York, p. 140.
17. Toffler, A. 1970. *Future Shock.* Random House, Inc., New York p. 22.
18. Wattenberg. *Op. cit.* pp. 49, 64. Anonymous. 1979. Family's Chances of Survival. *U.S. News and World Report.* Oct. 15, p. 72.
19. Anonymous. 1977. Can Carter Revitalize the American Family *U. S. News and World Report.* Feb. 28, p. 35. Anonymous. 1978. Rising Concern Over Surge in Illegitimacy. *U. S. News and World Report.* June 26. p. 60.
20. Wattenberg. *Op. cit.* p. 413. Delury. *Op. cit.* p. 966.
21. Wattenberg. *Op. cit.* p. 989. Anonymous. 1978. People Going Deeper in Debt: "It's Really Worrisome." *U. S. News and World Report.* Nov. 20 p. 77.
22. Davidson, J. 1979. *Statement of Account* (newsletter). National Taxpayer's Union, Washington, D. C. p. 1.
23. Wattenberg. *Op. cit.* p. 340.
24. Wattenberg. *Op. cit.* p. 73. Lewis, A. L. (ed.). 1978. *Information Please Almanac, Atlas, and Yearbook, 1979.* The Viking Press, New York. p. 86.
25. Rauscher, F. J., Jr. 1976. Latest in the Fight Against Cancer. *U. S. News and World Report.* Feb. 9. p. 60.

26. Reams, C. 1976. Interview with Dr. Carey Reams on correcting diabetes and hypoglycemia. *The Healthview Newsletter* 1 (6). p. 1.

27. Hall, R. H. 1974. *Food for Naught, the Decline in Nutrition.* Harper and Row, Publishers, Hagerstown, Maryland, p. 60.

28. Gibbon, E. 1960. *The Decline and Fall of the Roman Empire, Volume Two.* Abridged by D. M. Low. Washington Square Press, Inc., New York, p. 661.

29. Armstrong, H. W., and G. T. Armstrong. 1973. *The Wonderful World Tomorrow, What It Will Be Like.* Ambassador College Press, Pasadena, California. p. 67.

30. Meadows, D. H., D. L. Meadows, J. Randers, and W. W. Behrens III. 1972. *The Limits of Growth: A Report for the Club of Rome's Project on the Predicament of Mankind.* Universe Books, New York. p. 17.

Chapter Two

1. Berry, Wendell. 1977. *The Unsettling of America—Culture and Agriculture.* Sierra Club Books, San Francisco. p. 143.

2. USDA. 1978. *1978 Handbook of Agricultural Charts.* Agricultural Handbook No. 551. U. S. Government Printing Office, Washington, D. C. p. 34.

3. Wattenberg, B. J. 1976. *The Statistical History of the United States.* Basic Books, Inc., New York. p. 457. USDA. 1978. *1978 Handbook of Agricultural Charts.* Agricultural Handbook No. 551. U. S. Government Printing Office, Washington, D. C. p. 34.

4. Painted on the wall of the first floor hallway, Morrill Hall, North Dakota State University, Fargo, North Dakota.

5. *Ibid.*

6. Dorow, N. 1979 (June). *By Any Definition, Larger and Fewer Farms.* North Dakota State University Ag Communication (Mimeo). Fargo, North Dakota.

7. Young, R. 1939. *Analytical Concordance to the Holy Bible.* United Society for Christian Literature. London. p. 412.

Chapter Three

1. Gove, P. B. (ed.). 1965. *Webster's Seventh New Collegiate Dictionary*. G. and C. Merriam Co., Publishers, Springfield Massachusetts. p. 19.
2. Fels, R. 1961. *Challenge to the American Economy*. Allyn and Bacon, Inc., Boston. pp. 143-144, 201.
3. Tisdale, S. L., and W. L. Nelson. 1966. *Soil Fertility and Fertilizers,* 2nd edition, The Macmillan Company, New York. p. 453.
4. Sudjadi, M. 1978. Personal communication. Soil Research Institute, Bogor, Indonesia.
5. Halsell, G. 1976. *Los Viejos: Secrets of Long Life from the Sacred Valley.* Rodale Press, Inc., Emmaus. Pennsylvania.
6. Schumacher, E. F. 1973. *Small Is Beautiful, Economics As if People Mattered.* Harper and Row, Publishers, New York. p. 140.
7. *Ibid.*
8. *Ibid.* p. 139.
9. *Ibid.* p. 142.
10. Gilbert, L. 1968. Our Amish Neighbors. *Champaign-Urbana Courier,* Champaign-Urbana, Illinois. Mar. 10. p. 28.
11. Young, R. 1939. *Analytical Concordance to the Holy Bible.* United Society for Christian Literature, London. p. 237.
12. Milne, D. S. 1947. *Economics a Phase of Divine Law.* The Covenant Publishing Co., Ltd., London. p. 7.
13. *Ibid.*
14. Cameron, W. J. 1966. *Economics of the Bible.* Destiny Publishers, Merrimac, Massachusetts. p. 12-16.
15. McMaster, R. E., Jr. 1978. *Cycles of War.* The War Cycles Institute, Kalispell, Montana.
16. Cayne, B. S. (ed.). 1968. *Merit Students Encyclopedia,* Volume 5. Crowell-Collier Educational Corporation, New York. p. 550-551.
17. *Ibid.* p. 551.

18. Hoeh, H. L. 1979. Bible Study (October 19). Ambassador College, Pasadena, California.
19. Cayne, B. S. (ed.). 1968. *Merit Students Encyclopedia,* Volume 11. Crowell-Collier Educational Corporation, New York. p. 105.
20. Josephus, F. 1960. *Complete Works of Flavius Josephus.* The Antiquities of the Jews (I, II, 2). Kregel Publications, Grand Rapids, Michigan. p. 27.
21. Wattenberg, B. J. 1976. *The Statistical History of the United States.* Basic Books, Inc., New York. p. 989. USDA. 1978. *Agricultural Statistics 1978.* U. S. Government Printing Office, Washington, D. C. p. 478, 484.
22. Wattenberg. *Op. cit.* p. 490-491. USDA. *Op. cit.* p. 472.
23. Anonymous. 1979. Tax Burden That Grows and Grows. *U. S. News and World Report,* March 26. p. 64.

Chapter Four

1. Young, R. 1939. *Analytical Concordance to the Holy Bible,* 8th edition. United Society for Christian Literature, London. p. 652.
2. Hassing, A. 1972. Norway's Organized Response to Emigration. *Norwegian-American Studies,* Vol. 25. Norwegian-American Historical Association, Northfield, Minnesota. HLM Graphics, Minneapolis, Minnesota. p. 54-79.
3. Cayne, B. S. (ed.). *Merit Students Encyclopedia,* Vol. 9. Crowell-Collier Educational Corporation, New York, p. 18.
4. *Ibid.* Vol. 17. p. 419.
5. Wattenberg, B. J. 1976. *The Statistical History of the United States.* Basic Books, Inc., New York. p. 457.
6. *Ibid.*
7. *Ibid.*
8. Delury, G. E. (ed.). 1979. *The World Almanac and Book of Facts.* Newspaper Enterprise Association, Inc., New York. p. 151.
9. Estimate, based on a 3.7% farm population of total population in 1978. USDA. 1978. *1978 Handbook of Agricultural Charts.* Agricultural Handbook No. 551. U. S. Government Printing Office, Washington, D. C. p. 34.

10. Wattenberg. *Op. cit.* p. 457. Delury. *Op. cit.* p. 151.
11. Alexander, G. (ed.). 1974. *World Crisis in Agriculture.* Ambassador College Press, Pasadena, California. p. 32. Figures quoted in this booklet based on data from the early 1970s have been inflated to more closely reflect current economic conditions.
12. McConnell, C. R. 1963. *Economics: Principles, Problems, and Policies,* 2nd edition. Mc Graw-Hill Book Company, Inc., New York. p. 625.
13. Wattenberg. *Op. cit.* p. 8.
14. *Ibid.* p. 457.
15. *Ibid.* p. 8.
16. *Ibid.* p. 41.
17. Janick, J., C. H. Noller, and C. L. Rhykard. 1976. The Cycles of Plant and Animal Nutrition. *Scientific American,* Vol. 235, No. 5. p. 80.
18. Hall, R. H. 1974. *Food for Nought: The Decline in Nutrition.* Harper and Row, Publishers, Hagerstown, Maryland. p. 132.
19. Kononova, M. M. 1966. *Soil Organic Matter.* Pergamon Press, New York, pp. 323-324.
20. Commoner, B. 1971. *The Closing Circle.* Alfred A. Knopf, New York.
21. Tugwell, R. 1934. Tugwell Predicts New Regulations for Land With Federal Control. *Phillips County News,* Malta, Montana. January 4.
22. *Ibid.*
23. Anonymous. 1976. Tugwell: Government Will Control All Land. *Bulletin of the Committee to Restore the Constitution.* Ft. Collins, Colorado. August. p. 1.
24. Roberts. A. 1976. The Crisis of Federal Regionalism: A Solution. *Bulletin of the Committee to Restore the Constitution.* Ft. Collins, Colorado. September. p. 3. Quoted from a public hearing, sub-committee of the California Senate Committee on Local Government, February 19, 1968.
25. *Ibid.*
26. Ayres, Q. C., and D. Scoates. 1939. *Land Drainage and Reclamation.* Mc Graw-Hill Book Company, Inc., New York. p. 4.

27. Donahue, R. L., J. C. Shickluna, and L. S. Robertson. 1971. *Soils: An Introduction to Soils and Plant Growth.* Prentice-Hall, Inc., Englewood Cliffs, New Jersey. pp. 196-199.
28. Buckman, H. O., and N. C. Brady. 1969. *The Nature and Properties of Soils,* 7th edition. The Macmillan Company, New York. p. 60.
29. *Ibid.*
30. *Ibid.*
31. Buckman, H. O., and N. C. Brady. *Op. cit.* p. 174.
32. A practice currently promoted by some Purdue University (Lafayette, Indiana) crop scientists who assert that, for the average year, yield losses of corn may inexorably be expected once the April 31 planting date is passed.
33. Byrd, W. 1941. *The Land.* Vol. 1, No. 1. Winter. p. 60.
34. Barrows, H. L., and V. J. Kilmer. 1963. Plant Nutrient Losses from Soils by Water Erosion. *Advances in Agronomy,* Vol. 15. Academic Press, New York. p. 306.
35. *Ibid.* p. 305.
36. *Ibid.* p. 307.
37. Alexander, G. (ed.). 1979. *World Crisis in Agriculture.* Ambassador College Press, Pasadena, California. p. 10.
38. Puhr, L. F., and W. W. Worzella. 1952. *Fertility Maintenance of South Dakota Soils.* South Dakota Agricultural Experiment Station Circular No. 92.
39. *Ibid.*
40. Salter, R. M., R. D. Lewis, and J. A. Slipher. 1941. *Our Heritage the Soil.* Ohio Agricultural Experiment Station Bulletin No. 175.
41. Pimentel, D., et. al. 1976. Land Degradation: Effects on Food and Energy Resources. *Science,* Vol. 194, No. 4261. p. 151.
42. *Ibid.* p. 150.
43. Brink, R. A., J. W. Densmore, and G. A. Hill. 1977. Soil Deterioration and the Growing World Demand for Food. *Science,* Vol. 197, No. 4304. p. 626.
44. U. S. National Resources Board. 1935. *Soil Erosion: A Critical Problem in American Agriculture.* Land Planning Committee, supplementary report. U. S. Government Printing Office, Washington, D. C. p. 5.

45. Pimentel, D., et. al. *Op. cit.* p. 150.
46. *Ibid.*
47. Commoner, B. 1976. *The Poverty of Power.* Bantam Books, Inc., New York. p. 153.
48. *Ibid.*
49. Scott, F. I., Jr. 1978. The Editor's Page. *American Laboratory,* Vol. 10, No. 7. p. 6.

Chapter Five

1. Cayne, B.S. (ed.). *Merit Students Encyclopedia,* Vol. 6. Crowell-Collier Educational Corporation, New York. p. 356.
2. *Ibid.* p. 352-353.
3. Wattenberg, B. J. 1976. *The Statistical History of the United States.* Basic Books, Inc., New York. p. 469, 519-520. USDA. 1978. *Agricultural Statistics 1978.* U. S. Government Printing Office, Washington, D. C. p. 427.
4. *Ibid.*
5. Wattenberg. *Op. cit.* p. 469. USDA. *Op. cit.* p. 427.
6. USDA. *Op. cit.* p. 427.
7. Perelman, M. J. 1972. Farming With Petroleum. *Environment,* Vol. 14, No. 8. pp. 8-13.
8. Rappaport, R. A. 1968. *Pigs for the Ancestors.* Yale University Press, New Haven, Connecticut.
9. Perelman. *Op. cit.*
10. Wattenberg. *Op. cit.* p. 691-692. Delury, G. E. (ed.). 1979. *The World Almanac and Book of Facts.* Newspaper Enterprise Association, Inc., New York. p. 115.
11. Lobel, H. 1973. The Energy Hoax, Part 2: A Modern Myth. *Acres U. S. A.* August.
12. Commoner, B. 1976. *The Poverty of Power.* Bantam Books, Inc., New York. pp. 84-112.
13. *Ibid.* p. 128.
14. Pimental, D., et. al. 1976 Land Degradation: Effects on Food and Energy Resources. *Science,* Vol. 194, No. 4261. p. 149.

15. Toffler, A. 1970. *Future Shock*. Bantam Books, Inc., New York.
16. Wattenberg. *Op. cit.* p. 718.
17. Wattenberg. *Op. cit.* p. 64. Anonymous. 1979. Family's Chances of Survival. *U. S. News and World Report*. Oct. 15. p. 72.
18. Anonymous. 1977. Can Carter Revitalize the American Family? *U. S. News and World Report*. February 28. p. 35. Anonymous. 1978. Rising Concern Over Surge in Illegitimacy. *U. S. News and World Report*. June 26. p. 60.
19. Wattenberg. *Op. cit.* p. 55.
20. Beevers, H. 1961. *Respiratory Metabolism in Plants*. Harper and Row, Publishers, New York.
21. Lacher, J. R., A. Amador, and K. Snow. 1966. Effect of Dinitrophenol on the Heats of Respiration of Germinating Seeds of *Prosopis Juliflora, Kochia Scoparia*, and *Oxyria Digyna*. *Plant Physiology*, Vol. 41. pp. 1435-1438.
22. Figures given are thermal efficiencies. Taylor, C. F. 1968. *The Internal-Combustion Engine in Theory and Practice*. Vol. II. The M.I.T. Press, Cambridge, Massachusetts. Newell, A. B. (ed.). 1953. *Diesel Engineering Handbook*, 8th ed. Diesel Publications, Inc., New York.
23. Anonymous. 1979. When the Amish Run Head-on Into "Progress." *U. S. News and World Report*. June 25. pp. 46-49.
24. Clarke, A. *Clarke's Commentary*, Vol. 3. Abingdon Press, Nashville, Tennessee. p. 740.
25. Hardy, T. 1966. *Collected Poems*, 11th printing. New York.
26. Rolvaag. O. E. 1927. *Giants in the Earth*. Harper and Row, Publishers, New York. Wilder, L. I. 1935. *Little House On the Prairie*. Scholastic Book Services, New York. Brings, L. M. (ed.). 1960. *Minnesota Heritage*. T. S. Denison and Company, Inc., Minneapolis, Minnesota pp. 120-138.
27. Walvoord, J. F., and J. E. Walvoord. 1974. *Armageddon: Oil and the Middle East Crisis*. Zondervan Publishing House, Grand Rapids, Michigan.
28. Dobson, J. 1970. *Dare to Discipline*. Tyndale House Publishers, Wheaton, Illinois. Dr. Dobson correctly asserts that "children thrive best in an atmosphere of genuine love, undergirded by reasonable, consistent discipline. . . . Permissiveness has not just been a failure; its been a disaster!" pp. 13-14.

29. Wattenberg. *Op. cit.* p. 498. Anonymous. 1976. The Farmer and the Food Dollar. *Farm Profit.* Massey-Ferguson Corporation.
30. *Ibid.*
31. Wattenberg. *Op. cit.* p. 500-501. USDA. *Op. cit.* p. 32.
32. *Ibid.*
33. USDA. 1978. *1978 Handbook of Agricultural Charts.* U. S. Government Printing Office, Washington, D. C. p. 31.
34. *Ibid.*
35. *Ibid.*
36. *Ibid.*
37. Schumacher, E. R. 1973. *Small is Beautiful: Economics As if People Mattered.* Harper and Row, Publishers, New York. pp. 105-106.
38. Herber, L. 1963. *Our Synthetic Environment.* Jonathan Cape Ltd., London.
39. *Ibid.*
40. Schumacher. *Op. cit.* p. 106.
41. Mansholt, S. L. 1967. *Our Accelerating Century.* The Royal Dutch/Shell Lectures on Industry and Society, London.
42. Berry, W. 1977. *The Unsettling of America: Culture and Agriculture.* Sierra Club Books, San Francisco. pp. 9-10.
43. *Ibid.* p. 170.

Chapter Six

1. Anonymous. 1976. The Farmer and the Food Dollar. *Farm Profit.* Massey-Ferguson Corporation.
2. Rolvaag, O. E. 1927. *Giants in the Earth.* Harper and Row Publishers, New York. pp. 413-414.
3. Armstrong, H. W. 1979. *Tomorrow . . . What It Will Be Like.* Everest House Publishers, New York. p. 95.
4. Schumacher, E. F. 1973. *Small is Beautiful: Economics As if People Mattered.* Harper and Row, Publishers, New York. p. 140.
5. *Ibid.* p. 141.
6. *Ibid.* p. 141.
7. *Ibid.* pp. 141-142.
8. *Ibid.* p. 145.

9. Berry, W. 1977. *The Unsettling of America: Culture and Agriculture.* Sierra Club Books, San Francisco, California. pp. 51-52.
10. *Ibid.* pp. 52-53.
11. Toffler, A. 1970. *Future Shock.* Bantam Books, Inc., New York. pp. 103-104.

Chapter Seven

1. Josephus, F. 1960. *The Antiquities of the Jews,* Book I, 1, 4. Translated by W. Whiston. Kregel Publications, Grand Rapids, Michigan. p. 26.
2. Young, R. 1939. *Analytical Concordance to the Holy Bible,* 8th edition. United Society for Christian Literature, London. pp. 367, 1028.
3. Velikovsky, I. 1950. *Worlds in Collision.* Dell Publishing Co., Inc., New York. pp. 163-201.
4. Smith, U. 1907. *Daniel and the Revelation.* Pacific Press Publishing Company, Mountain View, California. p. 508.
5. *Ibid.* pp. 508-509.
6. *Ibid.* p. 509.
7. Clarke, A. *Clarke's Commentary,* Vol. 1. Abingdon Press, Nashville, Tennessee. p. 77.
8. Josephus. *Op. cit.* Book I, 3, 7. p. 29.
9. Reitan, C. H. 1960. Distribution of Precipitable Water Vapor Over the Continental United States. *Bulletin of the American Meteorological Society,* Vol. 41, February, p. 86.
10. Rand, H. B. 1964. *Primogenesis,* 3rd edition. Destiny Publishers, Merrimac, Massachusetts. p. 51.
11. *Ibid.* p. 38.
12. Josephus. *Op. cit.* Book I, 1, 3. p. 25.
13. *Ibid.*
14. Leet, L. D., and S. Judson. 1965. *Physical Geology,* 3rd edition. Prentice-Hall, Inc., Englewood Cliffs, New Jersey. p. 327.
15. *Ibid.* pp. 327-332.
16. Hallam, A. 1972. Continental Drift and the Fossil Record. *Scientific American,* Vol. 227, No. 5, November. pp. 57-66.

17. Figure taken from Leet and Judson. *Op. cit.* p. 327. Quote taken from Longwell, C. 1958. My Estimate of the Continental Drift Concept. *Continental Drift, a Symposium.* Tasamania University, Hobart, Australia.
18. Leet and Judson. *Op. cit.* p. 328.
19. Rand, H. B. *The World That Then Was.* Destiny Publishers, Merrimac, Massachusetts. p. 6.
20. *Ibid.* pp. 6-8. Data is taken from investigations by G. F. Carr.
21. Anonymous. 1974. Physiography of the Earth, pp. 42-48. In: *Encyclopedia Britannica,* 15th edition, Vol. 6. Encyclopedia Britannica, Inc., Chicago, Illinois. pp. 42-43.
22. Nevin, C. M. 1942. *Principles of Structural Geology,* 3rd edition. John Wiley and Sons, Inc., New York. pp. 261-262.
23. *Ibid.* p. 294.
24. *Ibid.*
25. *Ibid.*
26. Whitcomb, J. C., and H. M. Roberts. 1970. *The Genesis Flood.* The Presbyterian and Reformed Publishing Co., Philadelphia, Pennsylvania. pp. 125-126.
27. Thornbury, W. D. 1954. *Principles of Geomorphology.* John Wiley and Sons, New York. p. 475.
28. Shepard, F. P. 1948. *Submarine Geology.* Harper and Row, New York. pp. 231-233.
29. Thornbury. *Op. cit.* p. 472.
30. Hamilton, E. L. 1957. The Last Geographic Frontier: The Sea Floor. *Scientific Monthly,* Vol. 85. December. p. 303.
31. Bucher, W. H. 1953. The Crust of the Earth. *The Precambrian.* Manitoba Chamber of Mines, Winnipeg, Manitoba. March.
32. Rand. *Op. cit.* pp. 9-10.
33. Young, R. 1939. *Analytical Concordance to the Holy Bible,* 8th edition. United Society for Christian Literature, London. p. 240.
34. Rand. *Primogenesis. Op. cit.* p. 51.
35. *Ibid.* p. 52.
36. *Ibid.* p. 51.

Chapter Eight

1. Russell, E. W. 1961. *Soil Conditions and Plant Growth,* 9th edition. John Wiley and Sons, Ltd., New York. pp. 617-620.
2. Dymond T. S., and F. Hughes. 1899. *Report on Injury to Agricultural Land on the Coast of Essex by Innundation of Sea Water on 29th November, 1897.* Chelmsford, England.
3. *Ibid.*
4. *Ibid.*
5. Russell. *Op. cit.* p. 618.
6. Dymond and Hughes. *Op. cit.*
7. Murray, M. 1976. *Sea Energy Agriculture.* Valentine Books, Winston-Salem, North Carolina. pp. 15, 56-57.
8. Boyko, H. (ed.). 1968. *Saline Irrigation for Agriculture and Forestry.* Dr. W. Junk N. V., Publisher, The Hague, Netherlands.
9. Weast, R. C. (ed.). 1973. *Handbook of Chemistry and Physics,* 56th edition. CRC Press, Cleveland, Ohio. pp. D-158, D-165, F-95, F-206.
10. Koeppe, C. E., and G. C. DeLong. 1958. *Weather and Climate.* Mc Graw-Hill Book Company, Inc., New York. p. 23.
11. Whitcomb, J. C., Jr., and H. M. Morris. 1970. *The Genesis Flood.* The Presbyterian and Reformed Publishing Company, Philadelphia, Pennsylvania. pp. 156, 289-291.
12. Flint, R. F. 1957. *Glacial and Pleistocene Geology.* John Wiley and Sons, New York. p. 471.
13. Sanderson, I. T. 1960. Riddle of the Frozen Giants. *Saturday Evening Post,* January 16. p. 83.
14. *Ibid.*
15. Rand, H.B . 1954. *The World That Then Was.* Destiny Publishers, Merrimac, Massachusetts. p. 7.
16. Velikovsky, I. 1950. *Worlds in Collision.* Dell Publishing Company, New York. pp. 215-304.
17. *Ibid.* p. 30.
18. *Ibid.*

19. The concept of all new wealth coming from the soil has been outlined in a hard-to-find, concise book called *All New Wealth Comes from the Soil* by Carl H. Wilken. Only 5,000 copies were printed, in 1956.

Chapter Nine

1. Young, R. 1939. *Analytical Concordance to the Holy Bible,* 8th edition, revised. United Society for Christian Literature, London. p. 272.
2. *Ibid.* p. 560.
3. Josephus, F. 1960. *The Antiquities of the Jews,* Book I, 2, 1. Translated by W. Whiston. Kregel Publications, Grand Rapids, Michigan, p. 26.
4. Drawings from Partridge, M. 1973. *Farm Tools Through the Ages.* New York Graphic Society, Boston, Massachusetts. p. 37.
5. Young. *Op. cit.* p. 759.
6. *Ibid.*
7. *Ibid.*
8. *Ibid.*
9. Brown, Gerald. 1979. Rabbi of Fargo, North Dakota. Personal communication.
10. Josephus. *Op. cit.* Book I, 1, 4. p. 26.
11. Fukuoka, M. 1978. *The One-straw Revolution.* Rodale Press, Emmaus, Pennsylvania.
12. *Ibid.* p. xxi.
13. *Ibid.* pp. 65-69.
14. *Ibid.* pp. 53-57.
15. *Ibid.* pp. xxi-xvii.
16. De Oñate, D. J. 1601. True Account of the Expedition of Oñate Toward the East. In: *Our Natural World.* Edited by Hal Borland. Doubleday and Company, Inc., Garden City, New York. 1965. p. 335.
17. Deibert, E. 1979. No-till Competes With Conventional Tillage. *N. D. S. U. Ag. Communication* (mimeo). J. J. Feight, editor. Aug. 6.
18. *Ibid.*

19. Faulkner, E. H. 1943. *Plowman's Folly.* University of Oklahoma Press, Norman, Oklahoma.
20. *Ibid.* p. 3.
21. *Ibid.* Book jacket summary.
22. Triplett, G. B., Jr., and D. M. Van Doran, Jr. 1977. Agriculture Without Tillage. *Scientific American,* Vol. 236, No. 1. p. 33.
23. *Ibid.* p. 28.
24. *Ibid.*
25. *Ibid.*
26. Anonymous. 1979. The Great Insect Invasion. *U. S. News and World Report.* February 19. p. 44.
27. Committee on Genetic Vulnerability of Major Crops. 1972. *Genetic Vulnerability of Major Crops.* National Research Council, Washington D. C.
28. Cook, R. L. 1962. *Soil Management for Conservation and Production.* John Wiley and Sons, Inc., New York. p. 127.
29. De Oñate. *Op. cit.* pp. 331-332.
30. The pathway from field to ocean may take many devious routes, but the result is essentially the same: diminishing of the soils' fertility.
31. Jenny, H. 1941. *Factors of Soil Formation.* McGraw-Hill Book Company, New York.
32. Donahue, R. L., J. C. Shickluna, and L. S. Robertson. 1971. *Soils: An Introduction to Plant Growth,* 3rd edition. Prentice-Hall, Inc., Englewood Cliffs, New Jersey. p. 197.
33. Bartholomew, W. V. 1957. Maintaining Organic Matter. pp. 245-252. In: *Soil: the 1957 Yearbook of Agriculture.* Edited by Alfred Stefferud, USDA. U. S. Government Printing Office, Washington, D. C. p. 247.
34. Buckman, H. O., and N. C. Brady. 1969. *The Nature and Properties of Soils,* 7th edition. The Macmillan Company, New York. pp. 447-448.
35. Thompson, L. M. 1957. *Soils and Soil Fertility,* 2nd edition. McGraw-Hill Book Company, New York. p. 120.
36. Wattenberg, B. J. 1976. *The Statistical History of the United States.* Basic Books, Inc., New York. p. 469. USDA. 1978. *Agricultural Statistics 1978.* U. S. Government Printing Office, Washington, D. C. p. 469.

37. Wattenberg. *Op. cit.* pp. 510-512. USDA. *Op. cit.* p. 1.
38. Simonson, R. W. 1957. What Soils Are. p 17-31. *In: Soil: The 1957 Yearbook of Agriculture.* Edited by Alfred Stelfferud, USDA. U. S. Government Printing Office, Washington, D. C. p. 26.
39. Lowdermilk, W. C. 1953. *Conquest of the Land Through Seven Thousand Years.* USDA Agricultural Information Bulletin No. 99. U. S. Government Printing Office, Washington, D. C. p. 26.
40. *Ibid.*
41. *Ibid.*
42. *Ibid.*
43. *Ibid.* p. 30.
44. Ayres, Q. C., and D. Scoates. 1939. *Land Drainage and Reclamation,* 2nd edition. Mc Graw-Hill Book Company, Inc., New York. ppp. 4-10.
45. Faulkner. *Op. cit.* p. 10.
46. *Ibid.* p. 5.
47. Berry, W. 1977. *The Unsettling of America: Culture and Agriculture.* Sierra Club Books, San Francisco, California. pp. 175-179. Several of the statements used are from an unpublished paper by Stephen B. Bruch, Department of Anthropology, William and Mary College.
48. *Ibid.* p. 178.
49. *Ibid.*

Chapter Ten

1. Young, R. 1939. *Analytical Concordance to the Holy Bible,* 8th edition. United Society for Christian Literature, London. p. 943.
2. Gove, P. B. (ed.). 1967. *Webster's Seventh New Collegiate Dictionary.* G. and C. Merriam Company, Publishers, Springfield, Massachusetts. p. 874.
3. Young. *Op. cit.* p. 272.
4. *Ibid.* p. 560.
5. USDA. 1972. Genetic Vulnerability of Major Crops: A Challenge to Scientists and the Nation. *Agricultural Science Review.* Vol. 10, No. 4. p. 7.

6. Committee on Genetic Vulnerability of Major Crops. 1972. *Genetic Vulnerability of Major Crops*. National Research Council, Washington D. C.
7. USDA. *Op. cit.* p. 1.
8. Alexander, G. (ed.). 1974. *World Crisis in Agriculture*. Ambassador College Press, Pasadena, California. p. 9.
9. USDA. *Op. cit.* p. 3.
10. Griliches, Z. 1960. Hybrid Corn and the Economics of Innovation. *Science,* Vol. 132, Figure 1. pp. 375-290.
11. Sigurbjoernsson, B. 1967. Evolution of Agronomically Superior Genotypes in Natural Habitats. *Isotopes in Plant Nutrition and Physiology*. Food and Agriculture Organization, International Atomic Energy Commission, Vienna, Austria. pp. 569-573.
12. *Ibid.* p. 569.
13. *Ibid.* p. 573.
14. Berry, W. 1977. *The Unsettling of America: Culture and Agriculture*. Sierra Club Books, San Francisco, California. p. 177. Several of the statements used are from an unpublished paper by Stephen B. Bruch, Department of Anthropology, William and Mary College.
15. *Ibid.*
16. *Ibid.*
17. *Ibid.* pp. 177-178.
18. *Ibid.* p. 178.
19. Syltie, P. W. 1979. *The Influence of Fertilization on the Nutritional Value of Two Hard Red Spring Wheat Cultivars*. Ph.D. Thesis. North Dakota State University, Fargo, North Dakota. p. 3.
21. Howard, A. 1947. *The Soil and Health: A Study of Organic Agriculture*. Schocken Books, New York. pp. 77-78.
21. More, L. T. 1925. *Dogma of Evolution*. Lectures delivered at Princeton University during January. p. 117.
22. Nelson, B. C. 1967. *After Its Kind*. Augsburg Publishing House, Minneapolis, Minnesota. pp. 4-7.
23. Sigurbjoernsson. *Op. cit.* p. 569.
24. Walters, C., Jr. 1980. Opposing That Corner on Seeds; Seeds: An Update on Plant Patents. pp. 1-2, 12-14. *Acres, U.S.A.,* Vol. 10, No. 2. p. 1.
25. *Ibid.*

26. Committee on Genetic Vulnerability of Major Crops. *Op. cit.*
27. USDA. 1972. Genetic Vulnerability of Major Crops: A Challenge to Scientists and the Nation. Agricultural Science Review, Vol. 10, No. 4. p. 3.
28. Walters. *Op. cit.* p. 13.
29. Harlan, J. *In:* Walters. *Op. cit.* p. 2.
30. Wilkes, G. *In:* Walters. *Op. cit.* p. 2.
31. Fowler, C. *In:* Walters. *Op. cit.* p. 2.
32. Stevens, M. A. 1979. Varietal Influence on Nutritional Value. pp. 87-110. In: *Nutritional Qualities of Fresh Fruits and Vegetables.* Edited by P. L. White and N. Selvey. Futura Publishing Company, Mount Kisco, New York. p. 87.
33. Syltie. *Op. cit.* p. v.
34. Bear, R. E., S. J. Toth, and A. L. Prince. 1948. Variation in mineral composition of vegetables. *Soil Science Society Proceedings,* Vol. 13. pp. 380-384.
35. Nightingale, G. T. 1948. The nitrogen nutrition of green plants. II. *Botanical Review,* Vol. 14. pp. 185-221.
36. Shannon, S., R. F. Becker, and M. C. Bourne. 1967. The effect of nitrogen fertilization on yield, composition, and quality of table beets (*Beta vulgaris*). *Proceedings of the American Society of Horticultural Science,* Vol. 90. pp. 201-208.
37. Bear. *Op. cit.*
38. Beeson, K. C., and G. Matrone. 1976. *The Soil Factor in Nutrition, Animal and Human.* Marcel Dekker, Inc., New York. p. 40.
39. *Ibid.* pp. 62-65.
40. Thomke, S. O. S., and B. Widstromer. 1975. Nutritional Evaluation of High Lysine Barley Fed to Pigs. pp. 79-100. In: *Protein Nutritional Quality of Food and Feeds, Part 2. Quality Factors—Plant Breeding, Composition, Processing, and Antinutrients.* Marcel Dekker, Inc., New York.
41. Borlaug, N. E. 1971. *Mankind and Civilization at Another Crossroad.* 1971 McDougall Memorial Lecture, Wisconsin Agri-Business Council, Inc., Madison, Wisconsin.
42. Randall, G. 1974. Response of Soybeans to Iron Fertilizers in Southern and Western Minnesota. (mimeo). University of Minnesota Agricultural Experiment Station, Waseca, Minnesota.

43. Sigurbjoernsson. *Op. cit.* p. 569. Howard, A. 1943. *An Agricultural Testament.* Oxford University Press, New York. pp. 167-169.
44. Sigurbjoernsson. *Op. cit.* p. 569.

Chapter Eleven

1. Clark, A. *Clarke's Commentary, Vol. 1: Genesis —Deuteronomy.* Abingdon Press, Nashville, Tennessee. p. 79.
2. Edwards, E. E. 1948. The Settlement of the Grasslands. In: *Grass: The Yearbook of Agriculture, 1948.* U. S. Government Printing Office, Washington, D. C.
3. *Ibid.*
4. *Ibid.*
5. Young, R. 1939. *Analytical Concordance to the Holy Bible,* 8th edition. United Society for Christian Literature, London. p. 337.
6. *Ibid.* p. 271.
7. Cole, H. H. (editor). 1962. *Introduction to Livestock Production.* W. H. Freeman Company, San Francisco, California. p. 480.
8. Pieters, A. In: J. C. Whitcomb, Jr., and H. M. Morris (editors). 1970. *The Genesis Flood.* The Presbyterian and Reformed Publishing Company, Philadelphia, Pennsylvania. p. 468.
9. Leet, L. D., and S. Judson. 1965. *Physical Geology,* 3rd edition. Prentice-Hall, Inc., Englewood Cliffs, New Jersey. p. 396.
10. Monsma, E. Y. 1955. *If Not Evolution, What Then?* Published by E. Y. Monsma. p. 42.
11. Curry-Lindahl, K. In: W. H. Nault (editor). 1974. *Animals in Danger: the 1974 Childcraft Annual.* Field Enterprises Educational Corp., Chicago, Illinois. p. 9.
12. *Ibid.* p. 7.
13. Mc Clung, R. M. 1969. *Lost Wild America.* William Morrow and Company, New York. p. 9.
14. *Ibid.*
15. Leopold, A. 1949. "Wilderness." *A Sand County Almanac.* Oxford University Press, London. p. 197.
16. *Ibid.* p. 196.

17. Beeson, K. C., and G. Matrone. 1976. *The Soil Factor in Nutrition: Animal and Human.* Marcel Dekker, Inc., New York. p. 63.
18. Crampton, E. W., and L. E. Harris (editors). 1972. *Atlas of Nutritional Data on United States and Canadian Feeds.* National Academy of Sciences, Washington, D. C. pp. 128, 134, 154, 162.
19. Ambassador College. 1970. Grain—a Danger to Man. *Your Living Environment.* Vol. 1, No. 10. Ambassador College Press, Bricket Wood, England. p. 52.
20. *Ibid.*
21. *Ibid.* p. 54.
22. *Ibid.*
23. Whitaker, J. M. 1980. Three Steps to a Naturally Healthier Heart. *Prevention.* Vol. 32, No. 3. p. 124.
24. Hall, R. H. 1974. *Food for Nought: The Decline in Nutrition.* Harper and Row, Publishers, New York. p. 106.
25. *Ibid.* pp. 105-110.
26. Beeson and Matrone. *Op. cit.* p. 63
27. Lowdermilk, W. C. 1953. *Conquest of the Land Through Seven Years.* Agriculture Information Bulletin No. 99. USDA, SCS. U. S. Government Printing Office, Washington, D. C. p. 13.
28. Edwards, E. 1948. The Settlement of Grasslands. *Grass: The Yearbook of Agriculture,* 1948. In: *Our Natural World.* 1965. Edited by Hal Borland. Doubleday and Company, Inc., Garden City, New York. p. 284.
29. *Ibid.*
30. *Ibid.*, pp. 280-281.
31. *Ibid.*, p. 283.
32. Farb, P. 1963. Sea of Grass. *Face of North America; the Natural History of a Continent.* In: *Our Natural World.* 1965. Edited by Hal Borland. Doubleday and Company, Inc., Garden City, New York. p. 296.
33. Nelson, B. C. 1952. *After Its Kind.* Bethany Fellowship, Inc., Minneapolis, Minnesota. p. 4.
34. *Ibid.* p. 11.
35. Hoeh, H. L. 1962. *Compendium of World History,* Volume I. Ambassador College Press, Pasadena, California. p. 49.

36. Winchester, A. M. 1977. *Genetics: A Survey of the Principles of Heredity,* 5th edition. Houghton Mifflin Company, Inc., Atlanta, Georgia. p. 176.
37. *Ibid.* p. 376.
38. *Ibid.* p. 377.
39. *Ibid.* pp. 388-391.
40. Clark. *Op. cit.* p. 573.
41. Price, W. A. 1970. *Nutrition and Physical Degeneration.* Price-Pottenger Nutrition Foundation, Inc., Santa Monica, California. p. 137.
42. *Ibid.*
43. Cleave, T. L. 1974. *The Saccharine Disease.* Keats Publishing, Inc., New Canaan, Connecticut. p. 101.
44. *Ibid.* pp. 101-102.
45. *Ibid.* p. 102.
46. *Ibid.* pp. 102-103.
47. Cayne, B. C. (editor). 1968. *Merit Students Encyclopedia,* Vol 3. Crowell-Collier Educational Corporation, New York. p. 202.

Chapter Twelve

1. Young, R. 1939. *Analytical Concordance to the Holy Bible,* 8th edition. United Society for Christian Literature, London. p. 430.
2. *Ibid.* p. 166.
3. These points are summarized and discussed in the following excellent article: Meredith, R. C. 1969. The Seven Laws of Radiant Health. Ambassador College Press, Pasadena, California.
4. Cleave, T. L. 1975. *The Saccharine Disease.* Keats Publishing, Inc., New Canaan, Connecticut. p. 101.
5. A very interesting discussion related to this subject is found in the following book: McMillen, S. I. 1963. *None of These Diseases.* Fleming H. Revell Company, Old Tappan, New Jersey. pp. 12-16.
6. Schumacher, E. F. *Small is Beautiful: Economics As if People Mattered.* Harper and Row, Publishers, New York. p. 97.
7. Clarke, A. *Clarke's Commentary, Vol. 1: Genesis—Deuteronomy.* Abingdon Press, Nashville, Tennessee. p. 569.

8. Select Committee on Nutrition and Human Needs, U. S. Senate. 1977. *Dietary Goals for the United States,* 2nd edition. U. S. Government Printing Office, Washington, D. C. p. xi.

9. Anonymous. 1977. Are You Eating Right? *U. S. News and World Report,* November 28. p. 39.

10. Select Committee. *Op. Cit.* p. xiii.

11. *Ibid.*

12. *Ibid.*

13. Whitaker, J. M. 1980. Three Steps to a Naturally Healthier Heart. *Prevention,* Vol. 32, No. 3. p. 124.

14. Enos, W. F., R. H. Holmes, and J. Beyer. 1953. Coronary Disease Among United States Soldiers Killed in Action in Korea. *Journal of the American Medical Association,* Vol. 152. pp. 1090-1093.

15. Hall, R. H. 1974. *Food for Nought: The Decline in Nutrition.* Harper and Row, Publishers, New York. p. 218.

16. McNamara, J. J., M. A. Molot, J. F. Stremple, and R. T. Cutting. 1971. Coronary Artery Disease in Combat Casualties in Vietnam. *Journal of the American Medical Association.* Vol. 216. pp. 1185-1187.

17. Hall. *Op. cit.* p. 222.

18. *Ibid.*

19. Lieb, C. W. 1926. The Effects of an Exclusive, Long-Continued Meat Diet. *Journal of the American Medical Association,* Vol. 87. pp. 25-26.

20. Hall. *Op. cit.* pp. 224-225.

21. Young. *Op. cit.* p. 1,058.

22. *Ibid.* p. 237.

23. Lucia, S. P. 1963. *A History of Wine as Therapy.* J. B. Lippincott Company, Philadelphia, Pennsylvania. p. 23.

24. Hennekens, C. H., et. al. 1979. Effects of Beer, Wine, and Liquor in Coronary Deaths. *Journal of the American Medical Association,* Vol. 242 (Nov. 2). pp. 1973-1974.

25. Fredericks, C. 1980. Hotline to Health. *Prevention,* Vol. 32, No. 3. p. 38.

26. Anonymous. 1980. A Health Food Dictionary: Honey. *Prevention,* Vol. 32, No. 2. pp. 39-40.

27. Bromfield, R. 1973. Honey for Decubitus Ulcers. *Journal of the American Medical Association,* Vol. 224 (May 7). p. 905.

28. *Ibid.*

29. Anonymous. 1980. *Op. cit.* p. 40.
30. Cayne, B. C. (editor). 1968. *Merit Students Encyclopedia,* Vol. 4. Crowell-Collier Educational Corporation, New York. p. 166.
31. Burkitt, D. P., and H. C. Trowell. 1975. *Refined Carbohydrate Foods and Disease.* Academic Press, New York.
32. Cleave, T. L. 1974. *The Saccharine Disease.* Keats Publishing, Inc., New Canaan, Connecticut.
33. Gottlieb, W. 1980. Fire Down Below. *Prevention.* Vol. 32, No. 2. pp. 81-82.
34. Cleave. *Op. cit.* pp. 7, 82, 126, 135.
35. Price, W. A. 1970. *Nutrition and Physical Degeneration.* The Price-Pottenger Nutrition Foundation, Inc., Santa Monica, California.
36. *Ibid.* pp. 445, 455.
37. *Ibid.* p. 444.
38. Fine, P. A. 1977. Are You Eating Right? *U. S. News and World Report,* November 28. p. 40.
39. Hess, J., and K. Hess. 1977. Are You Eating Right? *U. S. News and World Report,* November 28. p. 40.
40. Hightower, J. 1975. *Eat Your Heart Out.* Crown Publishers, Inc., New York. p. 86.
41. Hunter, B. T. 1971. *Consumer Beware.* Simon and Schuster, New York. pp. 82-85.
42. Holman, R. A. 1960. The Answer to Cancer. *Journal of the Soil Association,* Vol. 11, No. 4. p. 371.
43. Schumacher. *Op. cit.* p. 99.
44. Schuphan, W. 1979. Nutritive Value of Crops as Influenced by Organic and Inorganic Fertilizer Treatments. *Qualitas Plantarum—Plant Foods for Human Nutrition,* Vol. 23, No. 4. pp. 333-358.
45. Warmock, J. W., and J. Lewis. 1978. *The Other Face of 2, 4 D.* South Okanagan Environmental Coalition, Penticton, British Columbia. pp. 1-13.
46. Van Overbeck, J. 1964. Survey of Mechanisms of Herbicide Action. *In: The Physiocology and Biochemistry of Herbicides.* Edited by L. J. Audus. Academic Press, New York.
47. Warnock and Lewis. *Op. cit.* p. I-12.

48. *Ibid.* pp. I-12-I-13.
49. *Ibid.* p. V-1-V-15.
50. *Ibid.* p. V-1.
51. *Ibid.* p. II-18, III-18, IV-11, VI-2.
52. Syltie, P. W. 1979. *The Influence of Fertilization of the Nutritional Value of Two Hard Red Spring Wheat Cultivars.* Ph.D. Thesis. North Dakota State University, Fargo, North Dakota. pp. 10-11.
53. *Ibid.* p. 4.
54. *Ibid.* pp. 9-18.
55. *Ibid.* p. 16.
56. Young. *Op. cit.* p. 260.
57. Albrecht, W. A. 1947. Our Teeth and Our Soils. *Annals of Dentistry,* Vol. 6. pp. 199-213.
58. Bear, F. E., S. J. Toth, and A. L. Prince. 1948. Variation in mineral composition of vegetables. *Soil Science Society of America Proceedings,* Vol. 13. pp. 380-384.
59. *Ibid.* Data from Bear's paper is generalized to illustrate directional trends east of the Rocky Mountains.
60. Le Clerc, J. A. 1910. Tri-local Experiments on the Influence of Environment on the Composition of Wheat. *USDA Bureau of Chemistry Bulletin No. 128.* U. S. Government Printing Office, Washington, D. C.
61. Webb, W. P. 1931. *The Great Plains.* Grosset and Dunlap, New York. p. 50.
62. Hawken, P. *The Macrobiotic Way.* Erewhon, Boston, Massachusetts. p. 1.
64. *Ibid.* p. 2.
65. Bragg, P. 1974 *The Miracle of Fasting.* Health Science, Santa Ana, California.
66. Cleave. *Op. cit.* p. 188.
67. Wight, F. H. 1953. *Manners and Customs of Bible Lands.* Moody Press, Chicago, Illinois. p. 56.
68. Skow, D. L. 1979. *The Farmer Wants to Know.* Box 286, Welcome, Minnesota. p. 5.
69. From an advertisement in *Prevention* entitled "The Shocking Sugar Story." General Nutrition Corporation.
70. Desor, J. A., O. Maller, and L. S. Greene. 1977. Preference for Sweet in Humans: Infants, Children, and Adults. pp. 161-172.

In: *Taste and Development: The Genesis of Sweet Preference.* Edited by James M. Weiffenback. U. S. Department of Health, Education and Welfare, U.S . Government Printing Office, Washington, D. C. p. 162.
71. Navarick, D. J.. 1969. *Effect of Saccharin and Sucrose Consumption on Adjustment to a Food Deprivation Schedule.* Master's thesis. Rutgers University, New Brunswick, New Jersey.
72. Bremer, M. K. 1975. *An Examination of Some Aspects of Two American Diets.* Ph.D. thesis. University of Massachusetts, Amherst Massachusetts. pp. iv-v.
73. Skow. *Op. cit.* p. 5.
74. *Ibid.* p. 6.
75. *Ibid.*
76. Oka, I. N., and D. Pimental. 1976. Herbicide (2, 4-D) Increases Insect and Pathogen Pests on Corn. *Science,* July. pp. 239-240.
77. Faulkner, E. H. 1943. *Plowman's Folly.* University of Oklahoma Press, Norman, Oklahoma. pp. 141-143.
78. Kurup. O. N. 1955. The Influence of Manuring on the Flavour of Fruits and Vegetables. *South Indian Horticulture,* Vol. 3. p. 66.
79. *Ibid.* p. 68.
80. Anonymous. 1979. *Prescott, Climate Capital of Arizona.* Chamber of Commerce, Prescott, Arizona.
81. Wurtman, R. J. 1975. The Effects of Light on the Human Body. *Scientific American,* Vol. 233, No. 1. p. 68.
82. Palmer. *Op. cit.* p. 28.
83. Ott, J. N. 1973. *Health and Light.* The Devin-Adair Company, Old Greenwich, Connecticut. pp. 45-58.
84. Taylor, R. 1964. *Hunza Health Secrets for Long Life and Happiness.* Prentice-Hall, Inc., Englewood Cliffs, New Jersey. p. 137.
85. Bricklin, M. 1980. Journey to Health: Walk Away from Illness. *Prevention,* Vol. 32, No. 3. pp. 28-29.
86. Mc Millen. *Op. cit.* p. 5.
87. *Ibid.* p. 144.
88. *Ibid.*
89. Schindler, J. A. 1965. *How to Live 365 Days a Year.* Prentice-Hall, Inc., Englewood Cliffs, New Jersey. p. 200.

90. McMillen. *Op. cit.* p. 103.
91. Hislop, A. 1959. *The Two Babylons,* 2nd American edition. Loizeaux Brothers, Neptune, New Jersey. pp. 22, 69.
92. Winchester, A. M. 1977. *Genetics: A Survey of the Principles of Heredity,* 5th edition. Houghton Mifflin Company, Boston, Massachusetts. p. 486.
93. *Ibid.* p. 176.
94. Bullinger, E. W. 1974. *The Companion Bible.* Zondervan Bible Publishers, Grand Rapids, Michigan. p. 11.
95. Gove, P. B. (editor). 1967. *Websters Seventh New Collegiate Dictionary.* G. and C. Merriam Company, Publishers, Springfield, Massachusetts. p. 383.
96. *Ibid.* pp. 238-239.
97. Scott, F. I. 1979. The Editor's Page. *American Laboratory,* Vol. 11, No. 2. p. 8.
98. *Ibid.* Vol. 10, No. 9. p. 8.
99. *Ibid.* Vol. 11, No. 2. p. 8.
100. *Ibid.* Vol. 11, No. 11. pp. 6, 8.
101. Halsell, G. 1976. *Los Viejos: Secrets of Long Life from the Sacred Valley.* Rodale Press, Inc., Emmaus, Pennsylvania. p. 7.
102. *Ibid.* p. 63.
103. *Ibid.* p. 43.
104. Taylor, R. 1964. *Hunza Health Secrets for Long-life and Happiness.* Prentice-Hall, Inc., Englewood Cliffs, New Jersey. pp. 52.
105. *Ibid.* pp. 51-52.
106. *Ibid.* p. ix.
107. Mc Carrison, R. 1921. *Studies in Deficiency Diseases.* Henry Froude and Hodder and Stoughton, London. p. 9.
108. Mc Carrison, R. 1953. *Nutrition and Health.* Faber and Faber Limited, London. pp. 22-35.
109. Taylor. *Op. cit.* p. 70.
110. *Ibid.* p. 135.
111. Benet, S. 1976. *How to Live to Be 100.* The Dial Press, New York. p. 159.
112. *Ibid.* p. 164.
113. Whitcomb, J. C., Jr., and H. M. Morris. 1970. *The Genesis Flood.* The Presbyterian and Reformed Publishing Company, Philadelphia, Pennsylvania. p. 24.

114. Keil, C. F. 1951. *Biblical Commentary on the Old Testament.* William B. Eerdmans Publishing Co., Grand Rapids, Michigan. p. 123.
115. Severs, R. K. 1978. Gerontology, Environment, and Geological Catastrophism. *Kronos,* Vol. 4, No. 1. p. 21.
116. Scott, F. I. 1979. The Editor's Page. *American Laboratory,* Vol. 11, No. 1. p. 8.
117. Rockstein, M., and M. L. Sussman (editors). 1976. *Nutrition, Longevity, and Aging.* Academic Press Inc., New York. p. 254.
118. Vis, W. R. 1950. Medical Science and the Bible. *Modern Science and Christian Faith,* 2nd edition. Van Kampen Press, Wheaton, Illinois. p. 242.
119. Selye, H. 1959. Is Aging Curable? *Science Digest,* Vol. 46, December. p. 1.

Chapter Thirteen

1. Hall, H. F. 1920. *The Soul of a People.* Macmillan and Company, Ltd., London.
2. Schumacher, E. F. 1973. *Small is Beautiful: Economics As if People Mattered.* Harper and Row, Publishers, New York. pp. 102-103.
3. *Ibid.* p. 102.
4. *Ibid.* p. 103.
5. *Ibid.* p. 105.
6. Sears, P. B. 1935. *Deserts on the March.* University of Oklahoma Press, Norman, Oklahoma. p. 1.
7. Scott, F. I. 1977. The Editor's Page. *American Laboratory,* Vol. 9, No. 10. p. 8.
8. Faulkner, E. H. 1943. *Plowman's Folly.* University of Oklahoma Press, Norman, Oklahoma. p. 73.
9. Fukuoka, M. 1978. *The One-straw Revolution.* Rodale Press, Emmaus, Pennsylvania. pp. xxi-xxii.
10. King, F. H. 1911. *Farmers of Forty Centuries.* Rodale Press, Inc., Emmaus, Pennsylvania. pp. 1-13.
11. *Ibid.*
12. *Ibid.*

13. Anonymous. 1980. Inflation Makes the Gardens Grow. *U. S. News and World Report,* March 10. p. 70.
14. Emerson, R. W. 1876. "Nature." *Essays: Second Series.* In: *Our Natural World.* Edited by Hal Borland. Doubleday and Company, Inc., Garden City, New York. pp. 802-804.

Appendix I

1. Udall, S. L. 1963. *The Quiet Crisis.* Holt, Rinehart, and Winston, New York. pp. 5-6.
2. *Ibid.* pp. 6-7.
3. *Ibid.* p. 7.
4. *Ibid.* pp. 7-8.
5. *Ibid.* p. 8.
6. *Ibid.*
7. *Ibid.*
8. Howard, A. 1943. *An Agricultural Testament.* Oxford University Press, New York. p. 4.
9. Faulkner, E. H. 1943. *Plowman's Folly.* University of Oklahoma Press, Norman, Oklahoma.
10. Sykes, F. 1949. *Humus and the Farmer.* Rodale Press, Emmaus, Pennsylvania.
11. Berry, W. 1977. *The Unsettling of America: Culture and Agriculture.* Sierra Club Books, San Francisco, California.
12. Lawrence, D. H. (at Taos). In: Udall. *Op. cit.* p. 3.
13. Hoeh, H. L. 1963. *Compendium of World History,* Volume Two. Ambassador College Press, Pasadena, California. pp. 93-94.
14. *Ibid.* p. 87.
15. Anonymous. *The Heritage of the Anglo-Saxon Race.* The Covenant Publishing Company, Ltd., London.
16. Mc Clung, R. M. 1969. *Lost Wild America: The Story of Our Extinct and Vanishing Wildlife.* William Morrow and Company, New York. pp. 21-22.
17. *Ibid.* pp. 22-23.
18. *Ibid.* p. 24.
19. *Ibid.* Udall. *Op. cit.* p. 3.

20. Mc Clung. *Op. cit.* p. 18.
21. Udall. *Op. cit.* p. 55.
22. *Ibid.* p. 84.
23. *Ibid.*
24. *Ibid.*
25. *Ibid.*
26. *Ibid.* p. 85.
27. Wilder, L. I. 1935. *Little House on the Prairie.* Scholastic Book Services, New York. p. 205.
28. Wilson, A. 1808. *American Ornithology: The Wild Pigeon.* In: *Our Natural World.* Edited by Hal Borland. Doubleday and Company, Inc., Garden City, New York. p. 692.
29. *Ibid.* p. 688.
30. *Ibid.* pp. 688-689.
31. *Ibid.* p. 689.
32. *Ibid.* p. 690.
33. *Ibid.*
34. Edwards, E. E. 1948. The Settlement of Grasslands. *The Yearbook of Agriculture, 1948.* USDA. U. S. Government Printing Office, Washington, D. C.
35. Graham, E. H. 1947. *The Land and Wildlife.* Oxford University Press, New York. pp. 20-21.
36. *Ibid.* p. 24.
37. Brereton, J. 1602. *A Briefe and True Relation of the Discouerie of the North Part of Virginia in 1602. In: Our Natural World.* Edited by Hal Borland. Doubleday and Company, Inc., Garden City, New York. pp. 792-794. The antique spelling has been altered to a more modern style for ease of reading.
38. Whitman, W. 1882. "May-Month." *Specimen Days.* In: *Our Natural World.* Edited by Hal Borland. Doubleday and Company, Inc., Garden City, New York.
39. Udall. *Op. cit.* p. 64.
40. Mc Clung. *Op. cit.* p. 39.
41. *Ibid.*
42. *Ibid.*
43. *Ibid.* p. 40.
44. *Ibid.* p. 45.
45. *Ibid.* pp. 51-52.
46. *Ibid.* p. 53.
47. *Ibid.* p. 66.

48. Bartram, W. 1791. "Flora and Fauna of Spanish Florida." *Travels Through North and South Carolina, Georgia, East and West Florida, the Cherokee Country, the Extensive Territories of the Muscogulges, or Creek Confederacy, and the Country of the Choctaws.* In: *Our Natural World.* Edited by Hal Borland. Doubleday and Company, Inc., Garden City, New York. p. 488.
49. Udall. *Op. cit.* p. 64.
50. *Ibid.*
51. Mc Clung. *Op. cit.* p. 60.
52. *Ibid.*
53. *Ibid.* p. 61.
54. *Ibid.* pp. 60-62.
55. Irving, W. 1849. "Up the North Platte." *The Adventures of Bonneville, U. S. A., in the Rocky Mountains and the Far West.* In: *Our Natural World.* Edited by Hal Borland. Doubleday and Company, Inc., Garden City, New York. p. 488.
56. Mc Clung. *Op. cit.* p. 64.
57. Errington, P. L. 1957. "Of Marshes and Fall." *Of Men and Marshes.* In: *Our Natural World.* Edited by Hal Borland. Doubleday and Company, Inc., Garden City, New York. p. 156.
58. Rolvaag, O. 1927. *Giants in the Earth.* Harper and Row, Publishers, New York. pp. 109-110, 194.
59. Farb, P. 1963. "Sea of Grass." *Face of North America; The Natural History of a Continent.* In: *Our Natural World.* Edited by Hal Borland. Doubleday and Company, Inc., Garden City, New York. p. 290.
60. Wilder. *Op. cit.* p. 121.
61. *Ibid.* pp. 49-50.
62. *Ibid.* p. 50.
63. Mc Clung. *Op. cit.* pp. 182-183.
64. Parkman, F. 1849. "Journey to the Arkansas." *The Oregon Trail.* In: *Our Natural World.* Edited by Hal Borland. Doubleday and Company, Inc., Garden City, New York. p. 345.
65. *Ibid.* p. 345.
66. *Ibid.*
67. Rolvaag. *Op. cit.* p. 193.
68. Syltie, P. 1977. *The Syltie Family in America.* Pronto Print, Inc., Fargo, North Dakota. p. 84.

69. Gregg, J. 1905. "The Prairies." *Commerce of the Prairies.* In: *Our Natural World.* Edited by Hal Borland. Doubleday and Company, Inc., Garden City, New York. pp. 308-309.
70. Irving. *Op. cit.* p. 398.
71. Parkman. *Op. cit.* p. 338.
72. Flint, T. 1826. "Down the Ohio." *Recollections of the Last Ten Years.* In: *Our Natural World.* Edited by Hal Borland. Doubleday and Company, Inc., Garden City, New York. p. 163-166.
73. De Tonti, H. 1683. *Account of La Salle's Expedition on the Mississippi.* In: *Our Natural World.* Edited by Hal Borland. Doubleday and Company, Inc., Garden City, New York. pp. 234-235.
74. Twain, M. 1883. "High Water on the Mississippi." *Life on the Mississippi.* In: *Our Natural World.* Edited by Hal Borland. Doubleday and Company, Inc., Garden City, New York. p. 242.
75. Muir, J. 1894. "Bee Pastures." *The Mountains of California.* In: *Our Natural World.* Edited by Hal Borland. Doubleday and Company, Inc., Garden City, New York. pp. 743-746.
76. Graham. *Op. cit.* pp. 25-26.
77. *Ibid.* p. 22.
78. Leopold, A. 1949. "Wilderness." *A Sand County Almanac.* In: *Our Natural World.* Edited by Hal Borland. Doubleday and Company, Garden City, New York. p. 60.
79. *Ibid.*
80. Irving. *Op. cit.* p. 402.
81. De Oñate, D. J. 1601. "Onate Goes East." *True Account of the Expedition of Oñate Toward the East.* In: *Our Natural World.* Edited by Hal Borland. Doubleday and Company, Garden City, New York. p. 329.
82. *Ibid.* pp. 330-335.
83. *Ibid.*
84. Leopold. *Op. cit.* pp. 58-59.
85. Udall. *Op. cit.* pp. 76-77.